MODERN BIOLOGY   Ma

The Made Simple series
has been created
especially for self-education
but can equally well
be used as
an aid to group study.
However complex the subject,
the reader is taken
step by step,
clearly and methodically,
through the course. Each volume
has been prepared by experts,
taking account of
modern educational requirements,
to ensure the most
effective way of
acquiring knowledge.

In the same series

MODERN BIOLOGY   Made Simple

Robert Barrass, BSc, PhD, FIBiol

Made Simple Books
HEINEMANN : London

Printed and bound in Great Britain
by Richard Clay (The Chaucer Press) Ltd, Bungay, Suffolk
for the publishers, William Heinemann Ltd,
10 Upper Grosvenor Street, London W1X 9PA

First edition, May 1979
Revised Reprint, December 1982

British Library Cataloguing in Publication Data

Barrass, Robert
    Modern biology made simple.—(Made simple books)
    1. Biology
    I. Title   II. Series
    574   QH307.2
ISBN 0-434-98538-4

Preface

Modern Biology, the science of biology as it is today, is both the knowledge accumulated about living things and a field of continuing scientific investigation. This book, therefore, presents a balanced and up-to-date introduction to what is known about biology and to the way biologists work.

No previous knowledge of biology is assumed. If you have not studied biology before, and you are working alone, start at the beginning and work through to the end. The information necessary for the proper understanding of each subject is provided not only on the page where the subject is considered but also in the preceding chapters.

Investigations are included in each chapter. Some of these enable you to see things described in this book; others provide guidance for further investigations. For some of these investigations you need only a pencil and a notebook: for others only inexpensive equipment and chemicals are required. However, some observations are possible only if you have the opportunity to use a microscope. For those who do not, colour transparencies provide an acceptable alternative in an introductory course (see Appendix 3). The investigations in which chemicals are required should be undertaken only in a laboratory in the presence of an experienced teacher.

To test your memory and your understanding, questions are included at the end of each chapter. The answers are given at the end of the book (Appendix 2). If you are preparing for an examination, read the advice on examination technique (Appendix 1).

The Further Reading (Appendix 4) is suitable for those who have read this book and wish to know more about biology.

For ease of reference, and to help students in the last year of an introductory course who are preparing for an examination, the topics included in biology syllabuses are set out in the List of Contents and a detailed Index is provided.

Technical terms are essential in science. They contribute to precision and to an economy of words. The technical terms used in this book are included in the Index, and after many entries one page number is printed in bold. On this page there is a definition, explanation or illustration which should make the meaning of the term clear. Synonyms of some of the terms used in this book are also given in the Index. Some other technical terms which you may see in other books, but which are not used here, are defined in the Glossary (Appendix 5).

Acknowledgements

I thank my wife for her help in preparing this book; and two teachers of biology, Mrs Alison Leadley Brown and Mr G. Swales, for reading the first draft and for their helpful comments. I am also grateful to Dr R. Morrison and Dr P. Wyn-Jones for advice on particular points.

I shall be pleased to receive suggestions for improving future editions.

Robert Barrass,
June 1978

The Polytechnic,
Sunderland

Key to Abbreviations and Symbols

Abbreviations

Fig.	figure (illustration)
e.g.	for example
L.	Latin
Gk.	Greek

Symbols

μm   micrometre (one thousandth of a millimetre $= 10^{-6}$ m)

mm   millimetre ⎫
cm   centimetre ⎬ length
m   metre ⎭
km   kilometre

cm²   square centimetre ⎫ area
m²   square metre ⎭

cm³   cubic centimetre ⎫ volume
m³   cubic metre ⎭

g   gram ⎫ mass
kg   kilogram ⎭

s   second ⎫
min   minute ⎬ time
h   hour ⎭

J   joule—energy, work, quantity of heat

MJ   megajoule (10^6 joules)

°C   degree Celsius; also called the degree Centigrade

Notes

1. The symbols for chemical elements are included in Table 8, p.54.
2. For other abbreviations see Index

Contents

PART 3: CELLS AND ORGANISMS

PART 4: LIFE GOES ON

Contents   xiii

PART 1: LOOKING AT LIFE

1

THE SCIENCE OF LIFE

You know quite a lot about life because *you* are alive and every day you see other living things. So you may not remember when you first became interested in biology—the science of life. Nor can we say when the study of life began. People have always taken an interest in living things. In cave paintings stone-age people depicted themselves and the animals they hunted. They used plants and animals as food and as sources of medicines, and they must have noted the changes in plant and animal life which mark the seasons of the year. In speaking to their children they passed on this knowledge.

With the beginning of agriculture, about 10 000 years ago, people started to use their knowledge of living things not only in hunting and food collecting but also in food production. They began to find out more about the relationship between crop plants and the soil, the influence of climate on soil conditions and plant growth, and the use of plants as food for farm animals. Before people knew how to write, and long before there was a science called biology, people were selecting seed from the best plants and using the best animals for breeding.

Because **science** is both the accumulated knowledge on any subject and the method by which discoveries are made and recorded, the development of writing made possible the growth of science. About 2500 years ago a number of Greek scientists began to organise and accumulate knowledge. They left records which for the next 2000 years were accepted as true. Aristotle was outstanding: his book *Historia Animalium* includes many of his own observations and deductions, and also many things said by other people. His work was a mixture of fact and fancy. Other Greek scientists wrote and illustrated books on the anatomy of man and other animals, and prepared illustrations of medicinal plants.

Science, as it is today, was made possible by the invention of the printing press in the 15th century. After this, the books by Greek scientists were printed and widely read, and new discoveries were quickly communicated to interested people everywhere. With these discoveries people slowly came to accept that earlier writings, by people who had been considered authorities, were not necessarily correct.

In the 16th and 17th centuries a common-sense procedure for acquiring scientific knowledge was established. This **scientific method** depends upon observation and discovery; not upon authority. Speculation by itself is not acceptable. Suggested explanations must be supported by evidence and tested by further observations in an attempt to establish the truth.

In the 17th and 18th centuries discoveries were made in botany, zoology and medicine (Table 1) but plants, animals and people were still considered to be essentially different. It was not until early in the 19th century that the word **biology**, meaning the study of life, was first used, by Jean Baptiste Lamarck in France and Gottfried Treviranus in Germany, for the study of *all* living things. With further discoveries other people came to accept that

3

the similarities between all living things were more fundamental than the obvious differences between different forms of life. We now emphasise that all living things are essentially alike by calling them all **organisms**.

In the 19th and 20th centuries the work of biologists has contributed to the control of many diseases and has helped farmers to increase food production. By making possible population growth, discoveries in biology have already had unforeseen social and economic consequences.

Table 1.   Some subjects in which biologists specialise.

Subject	Things studied
Agriculture	the cultivation of plants and animal husbandry
Anatomy	the structure of organisms
Biochemistry	the chemistry of life
Botany	plant life
Ecology	the interaction of organisms with their environment
Genetics	the mechanism of inheritance
Medicine	the prevention and treatment of disease
Morphology	the shape and form of organisms
Palaeontology	the fossil remains of organisms
Physiology	the functioning of organisms
Zoology	animal life

The further growth of populations presents new problems of disease control, food supply, pollution, conservation and the using up of limited resources, including living-space. Biology therefore, more than any other science, will continue to influence our future. This is one good reason for studying biology. You will also find out more about your body and how it works, and about the structure and functioning of other organisms and the way they interact with one another and with their physical environment. As a result you will have a better understanding of yourself and of our place in nature.

You can find out more about organisms in two ways. One is by **investigation**, and most people remember best the things they have seen. But there is a limit to what you can find out for yourself—even in a lifetime. The quickest way to learn is by listening to biologists talking about their subject and by reading articles and books. By reading you can find out what other people have selected from all that they know about biology. You can read about the ideas and problems which are now attracting the attention of biologists. However, remember that what you read is not necessarily either complete or correct. Scientists should not have too much respect for authority; and if you read books by specialists you will find that there are many subjects upon which experts disagree. Also, there are many questions to which scientists do not know the answer.

In the beginning the earth was without life (Fig. 1). Some books on biology start by considering how it came about that there are now organisms on this planet. But we do not know how life began: we can only speculate. Some books, about other subjects, begin with simple things and gradually work towards more complicated subjects. But we cannot do this in biology because all organisms have so much in common. They differ in size and shape, and

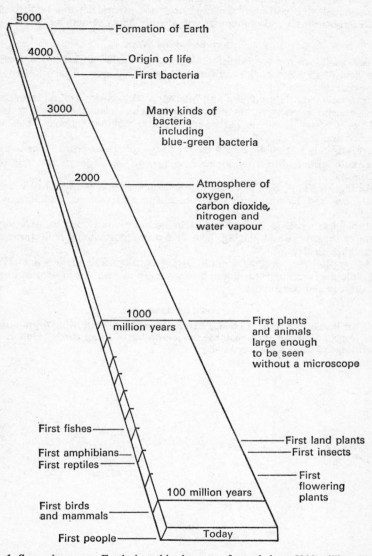

Fig. 1. Some changes on Earth since this planet was formed about 5000 million years ago. Time is represented by marks on a ruler.

in their organisation, but all are complex. Life goes on in all of them. Some are so small that you need a microscope to see them but this book begins with large animals and plants that you already know something about.

Where Biologists Work

Biologists work in schools, colleges, universities and polytechnics as teachers of biology, health education, human biology, social biology and environmental studies.

In government laboratories and international agencies biologists work as advisers and as research scientists in agriculture, defence, fisheries, forensic science, forestry, medicine, nature conservation, pollution control, veterinary science and water supply.

In hospitals and public health laboratories biologists work as biochemists, haematologists and microbiologists helping with the diagnosis and treatment of disease.

In industry biologists work on the development and testing of new drugs, pesticides and fertilisers, in food processing and storage, and in quality control.

Biologists work in museums and in botanical and zoological gardens; naming organisms and placing them in groups, maintaining collections and arranging displays.

Many biologists work as administrators, managers and advisers in all types of biological employment. Some biologists are self-employed—for example, as authors and consultants.

Test Questions

What is science? What is biology? Have there always been living organisms on this planet? How did early man use his knowledge of living things? How is our knowledge of living things used today?

2

ORGANISMS GROW

Like begets like. Young animals look like their parents and the seeds from a plant grow into the same kind of plant. However, organisms change as they grow. The young animal is neither the same size nor the same shape as either of its parents, and the seedling is very different from the fully grown plant. Another word for shape is form: organisms have a characteristic body form at each stage of their development and growth.

The Growth and Form of a Flowering Plant

The Seed

Seeds can be stored for a long time. This is one reason why we value them as foods. You cannot tell, just by looking at seeds, whether or not they are alive. How can you tell? One way would be to plant them in suitable soil at the right time of the year and if some started to grow you would say that those were alive. Growth is one of the characteristics by which we distinguish living from non-living things. But what is growth?

Investigation. Pour some water into a measuring cylinder. Add ten dry bean seeds that have been stored in a cool dry place since the last growing season. What is their volume? Keep these beans in water. After an hour remove the surface moisture from the beans and measure their volume again by adding them to a known volume of water. Measure the volume of the beans at intervals and keep them in water

Table 2. Change in volume of ten pea seeds *Pisum sativum* when soaked in water.

Time	Volume (cm³)			
	Water	Water + peas	Peas	Average
1025	5.0	7.2	2.2	0.22
1125	5.2	8.1	2.9	0.29
1305	6.0	9.4	3.4	0.34
1500	6.0	9.8	3.8	0.38
1700	5.5	9.6	4.1	0.41
1935	5.6	10.0	4.4	0.44
2255	5.2	9.8	4.6	0.46
0935	5.0	9.7	4.7	0.47
2035	5.1	9.8	4.7	0.47

between your measurements. Record in a table (as in Table 2) the date, the time at which you make observations and the details of your observations. Divide each of your measurements by ten to calculate the average volume of the beans. Plot these average values on a graph (similar to Fig. 2). Has the volume of these seeds

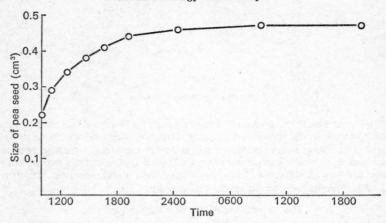

Fig. 2. Increase in volume of seeds of the garden pea *Pisum sativum* soaked in water.
Average values from Table 1.

changed since you started your observations? If so, how do you explain the
difference? Have they grown?

A **graph** is a useful way of showing how one thing varies in relation to
another. In this graph the average volume of the seeds is plotted against time.
In a graph you must always plot the thing that you can choose (the times at
which you choose to make your measurements in this example) in relation to
the horizontal axis (called the x axis) and the thing over which you have no
control (the volume of the seeds in this example) in relation to the vertical
axis (called the y axis).

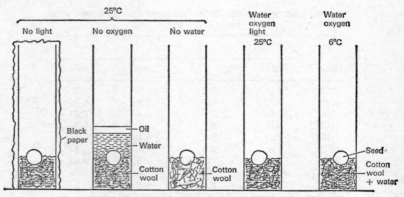

Fig. 3. Conditions necessary for germination.

Investigation: *conditions necessary for germination.* Arrange five tubes, as indicated
in Fig. 3, and look at them from time to time to see which seeds are germinating.
Make notes of your observations and answer the following questions. Is water
necessary for germination? Is oxygen necessary? Are light or darkness essential?
Will the seeds germinate in a refrigerator (at about 6 °C)?

In moist soil seeds absorb water, increase in volume, and the seed coat may split. A seed that has been soaked in water can be pulled apart and examined (Fig. 4B). There is a scar where the seed was attached to its seed stalk in the fruit. The dormant plant, within the seed coat, comprises the young root, two seed leaves and a young shoot.

Germination is the development of a seed or grain into a seedling.

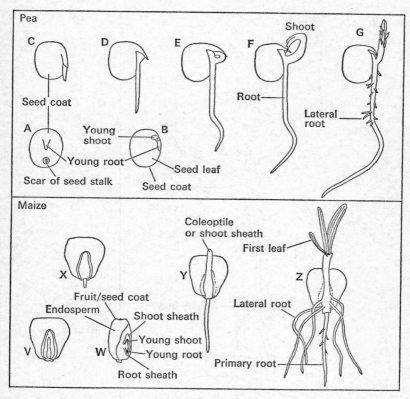

Fig. 4. Seed structure and germination: (A to G) the garden pea *Pisum sativum*; (V to Z) maize *Zea mais*. B = half seed; W = fruit cut in half.

Investigation: *observation of germination.* To make observations, soak a seed (of a pea, bean or sunflower, for example) and a grain (of a cereal plant) in water overnight and then roll a sheet of wet paper so that it holds the seed and grain against the side of a glass jar. Pour water into the jar to about 2 cm below the seed and grain. As the young root grows, note the root hairs near the root tip. Do the seed leaves remain in the seed? Compare the leaves formed, in succession, on one plant. Are they all the same shape and size?

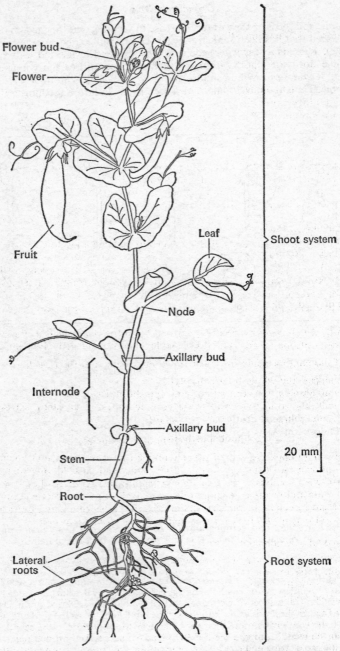

Fig. 5. The parts of a flowering plant: the garden pea *Pisum sativum.*

The Parts of a Flowering Plant

A flowering plant has two parts: a root (or root system) and a shoot (or shoot system)—see Fig. 5. Different kinds of plants have different kinds of roots. The shoots also differ from one kind of plant to another, but most plants have a stem which bears leaves, and in the axil of each leaf there is an axillary bud (see also Figs. 16 and 38).

Growth occurs at the tip of the shoot (as at the tip of the root—see Fig. 77) and if you make drawings of any plant, to scale, at intervals during the plant's growth, you will observe that new leaves develop at the shoot tip and then grow to their final size.

The leaves are green and flat, and in many plants they have two parts: the thin flat blade and the leaf stalk. Because of the growth of the stem, the leaves are spaced out. The leaves and axillary buds are at nodes and each space between nodes is called an internode. Each bud is a shoot tip, protected by scale leaves or by developing leaves, and it may grow into either a stem with leaves or into a flower.

If the flowers are in groups, then each group is called an inflorescence. Each flower has a stalk and four kinds of floral leaves arranged on a receptacle (Fig. 152A, p. 252). In a flower the outermost leaves, called sepals, form the calyx. Next to these are the petals, which form the corolla. The sepals and petals enclose and protect the stamens and the carpels. The parts of a stamen are the filament and anther; and the parts of a carpel are the ovary, style and stigma.

A fruit, which contains seeds, is formed from the ovary wall of the carpel (or carpels) of one flower. The flower stalk, therefore, is also the fruit stalk.

The following terms are used for flowering plants and their parts:

organism: the whole flowering plant
organ systems: the root system and the shoot system
organs: the roots (which form the root system) and the stem, leaves and fruits (which form the shoot system)

The Growth and Form of a Mammal

We are mammals. So are all other animals that have hair (fur), including horses, camels, cattle, pigs, sheep, rabbits, dogs and cats. Young mammals are born at an advanced stage of their development. At birth they resemble their parents and begin to feed on milk produced in their mother's mammary glands (Latin *mamma* = breast). In contrast to a flowering plant, most of the organs and organ systems of a mammal are not visible externally.

The Parts of a Mammal

The parts of the body of a mammal are the head, neck, shoulders, thorax, abdomen, hips and the tail. The fore-limbs are attached to the shoulders and the hind-limbs to the hips.

The head end of the body is called the anterior end (L. *ante* = before); and the tail end is the posterior end (L. *post* = after). The surface of the body furthest from the ground is the dorsal surface (L. *dorsum* = the back): and the surface nearest to the ground is the ventral surface (L. *venter* = the belly). Structures that are on the mid-line, including the mouth, anus and tail, are median in position (L. *medius* = the middle); and those that are to the sides of the mid-line, including the ears, eyes and legs, are lateral in position (L. *latus* = the side). Animals in which the right half of the body is the mirror image of the left half are described as bilaterally symmetrical.

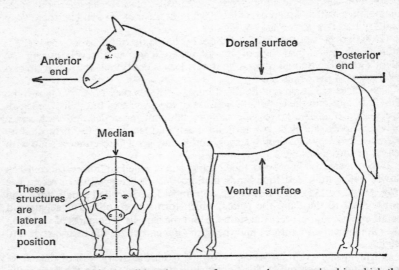

Fig. 6. Terms used in describing the parts of a mammal or any animal in which the right half of the body is the mirror image of the left half.

Investigation: *growth of a mouse*. Facts of any kind are called **data**. The measurements you make in any investigation are numerical data. These should be recorded in your practical notebook. You will find it easier to keep neat records, which you can understand later, if you prepare a table in your notebook before you make your measurements. The table should have a clear heading and the units of measurement

Table 3.   Length of the tail of a mouse.

Age (*days*)	0	1	3	6	10	17	24	35	51	78
Length of tail (*mm*)	12	14	18	25	36	45	64	80	88	88

must be included for every quantity shown (for example, age in days; length in millimetres). Table 3 is a record of measurements of the length of the tail of a male mouse from the day it was born until it was fully grown (see Fig. 7A). Tables are useful when you are recording data but a graph may be better when you start to analyse and interpret data. For example, in the graph (Fig. 7B) tail length is plotted against time. From the graph you can see, at a glance, how tail-length changes with time. Note, once again, that the thing that you can choose (the day on which you make each measurement in this investigation) is plotted in relation to the horizontal axis, and the thing over which you have no control (the length of the tail in this example) is plotted in relation to the vertical axis.

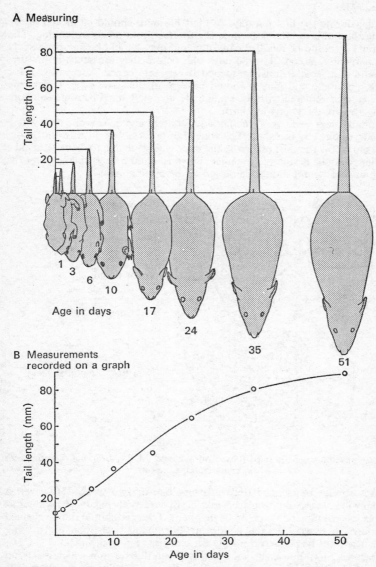

Fig. 7. The growth of a mouse: (A) measurements of the length of the tail; (B) the measurements recorded on a graph.

Rearing Mice

Except during the first ten days of their life mice should be picked up by holding the tail near the base while the forefeet hold on to something. The cage and lid should be handled carefully, and mice should be handled slowly and confidently. When 21 to 30 days old, before they are sexually mature, the males and females must be moved to separate cages. Alternatively, for mating, one male and female should be kept in the same cage. Unless the female is to be remated with the same male, the male must be removed from the cage before the young are born.

A suitable cage (see Fig. 8) includes a nest area; and an exercise area where food and water may be taken. The water bottle should be filled to not more than 2 cm below the cap; otherwise the mice will be unable to drink. Rat cake (a pelletted food) is suitable for mice. Sawdust should be sprinkled over the floor and wood wool should be placed in the nesting area.

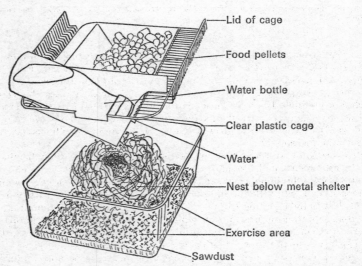

Fig. 8. A rearing cage for mice (based on Wallace, M. E., *Learning Genetics with Mice*, Heinemann, London).

Cages should be cleaned once in every one or two weeks. However, a pregnant female should be placed in a clean cage with plenty of bedding as soon as it is seen, by its shape, to be pregnant. The cage should not be cleaned again until a week after the young are born; and even then the nursing female need not be disturbed if only the exercise area is cleaned.

The cages should be kept in a quiet, well ventilated room which has good natural light in the daytime. If possible, the room temperature should be steady at 18 to 20 °C and it should not be too humid. Mice should be kept in a room where there are no other small mammals. To prevent disease, small numbers of mice should be kept, in clean cages, and they should be purchased only from a supplier of disease-free stock.

Table 4. Life of mice*.

Development
Days

Days	
0– 1	Naked and pink, become paler in a few hours.
5– 6	Darker pigments (if any) visible in skin.
8–10	Hair half grown. Colour visible. Easy to sex.
12–14	Eyes open. Weaning starts.
21–23	Weaning complete. Sexing hindered by fur.
26–35	Vagina open. Easy to sex.

Reproduction

Sexually mature in about 5 to 6 weeks after birth.
Pregnancy lasts 19 to 21 days; or up to 35 days if feeding young.
Breeding: females up to 6 to 12 months old;
          males up to 18 months old.

Life span: females up to 2 years; males up to 3 years.

---

*Note. For further information see Wallace, M. E., *Learning Genetics with Mice*, Heinemann, London.

The Measurement of Growth

A crystal grows by adding material to its surface. It gets bigger but remains the same shape. Its growth is not accompanied by a change in form. But when an organism grows it does not just get bigger. A mammal, for example, like a flowering plant, changes in many ways as it grows. We use the words babyhood, childhood, adolescence, maturity and old age for the phases of our own growth after birth. Plants and animals grow in different ways but it is not easy to measure their growth. How, for example, can the size of any organism be measured?

When we want to know how big people are we measure their height or weight; yet people of the same height may be very different in weight and people who are the same weight may be very different in physique. One may be physically fit with little fat and the other may be very fat and clearly over-weight. If a baby is getting too fat, is it growing more quickly than another baby that is putting on less fat? Or would it be better if we could ignore the fat when measuring growth? If the addition of fat is not part of growth, then how can we estimate growth? What is growth? Growth, which is not easy to define, is referred to again on many pages of this book because biology is the study of life: the study of the maintenance and growth of organisms, and of their reproduction and the start of new growth in each individual.

Keeping a Record

Keep a careful record of all your practical work so that you can refer to your own observations later or compare your notes with those of other people interested in similar subjects. Writing also helps you to concentrate and to arrange your thoughts, and preparing an accurate drawing makes you examine things carefully. However, your notes and drawings will help you to learn and to remember only if you understand what you are doing. Label your drawings and make notes, therefore, during your investigations, so that your record shows how well you understand your work.

Think of writing as part of a scientist's work. Use writing and drawing to help you to observe, to think, to describe and to remember.

Notes. Date all your work. Write in clear and carefully constructed sentences. Use headings and subheadings. Include your reasons for doing the work (*Introduction*), the materials and methods used in all preparations and your procedure during the investigation (*Materials and Methods*), your observations (*Data*) and the results of your analysis of the data (*Results*), and your interpretation of your results and any conclusions (*Discussion and Conclusions*).

Drawing. Use an HB pencil with a sharp point. Work on A4 paper (210 × 297 mm) and make it a habit to use a whole page for each drawing so that it is large and clear. Paper without lines is best for your drawings and it is also suitable for notes. Use drawings to augment your written record and not as an alternative to writing. Write notes next to your drawings and label each drawing clearly. Draw labelling lines with a ruler. Place your pencil on the point to be labelled and draw a straight line (as in Fig. 5). Mark a scale on each drawing (as in Fig. 5). Draw and label in pencil so that you can correct any mistakes.

Test Questions

1. In an investigation, the root of a broad bean seedling was marked into millimetre parts with waterproof ink (see Fig. 77A). Later, the distances between the marks were measured (Fig. 77B). What may be concluded about the growth of the root?

2. Prepare a diagram of the structure of a named seed that you have studied. Label four parts.

3. Write a concise summary of your observations of the growth of a named plant from seed.

4. (*a*) Estimate the length of the tail of a mouse, from the graph (Fig. 7B), when the mouse is one, two and three weeks old. (*b*) How old do you think the mouse was, under these rearing conditions, when it was fully grown? (*c*) What evidence do you have for this conclusion?

3

ORGANISMS VARY

All organisms of one kind comprise one **species**. They have many things in common. For example, the way each organism grows and its form at each stage in its growth are characteristic of all organisms of the same species. Yet, in any species, there are differences between organisms. The species we know best is our own. All people look very much alike: we have no difficulty in recognising them as people. Yet we can easily distinguish one person from another: we recognise individuals. Similarly, all maize plants or all house-flies look very much alike but if you looked at them carefully you would probably find that, as with people, no two are quite alike.

The development and growth of each organism is influenced by such things as climate, the lie of the land and the structure and properties of the soil (all of which are called **physical factors**). Growth is also influenced by the presence of other living organisms—that is to say, by **biotic factors**. The growth of plants is affected by the grazing behaviour of animals, and by the presence of other plants growing nearby. And the growth of animals is affected by the availability of resources such as shelter and food, and the presence of other animals sharing these same resources.

Some Environmental Factors that Influence Plant Growth

Soil Nutrients

In 1860 two German scientists, Sachs and Knop, cultured plants without soil in solutions containing different combinations of soluble salts in distilled water. They found, by these **water-culture** experiments, that for normal plant growth a nutrient solution containing calcium, potassium, iron, magnesium, nitrate, phosphate and sulphate ions was needed. The absence of any one of these nutrients resulted in abnormal growth.

If any essential element is not present in the soil in sufficient amounts, plants grown in this soil develop characteristic symptoms of the deficiency.

Soil deficient in	Deficiency symptoms
Calcium	Leaf margins folded, yellowing, poor root growth
Potassium	Little stem growth, scorching of older leaves
Iron	Yellowing of new growth but veins may be green
Magnesium	Older leaves become orange/red with dead patches
Nitrogen	Little growth, small leaves, older leaves yellow
Phosphorus	Thin stem, purple tints
Sulphur	Pale green, red/purple tints in younger leaves

The chemicals used by Sachs contained very small amounts of impurities because it was not possible to prepare pure chemicals at that time. Some of these impurities are now known to be essential for normal growth: boron, manganese, copper, zinc and molybdenum. Because these are needed in only very small amounts they are called **micronutrients**, or trace elements. Apart

17

from iron, which is a micronutrient, the essential elements listed by Sachs are all required in larger amounts. These, therefore, are called **macronutrients**.

Investigation: *growing plants without soil.* The growth of plants in water containing dissolved salts is called water culture. When used commercially, as a method of cultivation, the method is called hydroponics.

For this investigation, a culture solution in which plants will grow is prepared by adding the following to 1000 cm³ distilled water: calcium nitrate, 2.0 g; potassium nitrate, 0.5 g; magnesium sulphate, 0.5 g; potassium phosphate, 0.5 g; ferric chloride, trace.

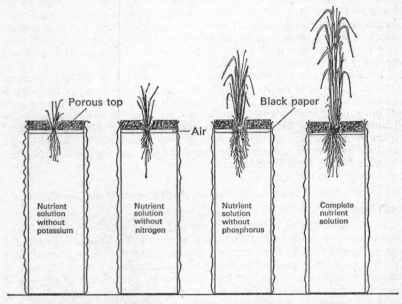

Fig. 9. Water culture experiment: barley *Hordeum* growing in different nutrient solutions (based on Baron, W. M. M., *Organization in Plants*, Edward Arnold, London).

Place young maize seedlings of about the same size in clean jars (see Fig. 9).

1. Complete culture solution.
2. Replace calcium nitrate by either potassium nitrate or potassium chloride to make a solution that lacks calcium.
3. Replace the potassium phosphate by potassium sulphate to make a solution that lacks phosphate.
4. Replace the calcium nitrate by potassium chloride, and the potassium nitrate by potassium chloride, to make a solution that lacks nitrogen.
5. Make a solution that lacks iron by leaving out the ferric chloride.
6. Add only distilled water to one jar.

Wrap the jars in foil or black paper to exclude light and so prevent the growth of algae in the nutrient solutions. Place the tubes so that they are all equally exposed to sunlight. Leave the seedlings to grow. Bubble air through the nutrient solution from time to time, and when necessary top up the tubes with distilled water.

Compare the plants grown in different jars. Record **qualitative differences** (for example, in the colour of their leaves) and **quantitative differences** (for example, in the number of leaves, the size of leaves, and the dry weight of the whole plants). What do you conclude from your observations? Remember that, apart from iron, all your nutrient solutions are without micronutrients. How does this fact affect your conclusions?

Investigation: *growing plants without light.* Grow six maize or bean plants in the dark; and another six in the light (until they are 5 cm high). Then compare the two lots of plants (see Fig. 10).

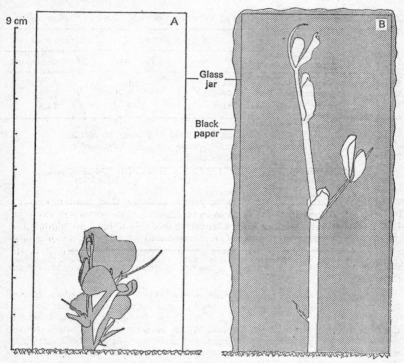

Fig. 10. Pea plants grown (A) in the light, and (B) in the dark.

Investigation: *differences between crop plants.* If you purchase seeds of a crop plant, all the seeds in the packet should be of good quality. Follow the instructions on the packet. If you plant the seeds the recommended distance apart, in the right kind of soil, and at the right time of the year, you will expect to get a uniform crop with the plants similar to one another though not identical. Plant some seeds in open ground and the same number in the shade. Plant some seeds the recommended distance apart and others closer together. When they are ready for harvest, compare the plants grown in these different conditions. For example, (1) compare the shape and area of the leaves growing in equivalent positions on different plants, and (2) weigh the edible part obtained from each crop plant. How have the different treatments affected growth? To measure leaf area, draw around the leaf on graph paper and count the squares within the outline. In this investigation you will have observed that various factors, such as light, water and soil nutrients, all influence growth. However, it is not easy to distinguish the effects of different physical factors because when plants grow close together they compete not only for light but also for water and nutrients from the soil.

Investigation: *the harmful effects of weeds.* Differences in the size of plants are due, in part, to the effects of other plants which are competing for the same resources. For example, the harmful effects of weeds on the growth of crop plants may be due to their removing nutrients and water from the soil, or to the effect of shading which cuts out heat and light.

Table 5. The effect of the position of weeds on the yield of red beet *Beta vulgaris.*

	Yield in kilogrammes per 15 metre row		
Treatments	*Whole shoots*	*Tap roots*	*Marketable roots*
Weed-free	41.9	43.6	23.3
Weeds left in rows	38.6	36.0	18.2
Weeds left between rows	31.6	30.9	14.8

Table 6. The effect on final yield of sowing 16 carrot seeds *Daucus carota* and 16 weed seeds *Stellaria media* at different times.

Treatments	*Weight of carrots*
Carrot and weed seeds sown together	60.7 g
Weed sown one week after carrot seed	106.3 g
Weed sown two weeks after carrot seed	126.3 g

Note. The results in Tables 5 and 6, obtained in investigations by J. K. A. Bleasdale at The National Vegetable Research Station in Britain, were reported in Harper, J. L., *The Biology of Weeds*, Blackwell, Oxford.

Crop plants are usually grown in rows. Study Table 5. Do weeds reduce the yield from the crop? Is it more beneficial to remove weeds in the row or between the rows? Why do you think this is so? Perhaps it is because weeding in the row disturbs or damages the crop plants. Study Table 6. Which weed seeds do most harm to crop growth, those that germinate at the same time as the crop plant or those that germinate later? Why do you think it makes any difference when the weed seeds germinate? Perhaps the plants that germinate first gain an advantage because their root systems become established and their shoots shade the later developing plants.

Investigation: *peas in a pod.* You have probably heard the expression 'as like as two peas in a pod'. But if you examine the peas in a pod (Fig. 155, for example) you will observe that although they are similar to one another (Fig. 155), they are all different. Most obviously, there are differences in size. Are these related to differences in their position in the pod? Each seed is a dormant plant within its seed coat, and the fruit is the environment in which they are formed. If you collect all the pods from one plant you will find that they differ in size and in the number of peas they hold. Do smaller pods contain smaller peas?

Some Environmental Factors that Influence the Growth of Animals

Rearing House-Flies *Musca domestica*

The house-fly lives in different places and behaves differently in the different stages of its life cycle. The sleeve cage (Fig. 11A) is large enough for several hundred flies. Provide a water fountain and a mixture of powdered milk and cane sugar as food. The abdomen of a mature female is swollen with eggs

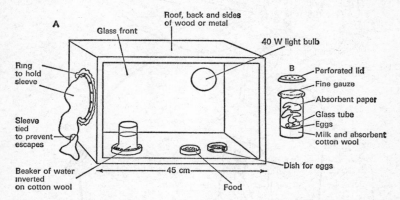

Fig. 11. Rearing house-flies: (A) observation cage; (B) culture jar for maggots (based on Barrass, R., Rearing house-flies *Musca domestica* L. and their use in laboratory practical work, *Journal of Biological Education*, **10**, 164–8).

and is creamy-white. When eggs are required, add enough cotton wool to a 50:50 milk/water mixture in a Petri dish so that there is no excess fluid. Then make small tunnels at the edge of the dish. Here the females will lay, and eggs of known age may be obtained by changing this pad every day.

Transfer some eggs to a culture jar (Fig. 11B). This should not contain excess milk that can be poured away; nor should there be dry cotton wool. If possible, keep this jar in an incubator at 25 °C. The eggs will develop into maggots (house-fly larvae). When they are fully grown the maggots start to leave the food. Then place crumpled absorbent paper in the jar. On this paper, the maggots will develop into pupae; and the pupae into flies. The change of form, from pupa to fly, within the puparial case (see Fig. 12) is called metamorphosis (Greek *meta* = change of; *morphē* = form).

Keep the sleeve cage as clean as possible. House-flies are a nuisance, and if they escape they may pick up and spread disease-producing bacteria (see p. 110). To prevent unpleasant odours and to prevent escapes, all waste materials from the cage and culture jars should be burnt or placed in disinfectant.

Investigation: *on the size of a fly*
1. Prepare a culture jar (see Fig. 11B) with absorbent cotton wool added to 20 cm³ fresh milk.
2. Collect the eggs laid by a female, in one batch, so that you have eggs of known age. Keep a record of their age.

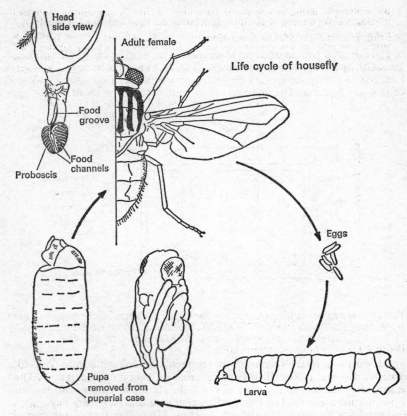

Fig. 12. The life cycle of a house-fly *Musca domestica* (based on Barrass, R., *Biology: Food and People*, Hodder & Stoughton, London).

3. Place the eggs on coloured absorbent paper, which must be wet, and use a small painting brush as you count 100 eggs on to a 10 mm square of this paper.
4. Place the paper in a culture jar so that the eggs are uppermost and the milk bathes the underside of the paper.
5. If possible, incubate the eggs at a constant temperature (about 25 °C). Otherwise, keep the jars in a warm place.
6. Replace the crumpled paper each day. Remove any puparia and place them in a Petri dish on a disc of dry absorbent paper. Mark the dish with the date on which these puparia were formed. Keep the puparia formed on different days in separate dishes.
7. As soon as you collect the puparia, or before they have completed their development, measure the length of each puparium and record your data in a table. Note that the puparia are not all the same size, even though they developed from larvae which hatched from one batch of eggs and which shared the same food and the same habitat. Present your data on the size of the puparia as a **histogram** (as in Fig. 13). Calculate the average size of the puparia. An **average**, also called

the **arithmetic mean**, is calculated by adding all the measurements and then dividing by the total number of measurements. What are the lowest and highest measurements? In statistics these values are called the **range**. Draw a graph in which you plot the average size of the puparia formed each day against time. As with all graphs, the thing that you can control (the times when you decide to collect puparia in this example) must be plotted in relation to the horizontal axis.

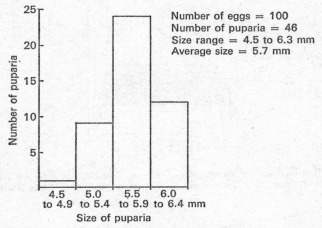

Number of eggs = 100
Number of puparia = 46
Size range = 4.5 to 6.3 mm
Average size = 5.7 mm

Fig. 13. Histogram: size of house-flies.

Rearing Locusts *Locusta migratoria*

The hard skin limits the growth of insects and they cast this skin, or moult, several times during their development. After each moult, while the new skin is soft, the insect gets bigger.

Female locusts lay in holes which they dig in the soil. When the eggs hatch, young locusts wriggle to the surface and moult. They are then called the first hopper stage. As they develop locusts moult five more times, at the end of each hopper stage. The hoppers (larvae of locusts) are similar to the adults but they do not have wings (see Fig. 15).

Up to 300 African migratory locusts *Locusta migratoria* can be kept in one cage (Fig. 14). Place long branching twigs across the cage, from corner to corner, so that the hoppers can hang head down when they moult. Place the light bulb near another corner, to give a day-time temperature of 28 to 34 °C in different parts of the cage.

Fresh but not wet grass is an adequate diet. Also, provide some dry grass and a small dish of wheat bran. When only dry food is available, a water fountain is essential (see Fig. 11). Remove any old grass, faeces and dead locusts each day.

Mature females will lay eggs in a glass jar (or in a metal container—see Fig. 14) full of sand (five parts clean, dry, sterilised sand to one part of water). The sand surface should be level with the cage floor (see Fig. 14). If possible, incubate the eggs at 28 to 33 °C. Otherwise, keep them in a warm place. Keep the jar covered with a loose-fitting lid. The eggs will hatch in about

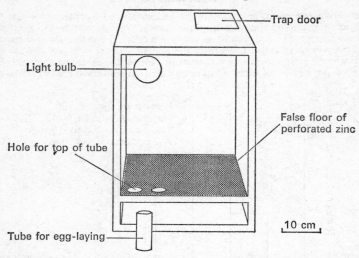

Fig. 14. Rearing cage for locusts, made from wood or metal and with a glass front (based on Barrass, R., *The Locust: A laboratory guide* (3rd edn.), Heinemann, London).

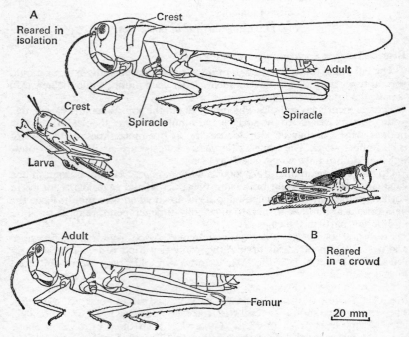

Fig. 15. Locusts reared (A) in isolation, (B) with other locusts.

two weeks. If the sand is too fine, or if too much water is used, the sand will be waterlogged and the eggs will not live (see p. 124).

Investigation: *some effects of crowding in locusts*
1. Prepare ten 1000 cm³ beakers so that each one is a small rearing cage. Put some dry sand in each, a few twigs, and some fresh grass. Cover the top with mosquito netting or similar material held in place by an elastic band.
2. Collect young locusts, from the eggs laid by one female, as they emerge to the surface of the sand.
3. Place ten first-stage hoppers in one jar, ten in another, and one in each of the remaining eight jars.
4. Place the beakers around a lamp, to keep the locusts warm, and provide them with fresh grass each day until they are fully grown.
5. Observe the difference between the locusts reared alone and those reared with other locusts (see Fig. 15). Remember that these insects are all of the same kind (that is, of the same species). Indeed, in your investigation they developed from eggs laid in one batch by one female and you might have expected them to look very similar to one another.

Investigation: *differences between people.* To take a fingerprint or thumb print: (1) wash your hands; (2) roll the tip of the finger lightly on a black-inked pad; and then (3) roll the inked finger on the edge of a piece of white paper.

Is the print of one finger similar to the prints from other fingers of the same hand? Compare your fingerprints with those of other people. You may see similarities but you will also find differences. Fingerprints may be left by criminals at the scene of their crime and the police use them as an aid in crime detection. So far, millions of people have been fingerprinted but no two people have been found to have identical fingerprints.

People differ from one another in many other ways. The differences we can measure are called **quantitative differences**. For example, people of the same sex who are about the same age differ in height and weight. Other differences are called **qualitative differences**. These are the differences which enable us to put people into groups according to the things they either have or do not have—such as brown eyes. You have no difficulty in recognising each person you know as an **individual**. No two people are exactly alike. Variety is a characteristic of human life.

Test Questions

1. In the water culture experiment (p. 18): (*a*) what is the purpose of the jar that contains only water; and (*b*) how could you modify the experiment so that you could be more certain that the differences between the plants were due to differences between the solutions and not the kind of differences that you might have observed if all the plants had been grown in one of the solutions?

2. (*a*) Describe how the life cycle of a locust or cockroach differs from that of a butterfly of house-fly. (*b*) Draw two diagrams and label them to indicate the differences. (*c*) List four differences between a larva and an adult house-fly.

4

ORGANISMS ARE ADAPTED

The place in which any organism lives is called its **habitat**. Some organisms, like the house-fly, live in different habitats and exploit different resources, at different times in their lives. House-flies lay eggs in a moist place (see Fig. 11); the maggots that hatch from the eggs (see Fig. 12) live in the liquid medium upon which they feed; the fully-formed maggots move to a dry but dark place where they develop into pupae; and flies live on the ground, on vegetation and in the air.

The **form** of any organism at each stage in its development and growth, and the way it lives (its way of life or its **mode of life**) at each stage, are **appropriate** to the environment in which it is living at the time. This **adaptation to environment** is a condition of life: that is to say, unless an organism is adapted to a particular environment it cannot live in that place. This is why organisms not only grow, and have a characteristic form at each stage in their growth, but also their form and mode of life is always appropriate to the place in which they are living.

This chapter includes other examples of the adaptation of different organisms to their environment in all aspects of their lives. We shall note this characteristic of living things whenever we study them, and therefore in all chapters of this book.

Differences between Plants and Animals

If anyone asked how animals differ from plants you might think, because they are so different, that you would not know how to begin your answer.

Plants   live in one place;
              have a branching body; and
              most of them are green and make their own food.
Animals eat plants or other animals;
              have a compact body; and
              most of them move from place to place.

These obvious differences between plants and animals (and other differences summarised on p. 141) should not cause you to think that plants and animals are essentially different. On the contrary, they are fundamentally alike (see p. 142) and the differences between them can be understood as adaptations to their different modes of life.

The Life of Vertebrates

Vertebrates are animals with vertebrae (or backbones, see Fig. 93). The vertebrae are part of the vertebral column that extends along the body from the brain case to the tip of the tail.

Differences in the **form** of different vertebrates can be related to differences in their habitat and **mode of life** at different stages in their lives.

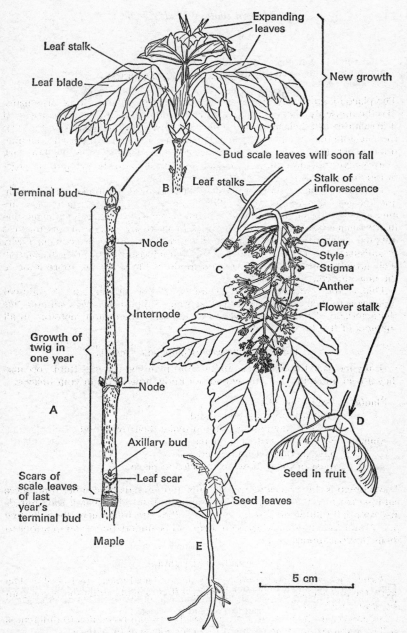

Fig. 16. A twig of a deciduous tree *Acer*, a maple, in four seasons: (A) without leaves (in winter); (B) new growth (in spring); (C) inflorescence (in summer); (D) ripe fruit (in autumn); and (E) a seedling (in the following spring).

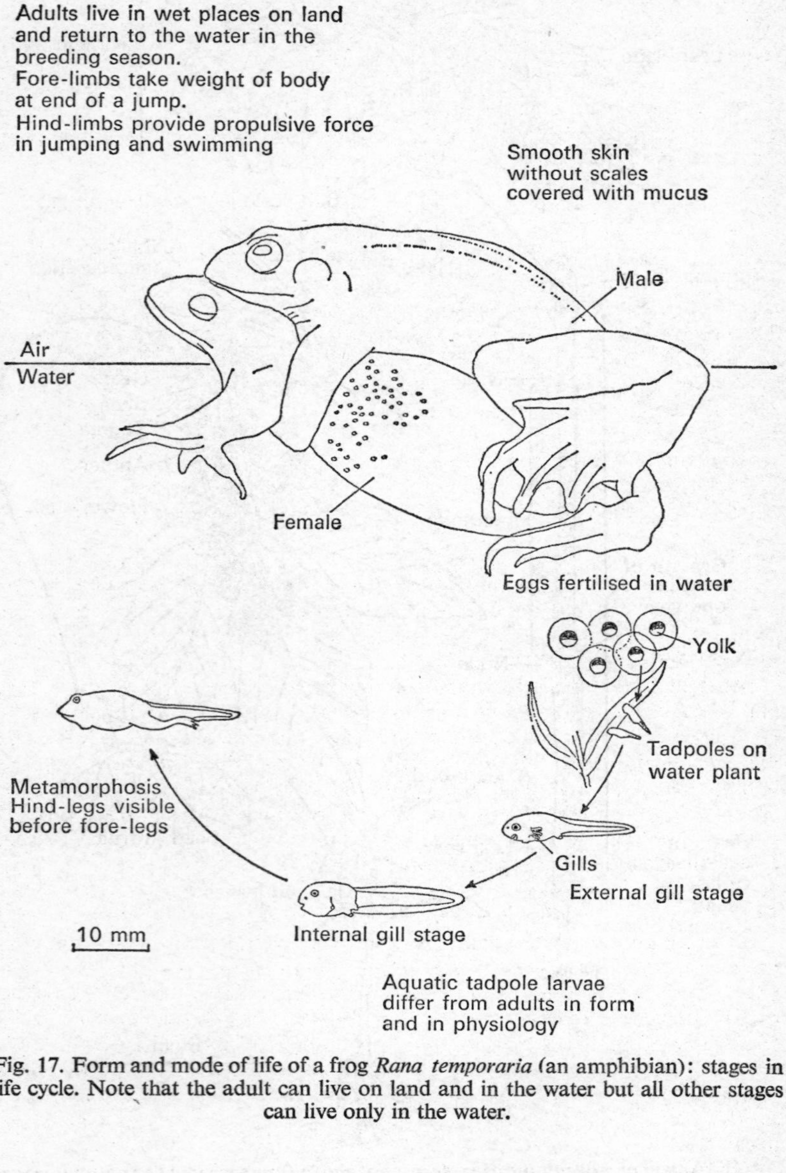

Adults live in wet places on land and return to the water in the breeding season.
Fore-limbs take weight of body at end of a jump.
Hind-limbs provide propulsive force in jumping and swimming

Smooth skin without scales covered with mucus

Male

Air
Water

Female

Eggs fertilised in water

Yolk

Tadpoles on water plant

Metamorphosis
Hind-legs visible before fore-legs

Gills
External gill stage

10 mm

Internal gill stage

Aquatic tadpole larvae differ from adults in form and in physiology

Fig. 17. Form and mode of life of a frog *Rana temporaria* (an amphibian): stages in life cycle. Note that the adult can live on land and in the water but all other stages can live only in the water.

Form and Mode of Life of the Frog *Rana temporaria*

Frogs spend most of their adult life on land but they discharge their eggs and sperm in fresh-water pools and ditches. The male frog clings to the female as the eggs and sperm are released, close together, and the eggs are fertilised in the water. Each egg contains yolk which nourishes the developing frog until it hatches as a tadpole (Fig. 17). Tadpoles obtain oxygen from the water, through the surface of their folded gills. They feed first on pond weed and later on small animals. They have a streamlined body and a long tail, similar to that of a fish, and they can move quickly through the water. Movement contributes to their survival by enabling them to feed and to move away from other animals that might eat them. In all respects they are aquatic animals.

The change from the tadpole to adult form (see Fig. 17) is another example of **metamorphosis** (see p. 21). Tadpoles, like house-fly maggots (p. 22) and locust hoppers (p. 24), are called larvae. A **larva** is an active stage in the life cycle of an animal which differs from the adult in its form and mode of life, and which does not breed. The frog tadpole develops four legs, its tail gradually becomes shorter, its gills cease to function, and the adult frog obtains all its oxygen either through its moist skin or, by breathing air, through the surface of its lungs. The frog's body is not streamlined. By walking and jumping, frogs find food and can move away from unfavourable habitats. Because of their moist skin, through which they lose water, most frogs (and other Amphibia, see p. 203) can live only in wet or humid places.

Form and Mode of Life of other Vertebrates

Fishes live only in the water. They have a **streamlined** body with paired **fins** and their skin contains calcareous scales. They have **gills** and obtain oxygen from the water. Their eggs are fertilised in the water and they develop in the water. There is no larval stage.

Most reptiles, birds and mammals live on the land. They all have **lungs** and breathe air. Reptiles have horny scales, and the birds have been described as feathered reptiles. Reptiles and birds lay eggs. The egg, which has a **box-like** shell, is fertilised before it is laid, and before the shell is formed. The young develop in a watery fluid inside the shell. Mammals have hair (fur). The egg of a mammal is fertilised, and the young develop, inside the female parent. The young are protected after birth, and fed on **milk**. **Parental care** is a feature of the life of both birds and mammals.

The Life of Flowering Plants

As a seed germinates the young root grows down into the soil and the shoot grows up, penetrating the soil and surface debris, into the air. The flowering plant, therefore, lives partly in the soil and partly in the air. It is adapted to life in two very different environments. If conditions in the soil and in the air are favourable, and if they remain favourable, the plant continues to grow. If at any time the environment where the plant is growing is unfavourable the plant either tolerates the adverse conditions and survives, or it dies. In form, structure and functioning, a flowering plant is adapted to life in one place.

The **root** anchors the plant in the soil; and water and mineral nutrients are absorbed from the soil through the surface of the root. The growth and branching of the root increases the anchorage and increases the area of contact between the root surface and the soil.

The **shoot** comprises the stem and leaves. At the shoot tip the stem grows longer and new leaves, with axillary buds, are formed. Each axillary bud may grow into a new branch (with leaves or flowers). The growth and branching of the shoot increases the number of leaves in contact with the air. The stem holds the leaves and flowers in the air and links all parts of the plant.

The leaf stalk holds the blade of the leaf away from the stem (usually in the sunlight). The leaf blade is flat and very thin and it has a large surface area in proportion to its volume. The large upper surface faces the sun and, because the leaf is so thin, sunlight penetrates to all parts of the leaf blade. **Chlorophyll**, the green pigment of leaves and young stems, absorbs light energy. This energy is used, with water from the soil and carbon dioxide from the air, in the synthesis of sugars. The carbon dioxide used in this **photosynthesis** is absorbed through microscopic openings in the surface of the leaf blade.

In the **flower** bud (Fig. 154) the sepals and petals enclose and protect the stamens and carpels. If pollen is transferred from the anthers to the stigma (Fig. 152), the ovary develops into a **fruit** containing seeds. The transfer of pollen from the anther to the stigma is called **pollination**. The pollen may be carried, for example, in the wind or on the bodies of insects. Some of the differences between the flowers of different kinds of plants can be understood as adaptations to different methods of pollination (see p. 251). Similarly, differences between the fruits of different kinds of plants result in their seeds being dispersed in different ways (see p. 253). As a result of the dispersal of seeds, plants colonise new habitats. This contributes to the survival of each kind of plant in some habitats even though it may be eliminated in others.

Survival during Unfavourable Periods

Flowering plants differ in their growth habit but, during any growing season, there is a period of **vegetative growth** (the production of all parts of the plant except flowers) after which flowers may be produced. Some plants grow from seed and flower in the same year, and they die after producing seeds. Such plants are called **annuals**. **Biennials** grow from seed in one year (vegetative growth only) and flower in the next year, after which they die. **Perennials** grow from seed in one year, flower in later years and may live for many years.

In cold climates and in the tropics the shoots of some **herbaceous** (non-woody) perennials die back each year and only their underground parts survive the cold or dry season. These parts contain food reserves which support the rapid growth and flowering of new shoots when conditions are again favourable. Bulbs and tubers make possible **perennation**—survival from year to year. Many crop plants, including onions (for bulbs) and potatoes (for tubers) (see Fig. 18), have been changed over thousands of years of cultivation. These are useful foods not only because they are good sources of essential food materials (see p. 184) but also because they can be stored for many months and eaten in a cold or dry season when most food plants are not growing.

Trees and shrubs (woody perennials) which lose their leaves before the cold or dry season are called deciduous plants to distinguish them from evergreens which do not lose all their leaves at one time. **Deciduous plants** survive the

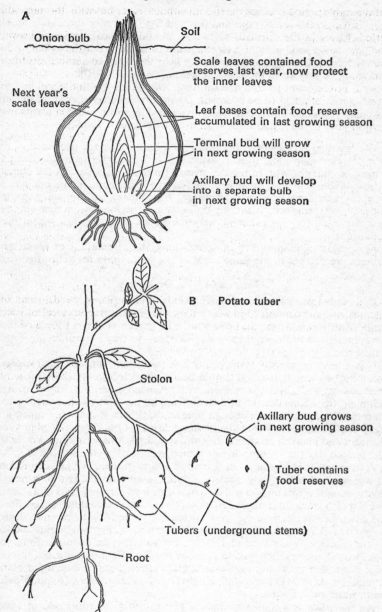

Fig. 18. Perennation and asexual reproduction: (A) bulb of onion *Allium cepa* (cut in half); (B) part of potato plant *Solanum tuberosum*, with tubers.

unfavourable period because the shoot, without leaves but with dormant buds (Fig. 16A), is resistant to cold and drought. At the end of the unfavourable period, leaves in the dormant buds expand and the scale leaves fall away. The new leaves soon present a large surface to sunlight but the axillary buds usually remain dormant and these may help the plant to survive any short unfavourable periods in the growing season.

Seeds are resistant to cold and drought. When they are in the soil but not growing they are said to be dormant. **Dormant seeds** may survive in the soil for many years and this is one reason why seedlings of unwanted plants may grow in your garden, year after year, even with careful weeding.

The **breeding seasons** of animals are such that young are produced at the time of year when most food is available. In the cold season (in cold and temperate climates) and in the dry season (in the tropics), when the climate is least favourable and when less food is available, some animals move to another place, some become inactive (see *Hibernation*, p. 236), and some die but leave offspring which survive unfavourable periods at another stage in their life cycle (as, for example, may the pupae of house-flies within their puparium).

As a result of many kinds of adaptations, the same kinds of plants and animals are present in the same place at the same times for year after year.

Observing Living Organisms

In a **garden** you can study different kinds of crop plants, weeds, pests and diseases, and the conditions in which they will grow and reproduce, and their methods of reproduction and dispersal. The garden is also a source of food for animals and of material for investigations—so that natural habitats need not be disturbed.

If you have no garden, grow plants in a pot or window-box. The **window-box** must be securely fixed. It should be almost as long as the window ledge, about 14 cm wide, and 16 cm deep, with drainage holes in the bottom. Add chippings (to 2.5 cm deep) and then soil and humus up to 2 cm from the top. Place each plant in a large enough hole so that there is space for roots, and leave enough space between the plants. Provide support for tall plants and climbers and plant them where they will not shade smaller plants. Water the plants each day (in the morning or evening) until they are established.

A **terrarium** (or vivarium) is a miniature indoor garden, in a glass container, in which small plants (and sometimes also small animals) live together. In establishing a terrarium you will learn not only how certain plants and animals live but also which organisms can be kept together in a confined space. Study the place in which the organisms normally live and try to provide similar conditions. An aquarium tank is a suitable container. Provide humus and leaf mould (previously sterilised at 120 °C). Try to grow, for example, fungi (on dead wood), mosses, lichens and ferns. Water the soil until it is moist but not wet. Cover the tank with an air-tight glass cover. Keep it where the plants will receive six to eight hours diffuse light from above each day. Do not provide more water or nutrients.

An **aquarium** is a miniature indoor pond, in a glass container, in which small water plants and small animals live together. In establishing an aquarium you will learn which organisms can be kept together in a confined space.

Unless you can maintain a balance between the water plants and a few small animals, a water filter and aeration equipment are necessary. Any animals must be fed regularly according to their needs.

Test Questions

1. Define the terms (*a*) habitat, (*b*) larva and (*c*) metamorphosis.
2. State four differences between plants and animals.
3. Prepare drawings of the larva of a named amphibian at two different stages in its development. Label your drawings to make clear similarities and differences in external appearance.
4. (*a*) Name two different kinds of dormant structures in the life of one named plant. (*b*) State two ways in which a dormant stage is important in the life cycle of this plant.

FORMS OF LIFE

Naming Organisms

People give names to things and to groups of things so that other people will know what they are talking about. Maize, pea, house-fly and mouse are some of the names used in this book. The names of these plants and animals immediately cause you to think about them and cause you to picture different kinds of organisms.

Biologists give each kind of organism two names. For example, the domestic cat is called *Felis felis* and the domestic dog is called *Canis familiaris*. This method of naming organisms, which is called the **binomial system** because every species is given two names, was devised by a Swedish naturalist called Linnaeus in the 18th century. *Canis familiaris* has a different name in different languages: the dog (English); *le chien* (French); and *el perro* (Spanish). The value of the scientific names, based on Latin or Greek words, is that they are the same in all scientific writing. Each kind of organism is called a species and its scientific name is therefore called its **specific name**. Like the technical terms biologists use, for example, for naming the parts of organisms, these specific names are part of the common language used by scientists in all nations.

Sorting Organisms into Groups

Principles of Classification

The way in which we classify things depends upon our purpose. If books in a library were classified for easy storage, so that the most books could be packed into the smallest space, they could be arranged according to their size. But if the classification was intended to help people to see all the books on one subject, in one place, the books would have to be arranged in groups according to their titles and contents.

A **classification** is simply an arrangement into groups; and the most useful classifications are those in which the members of each group have many things in common, which help us to recognise correctly the members of each group and so to distinguish them from the members of other groups.

Arranging things into groups and giving them names helps us to talk or write about them. Different kinds of tools are classified as hammers, saws, etc. There are many kinds of hammers. Each kind has a different name but they are all recognisable as members of one group (the hammers) and all kinds of saws are clearly members of another group (the saws). When we ask for a hammer people will know what we mean but we shall need to be more precise if we require a particular kind of hammer.

Classifying Organisms

Linnaeus, as well as the binomial system for naming organisms, devised a **natural system** for placing organisms into groups. The 12th edition of his book

Systema Naturae was published in 1766. His system is called 'natural' because he placed similar organisms together: so that those in each group had many things in common by which they could be distinguished from those in other groups.

Closely similar species are placed in the same genus and given the same generic name.

Canis familiaris	domestic dog	worldwide distribution
Canis lupus	wolf	North temperate regions
Canis latrans	coyote	North and Central America
Canis dingo	dingo	Australia
Canis aureus	golden jackal	Africa and Middle East

And closely similar genera are placed in the same Family. For example, in addition to all species in the genus *Canis*, the Family Canidae includes several other genera: the different kinds of foxes, the racoon dog of eastern Asia and Japan, the maned wolves of South America, the hunting dog of Africa, and the wild dog of India and east Asia.

Table 7. Some major groups of living organisms.

Viruses

Procaryota
  Bacteria
  Cyanobacteria; formerly called blue-green algae

Eucaryota
  Protista

  Algae
  Fungi
  Bryophyta } Plant kingdom
  Tracheophyta

  Porifera
  Cnidaria
  Platyhelminthes
  Nematoda
  Annelida } Animal kingdom
  Arthropoda
  Mollusca
  Echinodermata
  Chordata

Then, similar Families are placed in the same Order; and similar Orders in the same Class, according to the things they have in common by which they are distinguished from the members of other groups. For example, the animals placed in all the Orders of mammals have many things in common (see p. 29) by which they can be recognised as mammals and distinguished from other animals with backbones (see p. 29). But all the Classes of animals with backbones, because they have many things in common by which they can be distinguished, are placed in one major group. The domestic dog, for example, is classified as follows:

Species	*Canis familiaris*
Genus	*Canis*
Family	Canidae
Order	Carnivora (see p. 87)
Class	Mammalia (see p. 45)
Major group	Chordata (see p. 45)

This natural classification enables us to organise our knowledge of living things and to recognise the order which exists in nature (see Table 7). We then know something about any organism, even if we have not seen it, if we are told in which group the organism is classified. For example, if someone uses the word bird you think of an animal which has a beak and two eyes, and which walks on two legs, has two wings, has scales on its legs and feathers on the rest of its body.

Looking at Life

The study of organisms in their natural surroundings is called natural history. If you take an interest in natural history you will see a greater variety of organisms than you can see in a garden, a window-box, a terrarium or an aquarium. You will also see more of the ways in which different kinds of organisms affect one another; that is to say, you will be able to extend your observations.

Do anything you can to conserve plants and animals, and the places in which they live. Try not to damage the places you visit. Study the organisms without disturbing them. Make notes and drawings and take photographs as a record of what you have observed, but do not collect specimens. If you have to pick up an organism to examine it closely, replace it carefully. Try to leave it as you found it.

Investigation: *classifying living organisms.* In your garden, on derelict land, on a rubbish tip, in a woodland, on the sea shore, or in any place where there are living organisms, you will see many kinds of organisms. Observe some of them closely. From their external features, can you place each of them in one of the major groups described in this chapter?

How to use a Hand Lens

Some organisms are so small that you will need a good hand lens (a magnifying glass) if you are to see them clearly. A lens will also enable you to observe details that you could not otherwise see.

1. Use a lens that magnifies things ten times ($\times 10$ lens) or an instrument with both $\times 10$ and $\times 20$ lenses.
2. Keep both eyes open.
3. Hold the lens still (about 8 cm from one eye).
4. Move the object that you wish to examine until it is in focus (at about 16 cm from the lens).

The following list of some major groups of organisms, with brief notes on the external characteristics by which you can recognise the members of each group, should enable you to classify (place into the appropriate major group) those organisms that you are most likely to see.

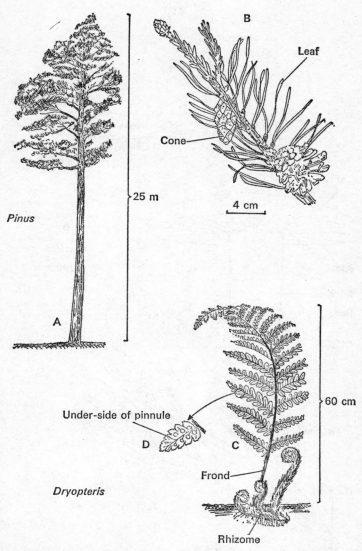

Fig. 19. Two tracheophytes: (A and B) a conifer *Pinus*; (C and D) a fern *Dryopteris*.

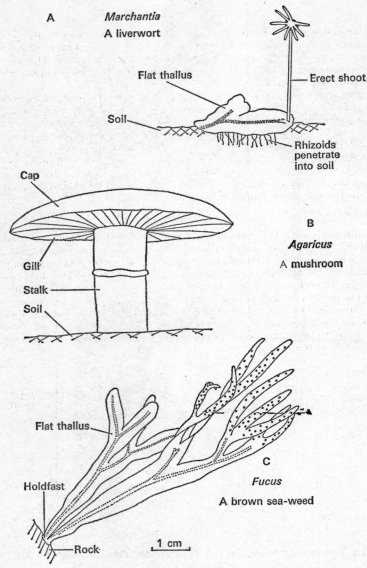

Fig. 20. (A) A bryophyte; (B) a fungus; (C) an alga.

Plants

Algae

All algae (about 13 000 species) have the green pigment chlorophyll and some have other pigments. The seaweeds which live on rocky shores, attached to the rocks, are all algae, and so are the green powder-like plants which live on the surface of some trees and the green scums (Fig. 27A, for example) that float on warm stagnant fresh waters.

Each seaweed (Fig. 20C) has a holdfast that anchors the plant to the rock and a leaf-like part (or frond) that is supported by the sea water. On a rocky shore many seaweeds are exposed at low tide. Green algae live high on the shore where they are not submerged every day; many brown algae live lower on the shore where they are covered by the tide twice each day; and other brown algae and also the red algae live even lower on the shore (and in rock pools) where except at very low tides they are always covered by the sea. Some seaweeds are used as food for people, some as fodder for farm animals and some are sources of useful chemicals.

Fungi

The fungi (about 90 000 species) are plants without chlorophyll. Some are **saprobionts**: they absorb nutriment from decaying organisms. For example, moulds grow on humus in the soil (and so contribute to the process of decay) and on stored foods (and so cause great economic losses especially in stored cereals); and mushrooms (Fig. 20B) and toadstools live on decaying humus. Yeasts are used in brewing and in bread-making. Other fungi are **parasites**, living on or inside other living organisms from which they obtain their nutriment. For example, there are many blights, mildews, smuts and rusts which are of great economic importance because they damage or kill crop plants and so reduce yields (p. 106).

Bryophyta

The bryophytes (about 25 000 species) are the liverworts and mosses (Fig. 20A). They live on land and are leaf-like plants which contain chlorophyll and have delicate thread-like processes that penetrate into the soil.

Tracheophyta

The tracheophytes are the club-mosses, horsetails, ferns, conifers (cone-bearing plants) and flowering plants. All these have well-developed roots and conducting tissues (see Figs. 84 and 126) in which materials are transported from one part of the plant to other parts. Their leaves contain chlorophyll.

The ferns (Class Filicinae: about 10 000 species) have roots, a perennial underground stem called the rhizome, and large leaves (Fig. 19C and D).

Many **cone-bearing plants** (Class Gymnospermae: about 700 species) are the large trees from which we obtain softwood timber and wood pulp for papermaking. These trees have roots and a shoot which has leaves (Fig. 19A and B) but they do not have flowers.

The **flowering plants** (Class Angiospermae: about 280 000 species) have roots, and a shoot which has leaves, flowers and fruits (enclosing the seeds). When the seed germinates there is either one seed leaf (Fig. 4Z) or two

(Fig. 16E). The flowering plants, therefore, are either monocotyledons (with one seed leaf), like the grasses which have narrow leaves with parallel veins (Fig. 4Z), or dicotyledons (with two seed leaves), which are broad-leaved plants with branching veins (Figs. 5 and 16).

All crop plants, grown as sources of food for man and for his farm animals, and all the trees from which we obtain hard-wood timbers, are flowering plants. Many chemicals and natural products (including many drugs and rubber) are extracted from flowering plants, as are many natural fibres (including cotton and flax). Honey is produced by bees from the nectar and pollen that they collect from flowers. Without flowering plants the life of many animals, including our own, would be impossible.

Animals

Porifera

The sponges (about 4500 species) nearly all live in the sea, fixed to rocks. Many of them live in deep water. Because sponges do not move they resemble plants (see Fig. 21D). However, they are animals and they feed upon small organisms that live suspended in sea water. You may not be able to study living sponges but you can see preserved specimens in most natural history museums.

Platyhelminthes

The flatworms (about 7000 species) are the free-living leaf-like animals called planarians which live in fresh waters and feed on decaying animals; and the parasitic flukes (Fig. 21B) and tapeworms (Fig. 21A) which live inside other organisms for most of their lives.

The liver-fluke, a parasite of sheep and cattle, lives in the liver of its host and is harmful to its health, greatly reducing milk and meat production in all countries. The blood-fluke of man causes the disease schistosomiasis (bilharzia).

Different species of tapeworms are parasites of different species of vertebrate animals, including farm animals and people, and they are harmful to health (see p. 105).

Cnidaria

The cnidarians (about 10 000 species) are animals with sting cells (see Cnidocil in Fig. 36C). *Hydra* (Fig. 36) lives in fresh water but most cnidarians live in the sea: sea anemones (Fig. 21C) live attached to rocks in the sea and in rock pools, and they are sometimes exposed on rocky shores; jelly-fishes swim in the surface waters of the sea and are sometimes stranded on the sea shore; and the corals form coral reefs and atolls.

There is a superficial resemblance between some cnidarians and some plants. All organisms that are fixed in one place, or floating in the sea, encounter their surroundings equally on all sides and, like a wheel, in which all radii are similar, such organisms are radially symmetrical (or nearly so).

In the flatworms (Fig. 21B), in contrast, one side of the body is the mirror image of the other side. This bilateral symmetry (see also Fig. 6) is characteristic of animals that move through their environment with one end leading

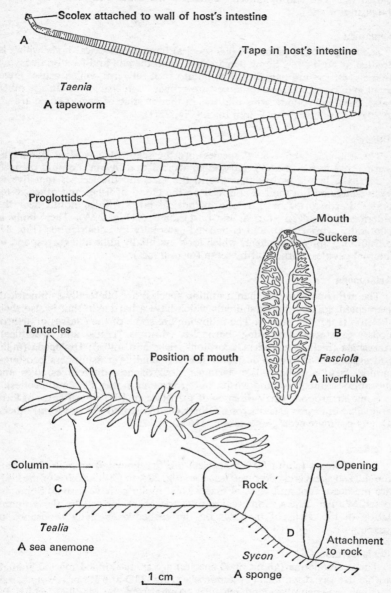

Fig. 21. (A and B) Two flatworms; (C) a cnidarian; (D) a sponge.

(called the head end or anterior end) and the other end following (called the posterior end).

Nematoda

The roundworms (about 10 000 species) have a cylindrical body which is pointed at both ends. Some nematodes live in the soil and feed on decaying animals. Others are parasites. The potato root eelworm, which causes great economic losses wherever potatoes are grown, is microscopic. On the other hand, the large roundworms that live in the intestine of some people are up to 20 cm long and about 5 mm thick (Fig. 22D).

Annelida

The annelids (about 8000 species) are the segmented worms: the earthworms that live in the soil and similar worms that live in the mud of fresh waters; the bristle worms that live in the sea; and the leeches that live in fresh waters and in the sea and feed on the blood of fishes and other vertebrates. Earthworms have a long cylindrical body with a mouth near the anterior end and an anus at the posterior end (Fig. 22A). Their body is bilaterally symmetrical, and is marked externally by constrictions (Fig. 87, p. 160) into units or **segments** which look essentially alike and correspond to internal cavities marked off by septa (membranes).

Arthropoda

The arthropods (more than a million species) are bilaterally symmetrical, segmented, jointed-limbed animals which have a hard skin that is also their skeleton (Fig. 22B and C). The following are some of the Classes of arthropods: **Crustacea** (including barnacles, shrimps, crabs and woodlice); **Arachnida** (including spiders, scorpions, ticks and mites); **Diplopoda** (millipedes); **Chilopoda** (centipedes); and **Insecta** (including grasshoppers, bed-bugs, aphids, head and body lice, termites, cockroaches, dragonflies, flies and mosquitoes, ants, bees and wasps, butterflies and moths, fleas and beetles).

Some arthropods carry diseases of man (see p. 107) and diseases of farm animals. Some are pests of crops. Others destroy stored foods. We eat others. Others pollinate crop plants (see p. 116 and p. 251).

Mollusca

The molluscs (about 80 000 species) are unsegmented animals, including the slugs, oysters and octopuses (see also Fig. 23A to C). The parts of the body are the head, foot and visceral mass. Most molluscs have a shell. Some are pests. We eat others. Some calcareous rocks are formed by the accumulation of the shells of molluscs on the seabed over many thousands of years.

Echinodermata

The echinoderms (about 5000 species) are spiny-skinned marine animals with a five-rayed symmetry: the starfishes (Fig. 23D and E), brittle-stars, seaurchins, sea-cucumbers and sea lilies. Apart from the sea-lilies, which are fixed by a stalk to the sea bed, the echinoderms are active animals.

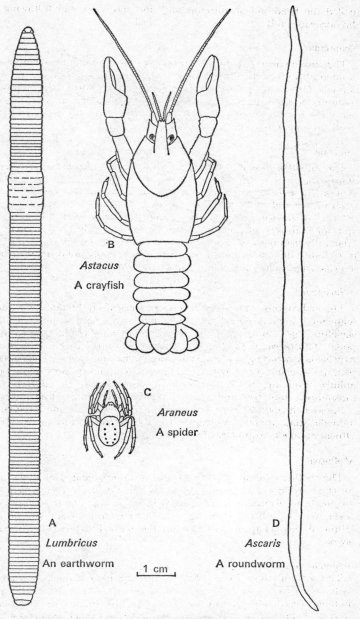

Fig. 22. (A) A segmented worm; (B and C) two arthropods; (D) a roundworm.

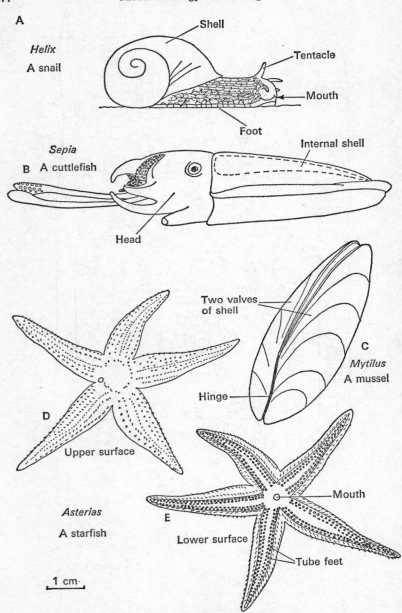

Fig. 23. (A to C) Three molluscs; (D and E) an echinoderm.

Chordata

The chordates (about 40 000 species) include some animals (the sea-squirts and lancelets) which do not have backbones as well as all the animals with backbones. They are all active bilaterally symmetrical animals with a well-developed head and a tail that extends posteriorly beyond the anus.

The Classes of chordates include the **Agnatha** (fishes without jaws—lampreys and hagfishes); **Chondrichthyes** (cartilaginous fishes including the dogfishes, sharks, skates and rays); **Osteichthyes** (bony fishes including sardines and cod); **Amphibia** (frogs and salamanders); **Reptilia** (turtles, crocodiles, snakes and lizards); **Aves** (birds); and **Mammalia** (**Monotremes**—egg-laying mammals, the spiny ant-eater and duck-billed platypus; **Marsupalia**—pouched mammals, including the opossums and kangaroo; and **placental mammals** in which the young are well developed when they are born—including the shrews, rats, rabbits, cats, dogs, cattle, monkeys, people, whales and bats).

Test Questions

1. Name (*a*) three different kinds of plants which have the green pigment chlorophyll, and (*b*) one kind of plant which does not have chlorophyll.

2. Make a list of the major groups of plants and animals referred to in this chapter. Give examples of members of each group that are of economic importance and state why each organism is either beneficial or harmful to man's interests.

6

MICRO-ORGANISMS

Many discoveries in biology follow the development of new techniques or the invention of new instruments, which make possible new kinds of observations or extend our ability to observe. For example, the first microscope was made by Leeuwenhoek in Holland in the 17th century. With this microscope he saw things which nobody had seen before—things that can be seen only with a microscope. These small organisms are now called **micro-organisms.**

With the unaided eye we can see things that are only 0.1 mm apart. If things are closer together than this, the limit of the eye's **resolving power,** we do not see them as separate objects. With a magnifying glass (a simple microscope), or with a compound microscope (Fig. 24), which has more than one lens and gives a greater magnification, we can see things that are closer together.

The limit of the resolving power of a light microscope is set by the wavelength of light and there is nothing to be gained from magnifying things more than about 1500 times. In practice, the highest magnification used with a light microscope is normally 1000 times (as with a × 10 eyepiece and a × 100 oil immersion objective). This enables us to see things that are only 0.1 μm ($\doteq$ 0.0001 mm) apart.

An electron miscroscope has a greater resolving power than a light microscope because the beam of electrons has a much shorter wavelength than has light and a 100 000 times magnification is commonly used, resolving structures that are only 0.000 001 mm apart.

The word **structure** is used for the parts of organisms that we can see with the unaided eye, or with a light microscope (Fig. 24); and the word **ultra-structure** for the smaller things and the greater detail that we see only in electronmicrographs (Figs. 29B and 76). An electronmicrograph is a photograph of the image produced by an electron microscope; and a photomicrograph is a photograph of the image produced by a light microscope.

Even though it is easy to use a microscope correctly, many people do not do so. Indeed, many qualified scientists have to use expensive and elaborate microscopes but do not learn to use them properly. As with any other instrument, you will get the most out of a microscope only if you use it carefully and correctly.

How to use a Microscope

If you are examining a prepared microscope slide make sure that it is clean. The lenses of the condenser, objective and eyepiece of the microscope should be cleaned with lens tissue to remove dust or fingerprints. Take care not to get mounting medium or any other fluid on the objective lens or on the stage of the microscope. Store the microscope under a dust cover.

1. Place the lamp 20 cm away from the mirror; and use the flat side of the mirror to reflect light through the microscope.

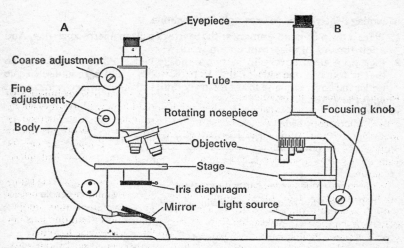

Fig. 24. Parts of a compound microscope: (A) microscope with a tube that moves up and down for focusing; (B) a microscope with a stage that moves for focusing and with built-in illumination.

2. Adjust the microscope so that the revolving nosepiece can be rotated without touching the stage.
3. The low-power objective should be in position immediately below the tube (as in Fig. 24).
4. Open the substage diaphragm fully.
5. Place a microscope slide on the stage and focus on the object that you wish to examine.
6. Move the mirror until the field is evenly illuminated.
7. If your microscope has a substage condenser (and if this is not fixed in one position), hold a mounted needle or a sharp pencil against the lamp and focus the condenser until you see a sharp image of the point through the microscope.
8. Remove the eyepiece and adjust the substage diaphragm until the light entering the tube is reduced to four fifths of the diameter of the lens. Replace the eyepiece.
9. To use a higher-power objective rotate the nosepiece carefully. Hold your head to the side, level with the stage, to ensure that the objective does not touch the slide. Click the objective into position. The object should still be in focus. If it is not, focus carefully.
10. Repeat step 8. The microscope is now adjusted for use with the high-power objective.

The distance between the objective and the object, when this is correctly in focus, is called the **working distance**. Take care not to break slides when you rotate the nosepiece or focus the microscope. Microscope slides are expensive and some are irreplaceable. Also, the objective lens may be damaged.

Mounting Material for Microscopic Examination

1. Place a drop of pond water near the centre of a clean microscope slide. Add a few threads of absorbent cotton wool.
2. Pick up a clean cover-slip by two opposite edges. Place a third edge so that it touches one side of the drop of water. Hold a mounted needle under the cover-slip and lower it slowly until its whole surface is in contact with the water.

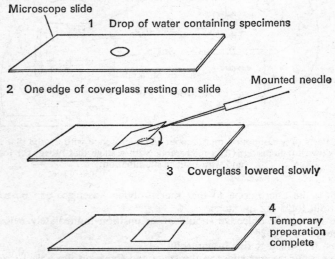

Fig. 25. Mounting material for microscopic examination.

3. To mount a small transparent object for examination (see p. 153), place this in a drop of water on the slide and lower the cover-slip as described above.

In a drop of pond water you will find a variety of microscopic organisms. The threads of cotton wool in your preparation will restrict their movement, making it easier for you to study them, and it will prevent them from being squashed below the cover-slip.

Protists

Amoeba, Euglena and *Paramecium* (Fig. 26) all live in fresh-water pools. *Amoeba* moves about on the bottom mud. It is just visible without a microscope but you need a microscope to see its structure. Sometimes there are so many *Euglena* in a pool that the water looks green but these are much smaller than *Amoeba* and you cannot see that the green colour is due to the presence of green micro-organisms unless you look at a drop of the water under a microscope. *Paramecium* is another kind of micro-organism. Many protists live in fresh water; others live in the sea; and others live in the body fluids of other organisms (see p. 107).

All protists have a **nucleus** (Fig. 26). A nuclear membrane is between the nucleus and the **cytoplasm**. The outermost part of the cytoplasm is the **plasmalemma** (or cell membrane). Outside this membrane there is, in some kinds of protists, a pellicle (Fig. 26C); and in other kinds there is a thicker structure called a cell wall (Fig. 27B). Neither of these should be confused with the cell wall of bacteria which is composed of different materials. In some protists the plasmalemma is the outermost part of the organism (Fig. 26A).

A **cell** may be defined as a nucleus and the cytoplasm associated with this nucleus. The protists are single-celled or **unicellular** organisms.

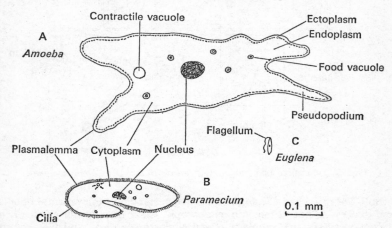

Fig. 26. Three protists: (A) *Amoeba*, (B) *Paramecium* and (C) *Euglena*.

Microscopic Algae

A librarian might have difficulty in trying to classify a book on physics and chemistry for biologists. Should it be put with books on physics or with books on chemistry, or with books on biology? Biologists have to make such decisions when they try to classify some organisms. There are many organisms which, like *Chlamydomonas* (Fig. 27B), can be classified as protists because they are similar to the protists (compare Figs. 26A and 27B) or as algae because they are similar to the algae (compare Figs. 27A and 27B).

Chlamydomonas and *Spirogyra* have many things in common but *Spirogyra* is classified as an alga, never as a protist. *Spirogyra* is an unbranched thread, which may be more than 100 mm long, and it is called a filamentous green alga. It differs from *Chlamydomonas* in that its body (the whole thread) is made up of many cylindrical cells (like a chain) whereas each *Chlamydomonas*, like the protists, is one cell. We say that *Spirogyra* is **multicellular**. Each cell is larger than the cell of *Chlamydomonas* but much of the space in the cell is occupied by the large fluid-filled vacuole. The nucleus is near the centre of the cell, suspended by threads of cytoplasm which connect the cytoplasm around the nucleus to the cytoplasm next to the cell wall. The cytoplasm contains one or more spiral chloroplasts.

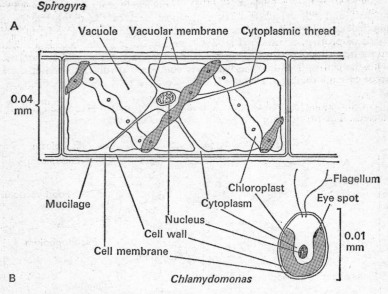

Fig. 27. Two microscopic algae: (A) *Spirogyra* and (B) *Chlamydomonas*.

Both *Spirogyra* and *Chlamydomonas* live in standing fresh waters: in pools and ditches. Although they are microscopic, water may appear green when it contains very large numbers of unicellular green algae and filamentous green algae may form a green scum over the water surface. The green colour is due to the presence of the green pigment, **chlorophyll**, which is in the **chloroplasts**.

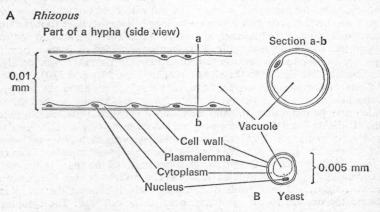

Fig. 28. Two microscopic fungi: (A) a mould; (B) a yeast.

Microscopic Fungi

Rhizopus and *Mucor* are microscopic thread-like organisms; but the structure of a single thread of one of these fungi is very different from a filament of *Spirogyra*. A thread of *Rhizopus* is called a **hypha**.

1. It branches and so forms a tangled mass of threads called a **mycelium**.
2. It contains no chlorophyll.
3. It has a wall that is not composed of cellulose.
4. It contains oil droplets or glycogen, as food reserves, but no starch.
5. It is not composed of cells (see Fig. 28A).

There is a large central vacuole of a fluid sap. The cytoplasm is near the surface of the hypha and there are many nuclei in this cytoplasm—that is to say, the hypha is not divided into cells but is an example of a **syncytium** (see also p. 95).

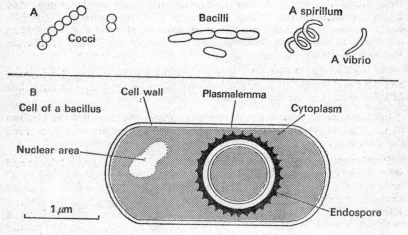

Fig. 29. Bacteria: (A) different kinds of bacteria; (B) the ultrastructure of a bacillus.

The larger fungi, with fruiting bodies called **mushrooms and toadstools**, are conspicuous only when they are fruiting. Their mycelium, in the soil or in rotting timber, is a tangled mass of microscopic threads like that of the bread moulds. The blights, mildews, smuts and rusts, which cause diseases of flowering plants, including crop plants, have a mycelium within the host plant. The yeasts (Fig. 28B), used in baking and brewing, are unicellular fungi (see pp. 93 and 94).

Bacteria

Because they are so small, you are not usually aware of bacteria but they are present in air, in water, in the soil, and upon and within other organisms. Leeuwenhoek, with his simple microscope, was the first person to see bacteria. Even with a compound microscope we cannot make out much detail of their structure. They are therefore classified according to their shape (see Fig. 29A) as **cocci** (spheres about 0.75 μm diameter); **bacilli** (rods up to 8 μm long); **spirilla** (spirals); and **vibrios** (curves).

Each bacterium is a unit of life, an individual, distinct from other individuals. The parts of one bacterium, its ultrastructure, are represented in Fig. 29B. The cell wall, unlike that of algae and other green plants, does not contain cellulose. Some bacteria have a chlorophyll pigment but this is not contained in chloroplasts and it is chemically different from the chlorophyll of algae and other green plants. Bacteria do not have mitochondria and their nuclear material is not enclosed in a nuclear membrane. Because of these differences, biologists place the bacteria in one group (the procaryotes); protists, plants and animals in another (the eucaryotes); and viruses (which are not cells and can live only in cells, see p. 111) in a third group: see Table 7.

Culture of Bacteria

Bacteria are cultured in transparent containers—for example, in glass Petri dishes—so that their growth can be seen as colonies develop. Any bacteria present on the surface of an agar jelly will multiply if this jelly contains suitable nutrients, if it has an appropriate pH, and if it is kept at an appropriate temperature. Different conditions favour the growth of different kinds of bacteria.

Culture medium. Dissolve 1 g beef extract, 0.2 g yeast extract, 1 g peptone and 0.5 g sodium chloride in 100 cm³ distilled water in a conical flask. Stir in 1.5 g agar. Plug the flask with non-absorbent cotton wool.

Sterilisation. To ensure that there are no organisms in the culture medium at the start of any investigation, sterilise the medium and the glass Petri dishes in a pressure cooker (15 min at 1 kg/cm²).

Pouring culture medium into Petri dishes. Close all windows and doors and work where there are no draughts. Allow the medium to cool to about 55 °C or heat flasks of solid medium in a beaker of water and then cool the liquid medium to about 55 °C for pouring. Place the Petri dishes on a flat surface. Raise the lid slowly at one side so that there is enough space to pour in some of the culture medium. Lower the lid slowly. The dish with the layer of culture medium is called a plate. Prepare all the plates you require.

Investigation: *detecting the presence of bacteria in air.* If you remove the lid of a Petri dish the nutrient medium is likely to be contaminated with the spores of bacteria and fungi. This is why such care is needed when you pour plates.

1. To detect the presence of bacteria in air, remove the lid from a Petri dish. Expose the plate to the air for 5 min on a clean working surface. Do not touch the plate or breathe upon it. Replace the lid. Secure the lid to the base in two places with adhesive tape. Label the dish on the base: 'exposed 5 min in laboratory'.
2. Expose another plate in the laboratory for 30 min. Secure and label.
3. Expose another plate in a refuse bin for 5 min. Secure and label.
4. Expose another plate outside for 5 min. Secure and label.
5. Secure the lid of another Petri dish, without exposing the plate, and label this **control.**

Keep the dishes upside-down at about 25 °C (or at room temperature). Each bacterium that can multiply in the conditions that you have provided will grow and reproduce and give rise to a separate colony. About one week after the start of this investigation, compare the plates and record your observations and conclusions.

Safety Precautions

Many bacteria, including some that are commonly present in the nose and on the skin, cause diseases. All bacteria, therefore, should be treated with caution.

(1) Secure each Petri dish lid to the base as soon as it has been exposed. (2) Do not remove the tape. (3) At the end of your investigation place the unopened Petri dish in disinfectant (fresh 40 per cent formaldehyde). (4) Do not eat, drink or put your fingers or anything else to your mouth. (5) Wash your hands before you leave the laboratory.

Test questions are included at the end of the next chapter.

7

LIFE IN ONE CELL

Consider your own life. Your body is separate from your environment and yet, all the time, you take in things from your environment and you lose things to your environment. These are characteristics of all living organisms by which we may distinguish them from non-living things: (1) their separate existence, distinct from their surroundings, which depends upon (2) a constant exchange of energy and materials between each organism and its surroundings.

The different parts of any organism, whether it is a single cell or is multi-cellular, are concerned with the intake of energy and matter from the environment, their use in the organism, and controlling the loss of energy and matter to the environment. The result of these different kinds of activities is the **maintenance** of the organism, and its **growth** and **reproduction**.

What Living Things are Made of

The matter and energy of which all living organisms are composed conform to the same laws of chemistry and physics as the matter and energy outside living organisms. Of the 92 elements that occur naturally in the universe only about 22 (all of low atomic mass—Table 8) are essential constituents of organisms. The elements are combined as molecules. Some molecules contain only one kind of atom (for example, hydrogen $= H_2$ and oxygen $= O_2$). Other molecules contain more than one kind of atom (for example, water $= H_2O$; carbon dioxide $= CO_2$; and sodium chloride $=$

Table 8. Essential elements in living organisms.

Atomic number	Element	Symbol	Atomic mass	Atomic number	Element	Symbol	Atomic mass
1	Hydrogen	H	1.01	17	Chlorine	Cl	35.46
5	Boron	B	10.82	19	Potassium	K	39.10
6	Carbon	C	12.01	20	Calcium	Ca	40.08
7	Nitrogen	N	14.01	24	Chromium	Cr	52.01
8	Oxygen	O	16.00	25	Manganese	Mn	54.91
9	Fluorine	F	19.00	26	Iron	Fe	55.85
11	Sodium	Na	22.99	27	Cobalt	Co	58.94
12	Magnesium	Mg	24.32	29	Copper	Cu	63.54
14	Silicon	Si	28.09	30	Zinc	Zn	65.38
15	Phosphorus	P	30.98	34	Selenium	Se	78.96
16	Sulphur	S	32.07	53	Iodine	I	126.90

NaCl). These four molecules (oxygen, water, carbon dioxide and sodium chloride), like many other molecules of cells, occur outside as well as inside living organisms. They are therefore called inorganic molecules.

Living organisms contain more **water** than anything else. About 65 per cent

54

Life in One Cell

of your mass is water, and a flowering plant contains even more (Fig. 30). Some of the oxygen and carbon dioxide in living organisms is in solution in the water, and some is chemically combined as part of larger molecules. The sodium chloride in living organisms is dissolved in water. In solution it is present not as molecules of sodium chloride but as separate parts, one of which has lost an electron (Na+) and is therefore positively charged, and the other has gained an electron (Cl−) and is therefore negatively charged. The sodium chloride, like other salts present in living organisms, dissociates in water. That is, it is present as separate sodium or chloride ions (Na+ and Cl−).

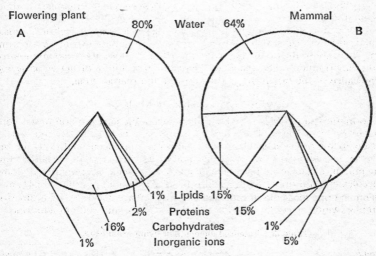

Fig. 30. Chemical composition of (A) a flowering plant and (B) a mammal (expressed as a percentage of each organism's mass).

Acids dissociate in water. For example, hydrochloric acid dissociates, giving hydrogen ions (H+) and chloride ions (Cl−). As more acid is dissolved in the water, more H+ and Cl− ions are present. Hydrogen ion concentration is therefore a measure of acidity and this is expressed on a scale: pH 0 (very acid) to pH 14 (very alkaline). Alkaline solutions have an excess of hydroxyl ions (OH−). The body fluids of organisms are either neutral (pH 7) or nearly so.

Organic molecules all contain carbon. They are produced from inorganic molecules, in nature, only in the bodies of living organisms. Many of these organic molecules contain many atoms and therefore have a very large mass. They are part of the complex organisation maintained throughout the life of any organism.

Carbohydrates, such as sugar and starch, are compounds of carbon, hydrogen and oxygen, in which the ratio of hydrogen to oxygen atoms is the same as in water—for example, glucose ($C_6H_{12}O_6$), sucrose ($C_{12}H_{22}O_{11}$). In glucose the atoms are arranged in a ring (Fig. 31), which can be represented as a hexagon. Glucose is a monosaccharide, a simple sugar. In the formation of maltose, a disaccharide, two glucose units are linked together (Fig. 31) and water is formed. Starch $(C_6H_{10}O_5)_n$ is called a polysaccharide because it is made up of many six-carbon units (n = a large whole number). Other polysaccharides are cellulose (the main constituent of plant cell walls—see Fig. 75) and glycogen (which is sometimes called animal starch).

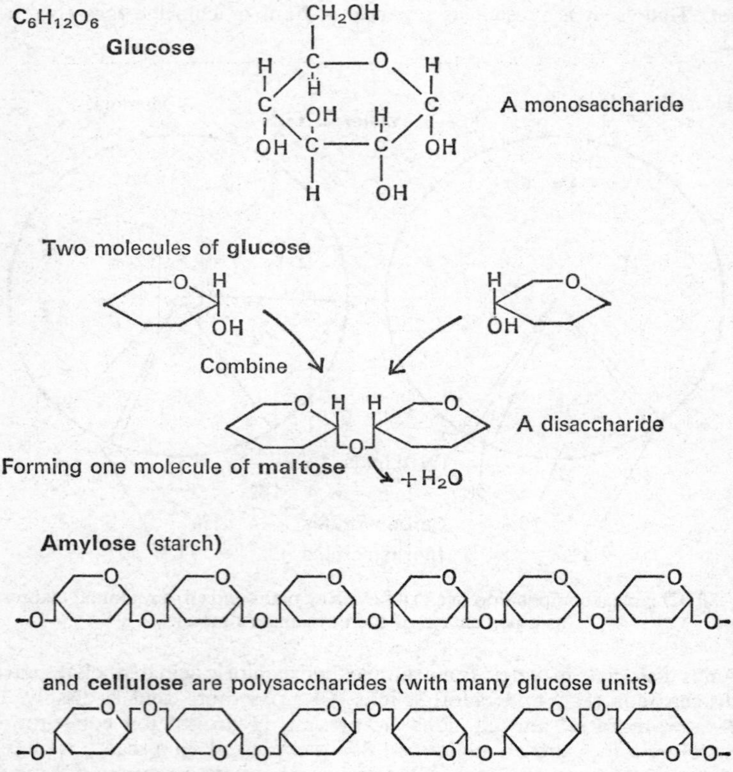

Fig. 31. Carbohydrates. Larger molecules are formed by the combination of small molecules of sugars, such as glucose, with the elimination of a molecule of water as each new link is added to the chain.

Lipids (fats and oils) also contain only carbon, hydrogen and oxygen, but the hydrogen and oxygen are not in the same proportions as in water. Each lipid molecule (formed from one molecule of glycerol linked to three fatty acid molecules) is a triglyceride. Some lipids are constituents of cell membranes; others are food reserves in cells (e.g. Fig. 89).

Proteins are formed by linking together amino acid molecules. Each amino acid contains nitrogen as well as carbon, hydrogen and oxygen. Twenty-three amino acids are present in living organisms but each organism has only some of them. In man, for example, there are 18. Just as you could build many different structures if you had 23 kinds of brick, and many bricks of each kind, so each organism makes many kinds of proteins. Each protein has some (but not all) of the different amino acids, linked in a chain. Many proteins are very large molecules, with several thousand amino acids in a particular order. Some are structural materials. Others are organic catalysts (see *Enzymes*, p. 183).

The Life of a Bacterial Cell

Some bacteria are able to oxidise inorganic molecules. For example:

$$\underset{\text{ammonia}}{NH_3} + \underset{\text{oxygen}}{2O_2} \longrightarrow \underset{\text{nitrate ion}}{NO_3^-} + \underset{\text{water}}{H_2O} + H^+ + \text{Energy}$$

The processes of synthesis, in which the bacterium uses this energy available from a chemical reaction, are called **chemosyntheses**.

Some bacteria have a green pigment, called bacterial chlorophyll, which traps light energy from the sun. This energy is then used in the formation of organic molecules from inorganic molecules:

$$\underset{\substack{\text{carbon}\\\text{dioxide}}}{6CO_2} + \underset{\text{water}}{6H_2O} + \underset{\text{sunlight}}{\text{Energy of}} \xrightarrow[\substack{\text{In presence}\\\text{of chlorophyll}}]{} \underset{\text{sugar}}{C_6H_{12}O_6} + \underset{\text{oxygen}}{6O_2}$$

This process of synthesis is called **photosynthesis**. The equation is a summary of the materials used and the products. Note that in this reaction, as in all reactions in the cell, the equation must balance. The number of atoms of each element must be the same in the reactants (carbon dioxide and water) as in the products (sugar and oxygen) since in a chemical reaction matter is neither created nor destroyed.

The organic molecules formed in chemosynthesis and photosynthesis contain energy. For example, when sugar is burned in air there is a release of heat energy. In combustion the chemical energy of the sugar is converted entirely to heat energy. Organic molecules are a source of energy in all living organisms. The controlled use of this energy, in which most of the energy is used to do work in the organism and only a small proportion is converted to heat energy, is called **respiration** (or cellular respiration because it takes place only in cells):

$$\underset{\text{sugar}}{C_6H_{12}O_6} + \underset{\text{oxygen}}{6O_2} \longrightarrow \underset{\substack{\text{carbon}\\\text{dioxide}}}{6CO_2} + \underset{\text{water}}{6H_2O} + \text{Energy}$$

The amount of energy on the two sides of this equation must balance. Energy may be converted from one form to another—for example, from chemical to mechanical—but it cannot be destroyed.

Some bacteria produce organic molecules in chemosynthesis or in photosynthesis. They use these in the production of other organic molecules that play a part in the life of the cell. However, most bacteria are unable to produce organic molecules from inorganic molecules. They are capable neither of chemosynthesis nor of photosynthesis. The organic molecules that they use in respiration, and in maintenance and growth, are absorbed ready made from their environment. These bacteria either live inside other organisms (and absorb organic molecules from their host organism) or they live in dead organisms (and absorb the organic molecules released in the process of decay).

The way in which an organism obtains organic molecules is called its **mode of nutrition**. Bacteria are called, according to their mode of nutrition, chemosynthetic bacteria, photosynthetic bacteria, parasitic or symbiotic bacteria (which live inside other organisms), or saprobiotic bacteria (which live in dead organic matter).

Table 9. Differences between photosynthesis and respiration.

Photosynthesis	*Respiration*
Chlorophyll essential	Chlorophyll not involved
Light essential	Occurs at all times
Energy stored	Energy released
Carbon dioxide used	Oxygen used
Oxygen produced	Carbon dioxide produced
Increase in mass of organism	Decrease in mass of organism

In their nutrition and respiration bacteria absorb energy and matter (food materials and oxygen) and lose energy and matter (heat and carbon dioxide) to their environment. Photosynthetic bacteria, in sunlight, absorb light energy and carbon dioxide. The surface of any organism, in contact with its environment, is the surface through which such **exchanges** of energy and matter take place.

In studying different forms of life and the structure and functioning of organisms and their parts, the biologist must always be aware of the relationship between size and surface area. Because it is so small, each bacterium has a very large surface area in proportion to its volume. To help you to understand this, compare the surface area and volume of cubes of different dimensions:

	surface area	*volume*	*ratio surface : volume*
2 cm cube	24 cm^2	8 cm^3	3 : 1
1 cm cube	6 cm^2	1 cm^3	6 : 1

The smaller the organism, the shorter the distance from its centre to the outside and the larger its surface area in proportion to its volume. All parts of a bacterium are very close to its environment and the organism has, in proportion to its size, a very large surface of contact with its environment.

One result of the input of materials is that the organism grows. However, bacteria remain small, in spite of growth, because after a period of growth each bacterium divides into two. This production of new individuals is called **reproduction**. In favourable conditions bacteria may divide every 30 min. In a suitable medium, therefore, their numbers increase rapidly at first and then gradually as food materials are used and their waste products accumulate. In these and other ways the environment may become unfavourable. Then an **endospore** may be formed within the bacterial cell (see Fig. 29B). This is resistant to many unfavourable conditions and it may be carried to other places. The **survival** and **dispersal** of individuals contributes to the continuance of the species. When conditions are again favourable the endospore develops into a bacterial cell which grows and reproduces.

The Life of Unicellular Protists and Algae

Amoeba moves over the bottom mud of fresh water pools. It is just visible without a microscope but you need a microscope to see its structure (Fig. 26A).

The surface of an *Amoeba* is its plasmalemma. The shape of the body changes constantly. Projections (Fig. 26A, pseudopodia; Gk. *pseudōs* = false; *pous* = foot) are extended and retracted. The firmer cytoplasm, just inside the plasmalemma, is called ectoplasm. This forms a tube in which the more fluid cytoplasm, called endoplasm, flows. As a pseudopodium is extended more plasmalemma must be formed at its tip and more ectoplasm must be formed from endoplasm (Fig. 32) and at the other end of the body the reverse changes must be taking place as endoplasm streams from one part of the body to another. You can observe this cytoplasmic streaming, if you have a microscope, but we do not know how these changes come about.

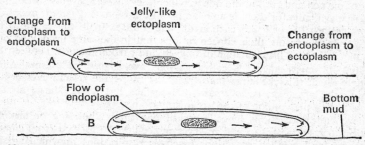

Fig. 32. Amoeboid movement: (A) the formation of endoplasm at the posterior end of the body and of ectoplasm at the anterior end; (B) the movement forward that results from the flow of endoplasm within the firmer ectoplasm.

The *Amoeba* moves over the bottom mud, feeding on smaller organisms. Movement and feeding are closely associated, as in most animals, and these are usually considered to be two characteristics of animal life. As it moves along, *Amoeba* feeds (Ingestion, Fig. 33) by enclosing smaller organisms in cup-shaped structures formed from the plasmalemma. In the formation of each of these food vacuoles the food is enclosed with some pond water. The contents of the food vacuole are always separated from the cytoplasm by the plasmalemma (now called the vacuolar membrane). Within food vacuoles the food organisms are digested (Fig. 33): that is, digestive juices produced in the cytoplasm are passed into the food vacuole (a process called secretion) and the large organic molecules in the food are broken down chemically into smaller organic molecules. Then these products of digestion are absorbed, through the vacuolar membrane (Fig. 33), into the cytoplasm. Water and inorganic ions are also absorbed. The incorporation of these absorbed materials into the materials of the living cell is called assimilation. The part of the food which cannot be digested, which we therefore describe as indigestible, is returned to the pond water (Fig. 33). Egestion is the reverse of ingestion; and the vacuolar membrane again becomes part of the plasmalemma.

As in bacteria, and in all other living cells, energy is released from sugars and from other organic molecules during **respiration**. This process can be summarised, as on p. 57, by the equation:

$$C_6H_{12}O_6 + 6O_2 \longrightarrow 6H_2O + 6CO_2 + Energy$$

In *Amoeba* oxygen is used in the cell and carbon dioxide is produced. As a result you might expect the amount of oxygen in the cell to decrease and the amount of carbon dioxide to increase. Neither of these things happens because small molecules, like oxygen and carbon dioxide, move about all the time. This random movement evens out their distribution. If oxygen molecules are being used in one place (for example, in *Amoeba* in respiration) other oxygen molecules will move from places where they are in higher concentration (for example, in the surrounding pond water). Similarly, if carbon dioxide molecules are being produced in one place (for example, in *Amoeba* in respiration) some of them will move to places where there is a lower concentration of carbon dioxide (for example, in the surrounding pond water). This movement of oxygen and carbon dioxide in which they disperse evenly throughout the space available for them is an example of **diffusion**. Oxygen diffuses from the water into the cell and carbon dioxide diffuses from the cell into the water and, as a result, their concentrations remain the same inside and outside the *Amoeba*. This exchange of oxygen and carbon dioxide, between the cell and its environment, is called **gaseous exchange**. The plasmalemma, through which this exchange takes place, is called the **respiratory surface**. Because the organism is so small, this surface has a very large area in proportion to the volume of the organism (see p. 58).

The chemical reactions in cells are of two kinds: building or **anabolic** reactions (or syntheses) in which larger molecules are formed from smaller molecules; and **catabolic** reactions (such as respiration) in which smaller molecules are formed from larger molecules. Both anabolic and catabolic reactions are going on in all living cells at all times and the relatively constant composition of cells is due to the balance between anabolism and catabolism. The sum total of all the chemical reactions in cells (anabolic + catabolic) is called **metabolism**.

Some of the anabolic reactions result, when food is plentiful, in the production of **storage** materials such as lipids which are used later in times of food shortage. Anabolic reactions also result in **growth**. For example, some of the amino acids absorbed from the food vacuoles are used in the production of proteins. In this way the amount of cytoplasm and nuclear material increases. This increase in size is called growth.

Storage and growth indicate that there is an excess of anabolic over catabolic reactions in the cell.

Some of the amino acids absorbed from the food vacuole are not used in the synthesis of proteins, and *Amoeba* (like the multicellular animals—see p. 187) is unable to store any amino acids that are in excess of its immediate requirements. These excess amino acids (nitrogen-containing compounds—see p.56) are broken down and ammonia (NH_3) is produced. This diffuses from the cell through the plasmalemma: this loss of ammonia is called **nitrogenous excretion**.

Similarly, the loss of carbon dioxide by diffusion through the cell membrane is called **carbonaceous excretion**. **Excretion** is defined as the loss from the body of waste chemicals produced in chemical reactions (metabolic reactions) inside living cells. These are called waste products because they are either of no use within the body or they are present in excess of the body's immediate requirements.

We can observe an organism's **responses**, such as the feeding behaviour of an *Amoeba*, and see that it is sensitive to certain changes in its environment. *Amoeba* is also sensitive to light: it will move away from bright light. It is also sensitive to certain chemicals in the water and to touch. **Sensitivity** is a property of the surfaces of all cells.

The characteristics of the environment to which an organism is sensitive are called **stimuli**. The receipt of stimuli is called **reception** and biologists use the terms photoreception (for the receipt of light or electromagnetic energy), chemoreception (for the receipt of chemical energy) and mechanoreception (for the receipt of mechanical energy).

A part of a cell which has a particular function is called an **organelle**. In *Amoeba* the pseudopodia are concerned in locomotion but as they extend through the water they encounter different stimuli. The *Amoeba* **responds** to some of these stimuli. Clearly pseudopodia, although we may call them locomotor organelles, have more than one function.

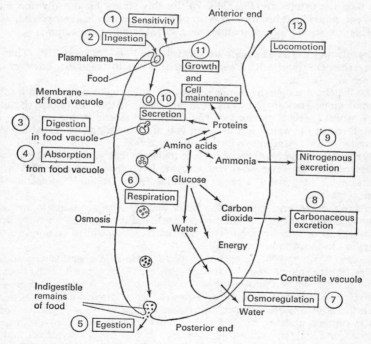

Fig. 33. Some processes that contribute to cell maintenance and growth in *Amoeba*: (1) sensitivity (e.g. to chemical characteristics of food); (2 to 5) nutrition; (6) respiration; (7) osmoregulation; (8 and 9) excretion; (10 and 11) the synthesis of enzymes and structural proteins; (12) locomotion.

A living *Amoeba* is almost transparent. If you observe one through a microscope you will see the streaming of the cytoplasm and the formation of pseudopodia. Then look for the contractile vacuole at the other end of the body (Fig. 26A). This alternately increases and decreases in size (like the inflation and deflation of a balloon) as it fills with water (from the cytoplasm) and then pumps this water through the plasmalemma into the pond. The **contractile vacuole** is an osmoregulatory organelle. Water is taken into the cell all the time by osmosis (see p. 157) and the contractile vacuole first accumulates water and then pumps it out of the cell. It keeps the water content of the body constant by eliminating the excess water. The regulation of the water content of the body is called **osmoregulation**. So far as we know, the contractile vacuole has no other function.

The *Amoeba* is able to maintain itself and to remain fairly constant in composition from day to day because of all the activities going on within it at all times (see Fig. 33). All parts of the cell are interdependent and the condition of constancy, which is the result of continuous change, is called **homeostasis**.

In addition to self-maintenance, in favourable conditions, an *Amoeba* grows. After a period of growth it divides into two. First the nucleus divides and then the cytoplasm (Fig. 34X–Z). By this binary fission (division into two) two individuals are formed from one. The *Amoeba* has **reproduced**. The nucleus is essential for cell maintenance, growth and reproduction.

Euglena and *Chlamydomonas* are protists (see Figs. 26C and 27B). That is to say, they are single cells. *Chlamydomonas* is usually classified, however, as a green alga (see p. 39).

The flagella are cylindrical projections of the cytoplasm, bounded by the plasmalemma. They are free to move in the water and their movement (lashing like a whip) exerts a pressure on the water and so causes the organism to move through the water, just as when you are swimming you thrust against the water one way and move in the other direction.

By moving, both organisms are able to maintain their position in the surface waters of a fresh water pool. In sunlight, like other organisms that have chlorophyll, they make organic molecules from inorganic molecules by photosynthesis.

In both organisms, part of the body acts as a photoreceptor and the pigmented spot near to this photoreceptor shades the receptor when the light is coming from one direction. This enables the organism to respond to the stimulus: to move towards the light.

Euglena has a contractile vacuole which functions in a similar way to the contractile vacuole of *Amoeba*. It maintains the water content of the body.

In the dark, when photosynthesis is not taking place, respiration decreases the oxygen concentration and increases the carbon dioxide concentration in the cell. As in *Amoeba*, oxygen diffuses in and carbon dioxide diffuses out. But in sunlight photosynthesis proceeds much more rapidly than respiration. The carbon dioxide produced in respiration is used in photosynthesis and as a result there is less carbon dioxide in the cell than in the pond water. Carbon dioxide diffuses into the cell. Similarly, more oxygen is produced in photosynthesis than is used in respiration and oxygen diffuses from the cell.

Because organisms with chlorophyll can produce organic molecules from

Table 10. Interdependence of parts in *Amoeba* and *Chlamydomonas*.

Function	Part of organism concerned
Sensitivity	Light receptor in *Chlamydomonas*
	Plasmalemma in *Amoeba*
Locomotion	Flagella of *Chlamydomonas*
	Pseudopodia of *Amoeba*
Nutrition	Organic molecules produced by *Chlamydomonas* in chloroplasts and in cytoplasm
	Organic molecules absorbed from food vacuoles in *Amoeba*
Respiration	Cytoplasm (especially in mitochondria)
Gaseous exchange	Across plasmalemma
Osmoregulation	Cell wall limits water intake in *Chlamydomonas*
	Contractile vacuole pumps out excess water in *Amoeba*
Information store and control centre	Nucleus
Reproduction	Division of nucleus followed by division of cytoplasm

inorganic materials they do not have, for example, an excess of amino acids. Also, any inorganic molecules or ions produced in catabolic reactions (as are ammonium ions) can be used in anabolic reactions. These organisms, therefore, do not have nitrogenous excretory products. However, in sunlight they excrete most of the oxygen produced in photosynthesis (the rest is used in respiration) and at night they excrete the carbon dioxide produced in respiration (which in sunlight is used in photosynthesis).

Animals, therefore, absorb oxygen and excrete carbon dioxide. But plants,

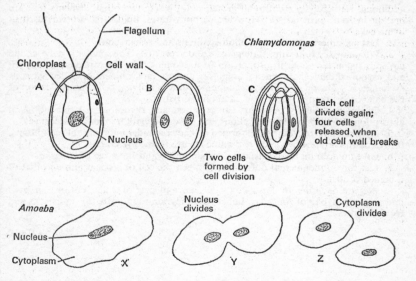

Fig. 34. Asexual reproduction (A to C) of *Chlamydomonas* and (X and Z) *Amoeba*. Diagrams not to scale.

in sunlight, absorb carbon dioxide and excrete oxygen. The result of this interdependence of animals and plants is that the concentration of oxygen and carbon dioxide in the Earth's atmosphere remains constant.

Investigation: *diffusion through gelatin.* Dissolve 5 g gelatin in 50 cm³ hot water. Pour some clear gelatin into a specimen tube and allow this to set. Add a layer of cool liquid gelatin which you have dyed with methylene blue. Cool this layer quickly; then add another layer of clear gelatin and cool this quickly. You should now have distinct clear, blue and clear layers. Look at the tube each day and record your observations. Do the methylene blue molecules move (*a*) down only, (*b*) up and down equally or (*c*) up only?

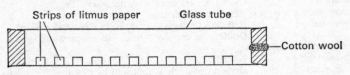

Fig. 35. Diffusion of ammonia vapour in air.

Investigation: *diffusion through air.* Place squares of wet litmus paper at intervals in a horizontal glass tube (Fig. 35). Close both ends of the tube so that there is no air current through the tube. Add one drop of ammonia to the cotton wool plug. The litmus paper turns blue as molecules of ammonia diffuse in the tube. Do ammonia molecules diffuse through air (*a*) more rapidly or (*b*) more slowly than methylene blue molecules diffuse through gelatin?

Test Questions

1. (*a*) Name three elements present in starch, glycogen and cellulose. (*b*) Which additional element is present in all proteins? (*c*) Name two other elements that are present in some proteins. (*d*) How are carbohydrates, lipids and proteins used in living cells?

2. List six differences between photosynthesis and respiration.

3. Which of the following statements are correct? (A) The smaller a cube is, the larger is its surface area in proportion to its volume. (B) The exchange of oxygen and carbon dioxide between an organism and its environment is called gaseous exchange. (C) The relatively constant composition of a living cell is an indication of the balance between anabolic and catabolic activities.

4. Distinguish clearly between: (*a*) ingestion and digestion; (*b*) secretion and absorption; (*c*) egestion and excretion; and (*d*) osmoregulation and homeostasis.

5. (*a*) Name the resistant stage formed by bacteria under unfavourable conditions. (*b*) Name the process by which two amoebae are formed from one.

6. Give an account of the structure, mode of life and life cycle of *Amoeba*.

7. List three fundamental differences between the cell of a bacterium and that of a named protist.

8. Prepare diagrams to illustrate the structure of part of a filament of *Spirogyra* and part of a hypha of *Rhizopus*. Label your diagram to indicate (*a*) similarities and (*b*) differences.

8

MULTICELLULAR ORGANISMS

One thread of *Spirogyra* is composed of many cells (see Fig. 27A). Note that any one cell looks essentially similar to all other cells of the thread. It absorbs materials from the water and light energy from the sun and makes its own food materials: it is self-sufficient and is in no way dependent upon the other cells of the thread. In all respects, each cell is essentially similar to one *Chlamydomonas*. However, when a cell of *Spirogyra* divides, after a period of growth, the two cells produced remain attached to one another and so the thread grows longer.

Hydra, a cnidarian (see p. 40), is a multicellular animal. It lives in fresh water pools and lakes. Its body is a cylinder, about 15 mm long, which has a basal disc at one end and a mouth surrounded by tentacles at the other. The basal disc is attached to stones or to underwater plants. When smaller animals touch the body, especially the tentacles, they are captured. The tentacles bend, the mouth opens and the prey (any organism killed as food by a predator) is taken in through the mouth. The cylindrical body and the tentacles are hollow (Fig. 36B). This cavity is the gut or enteron. The mouth is the only opening.

Just as the parts of a unicellular organism are interdependent (see Table 10) so are the parts of a multicellular organism. The body of *Hydra* is made up of layers of cells (Fig. 36B). The outer layer, next to the water, is called the **ectoderm** (Gk. *ektos* = outside; *derma* = skin). The inner layer, next to the enteron, is called the endoderm (Gk. *endon* = within). The thin layer between the ectoderm and the endoderm is called the **mesogloea** (Gk. *mesos* = the middle).

Interdependence of Cells, Tissues and Organs in *Hydra*

Interdependence of Cells in the Ectoderm and Endoderm

Seven kinds of cells form the ectoderm of a *Hydra*. Note that each cell has a nucleus and cytoplasm (see Fig. 36C) but the seven cell types can be distinguished by differences in their structure.

Musculo-epithelial cells, on their outer surface, form an almost complete surface cover. From their inner surface, long contractile processes extend vertically (see Fig. 36C).

Gland cells on the basal disc secrete a sticky material which enables the *Hydra* to hold on to underwater surfaces; and gland cells around the mouth secrete a lubricant which facilitates feeding.

Receptor cells project at the surface, between the musculo-epithelial cells, into the water. They also have projections at their inner ends, and these extend between the other cells (see Fig. 36C).

Nerve cells (neurones) have a spherical cell body containing the nucleus, and a number of projections. The end of each of these projections is close to a similar projection from another nerve cell, or to a projection from a receptor cell, or to a contractile projection from a musculo-epithelial cell.

Nematoblasts or sting cells produce nematocysts (see Fig. 36C).

Interstitial cells are so called because they fill the spaces (or interstices) between other cells.

Sex cells (gametes) are formed in the ectoderm, from interstitial cells, but these are present only at certain times of the year.

Adaptation is as characteristic of the different cell types of multicellular organisms, as it is of their organs or of the organism as a whole (see Chapter 4). The structure of the different cell types in the ectoderm of *Hydra*, for example, is appropriate for their different functions:

Structure	*Function*
Musculo-epithelial cell	Protection and contraction
Gland cell	Secretion
Receptor cell	Sensitive to stimuli
Nerve cell	Conducts nerve impulses
Nematoblast	Produces and discharges nematocyst
Interstitial cell	Can develop into any other kind of cell (including a sex cell)
Sex cell (Gamete)	Sexual reproduction

Note that the different kinds of cells in the ectoderm of *Hydra* have many things in common. Each one has all the characteristics of a cell. But the functioning of the ectoderm as a skin depends upon the working together of the different kinds of cells. For example, when a receptor cell is affected by a stimulus nerve impulses may be produced in a nearby nerve cell (Fig. 36C). These travel in the nerve cell and may cause a musculo-epithelial cell to contract. The three kinds of cell involved are interdependent. One could not function without the others.

The nematoblasts are held between other ectodermal cells. The trigger or cnidocil projects into the water. When a small animal touches the cnidocil the nematocyst turns inside out and its tip penetrates the prey animal. The many nematocysts discharged hold and paralyse the prey.

A nematoblast that has released its nematocyst cannot make another. The maintenance of a supply of nematoblasts, containing nematocysts, depends upon some of the interstitial cells developing into nematoblasts. And each new nematoblast produces one nematocyst. The interstitial cells are also important when a *Hydra* is injured. The damaged cells are replaced by interstitial cells developing into other kinds of cells. The continued functioning of the ectoderm, therefore, depends upon the interdependence of all the different kinds of cells.

Similarly, the cells of the endoderm are interdependent. Most of them have muscle tails and are musculo-epithelial cells (Fig. 36C) but they have different functions. Some, called gland cells, produce digestive juices and secrete these into the enteron where digestion begins, breaking the food into smaller pieces. Other cells ingest small food particles, by forming food vacuoles in which further digestion takes place (as in *Amoeba*, see p. 59). Digestion in the enteron is called extra-cellular digestion (because it takes place outside the cell) and digestion in a food vacuole is called intracellular digestion. Some

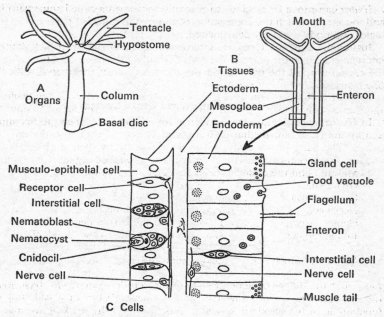

Fig. 36. Interdependence of parts of *Hydra*: (A) organs; (B) tissues (in a vertical section); (C) cells (in a vertical section of part of the body wall). Diagrams not to scale.

cells have flagella which move the food within the enteron. Note the other kinds of cells in the endoderm (see Fig. 36C).

Interdependence of Tissues

The ectoderm is a skin. It protects the endoderm from the effects of surface damage. Its nematocysts are essential in the capture of food. On the other hand, the endoderm is essential in the digestion of food and absorption; and the food molecules required by the cells of the ectoderm can be obtained only from the nearby cells of the endoderm. Contraction of the musculo-epithelial cells of the ectoderm makes the body or tentacles shorter; but contraction of the musculo-epithelial cells of the endoderm makes the body or tentacles longer.

Note that most nerve cells are in the ectoderm. There are very few in the endoderm and none in the mesogloea. The mesogloea, therefore, contains no cells.

Interdependence of Organs

Because the tentacles are spread like a net, and there are more nematocysts on the tentacles than on other parts of the body, the prey animal is usually held by a tentacle. Other tentacles then move over to the prey and contribute to food capture and to carrying the food to the mouth.

Hydra can move from place to place by movements called somersaulting and looping in which the contraction of muscles in different parts of the tentacles and body is closely coordinated.

Just as different cell types are interdependent, and the two cell layers are interdependent, so the parts of the body (including the basal disc, the column, the region around the mouth and the tentacles) work together as parts of one individual.

Cells, Tissues, Organs and Organ Systems

In *Hydra* we distinguish the ectoderm from the endoderm by their position and by the kinds of cells that they contain. The ectoderm and endoderm are tissues. The parts of the body, which we recognise by their position, shape and function (not by the cells that they contain), are called organs: for example, the basal disc and the tentacles (Fig. 36A).

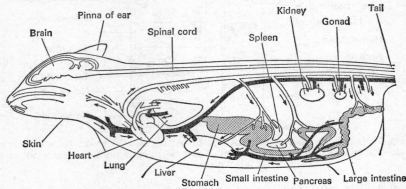

Fig. 37. Some parts of a mammal (simplified). The blood vessels are not labelled but the arrows indicate the direction in which the blood flows.

The body of a flowering plant comprises different organs (for example, the root and the leaf), as does the body of a mammal (for example, the eye, the brain and the kidney). Each organ is made up of different kinds of cells associated in tissues. As in *Hydra* we recognise **tissues** by their position and by the kinds of cells they contain and we recognise **organs** by their position, shape and functions.

In studying multicellular organisms we also recognise different **systems**—for example, the root system and the shoot system of a flowering plant. All the bones and cartilages of your body form the skeletal system; and all your muscles the muscular system. Your stomach is part of the digestive or alimentary system. Your lungs are part of the respiratory system. Your heart is part of the blood circulatory system. Your kidneys are part of the urinary system. Your brain is part of the nervous system.

Interdependence of Parts in a Mammal

As with a flowering plant (see Fig. 38), the parts of a mammal are interdependent—that is to say, there is a division of labour between the different parts (see p. 70).

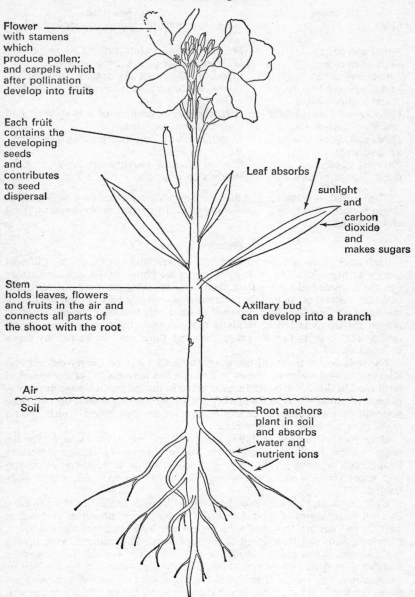

Flower with stamens which produce pollen; and carpels which after pollination develop into fruits

Each fruit contains the developing seeds and contributes to seed dispersal

Leaf absorbs sunlight and carbon dioxide and makes sugars

Stem holds leaves, flowers and fruits in the air and connects all parts of the shoot with the root

Axillary bud can develop into a branch

Air

Soil

Root anchors plant in soil and absorbs water and nutrient ions

Fig. 38. Interdependence of parts of a flowering plant *Cheiranthus cheiri*, the wallflower. Diagram not to scale.

Structure	Some functions
Skin	Support, protection, sensitivity, control of heat loss
Bones and joints	Maintenance of posture, protection, movement
Skeletal muscles	Maintenance of posture, movement
Alimentary canal	Ingestion, digestion, absorption, egestion
Lungs and other parts of respiratory system	Intake of oxygen and excretion of carbon dioxide
Kidneys and other parts of urinary system	Osmoregulation, control of salt content and nitrogenous excretion
Heart and blood vessels	Circulation of blood through all other parts
Sense organs	Receipt of stimuli
Nervous system	Control of many activities, memory
Reproductive system	Production of young

The normal functioning of a mammal, as with any other kind of organism, depends upon the normal functioning of all its parts (see *Homeostasis*, p. 62 and p. 233).

Technical Terms

Technical terms are useful because, as with the names of the different groups of organisms (Table 7, p. 35), once we know what a word means we can use it instead of having to explain what the thing or process means. For example, instead of writing that mammals *alternately take air into their lungs and expel air from their lungs* we need to write only that they *breathe*. Another reason for using technical terms is that, as with the names of organisms (see p. 34), in every-day language the same thing may be known by many different names.

The only useful technical terms are those that can be clearly defined and then understood and used correctly. You can find the meaning of any technical term used in this book by finding the word in the index. One page number is printed in bold (which looks blacker than the other numbers): on that page you will find a definition, an explanation or an illustration which should make the meaning of the term clear.

Once you are familiar with any term, you can use it, for example, for the same process in different organisms or for essentially similar structures in different organisms. The more you know about biology the more you will appreciate the value of words that help you to think about your subject.

Unfortunately, although scientists would like each process or thing to have its own internationally agreed technical name, some processes and things have more than one technical term. When you look up a word in the index, therefore, you may be referred to another word. For example, look up the word *atrium* in the index. Atrium is a synonym for auricle. To reduce the number of technical terms and to avoid confusion, where a thing has two or more names only one of them is used in this book (auricle, for example) but some synonyms are included in the index (*atrium*, for example) because you may see them in other books.

Many English words are formed from Latin (L.) or Greek (Gk.) words. For example:

	prefix	root word	English word
from Latin	*ex* (out of)	*tract* (drag)	extract
	trans (across)	*fer* (carry)	transfer
from Greek	*mikros* (small)	*skopeo* (to see)	microscope

If you know the following prefixes you will find it easier to understand the meaning of many technical terms: *a* (Gk. without); *ab* (L. from); *ad* (L. next to or towards); *ante* (L. before); *anti* (Gk. against); *de* (L. away or down); *ecto* (Gk. outside); *endo* (Gk. within); *epi* (Gk. upon); *hetero* (Gk. different); *homeo* (Gk. alike); *homo* (Gk. same); *hyper* (Gk. over); *hypo* (Gk. under); *meso* (Gk. middle); *meta* (Gk. after); *para* (Gk. beside); *post* (L. after); *pre* (L. before); *semi* (L. half); *sub* (L. under); *sym* or *syn* (Gk. together); *zygo* (Gk. joined).

Some adjectives and the parts of the body they refer to, are gastric (the stomach), hepatic (the liver), optic (the eye), pulmonary (the lungs), pelvic (the hip), pectoral (the shoulder), auditory (the ear) and dermal (the skin).

Investigations

1. If you have a microscope, examine prepared slides of *Spirogyra* and *Hydra*. Note that the cells of a filament of *Spirogyra* are similar to one another. Prepare a drawing of one cell. Label the parts that you have seen (see Fig. 27A). In sections of *Hydra* note the ectoderm, mesogloea and endoderm.
2. If you are working in a biology laboratory, or when you visit a museum, examine prepared specimens of whole animals, and demonstration dissections, and try to identify the different organs of each animal's body.
3. Examine plants that are living in different habitats. Note the adaptations that enable the plant to live in its habitat. Examine the organs of the plant body and consider how each organ contributes to the life of the plant as a whole.
4. Biologists construct keys to help people to identify plants and animals. Some keys enable you to identify different species but the following simple keys just allow you to begin to classify those multicellular organisms that you are most likely to see.

   Each key comprises numbered questions. To find out whether A or B applies, you must look at the external features of the organism that you are trying to identify. Your answer to A or B will be yes; and the words to the right of this answer tell you *either* the name of the major group in which the organism is classified *or* the number of the next question.

---

*Key to some major groups of plants**

1.	A With green pigment?	(see 2)
	B Without green pigment?	**a fungus**†
2.	A With roots or rhizoids?	(see 3)
	B Without roots or rhizoids?	**an alga**
3.	A With rhizoids?	(see 4)
	B With roots?	(see 5)
4.	A Leaf-like or leaves with no midrib?	**a liverwort**
	B Leaves with a midrib?	**a moss**
5.	A With flowers, fruits or cones?	(see 6)
	B Without flowers, fruits or cones?	**a fern**
6.	A Leaves like needles or scales?	**conifers** and their relations
	B Leaves not needles or scales?	**a flowering plant**

---

*Key to some major groups of animals**

1.	A With paired limbs or fins	(see 2)
	B Without paired limbs or fins	(see 3)
2.	A With more than two pairs of limbs	**an arthropod**
	B With no more than two pairs of limbs or fins	**a chordate**
3.	A Body flat	**a flatworm**
	B Body not flat	(see 4)
4.	A With shell and/or with flat foot	**a mollusc**
	B With no shell or flat foot	(see 5)
5.	A Body obviously segmented	**a segmented worm**
	B Body not obviously segmented	(see 6)
6.	A Bilaterally symmetrical (left side of body mirror image of right side)	**a roundworm**
	B Not bilaterally symmetrical	(see 7)
7.	A With radial symmetry	**Sea anemones** and their relatives
	B With five-rayed symmetry	**Starfishes** and their relatives

*Having found that an organism is an alga or a mollusc, for example, you would need to consult a key for identifying algae or molluscs if you wished to classify further or identify this organism.
†Some fungi are green but with experience you will soon be able to distinguish fungi from other kinds of plants by other features than their colour.

Test Questions

1. (*a*) Define the terms cell, tissue and organ as concisely as you can. (*b*) After each of your definitions give two examples, known to you from your study of *Hydra*.

2. Explain concisely what is meant by division of labour. Give two examples from your knowledge of a flowering plant or a mammal, and state how their structure is appropriate for their function.

PART 2: THE INTERDEPENDENCE OF ORGANISMS

9

ENERGY FROM SUNLIGHT

How Scientists Work

Observation is the basis of science. When a scientist sees something that he does not understand his curiosity is aroused. He tries to think of possible explanations, and makes more observations in an attempt to collect evidence that may help him towards a better understanding of the problem. For example, you may observe that crop plants grow best on weed-free land. Here is a **problem**: 'Why is a smaller yield obtained from crop plants which have grown amongst weeds?' You may think of several possible answers to this question.

1. The weeds shade the crop plants and the soil, and cut out light and heat which are essential for plant growth.
2. The roots of the weeds remove water and nutrients from the soil with the result that less is available to the crop plants.
3. The weeds produce chemicals which are harmful to the growth of crop plants.

Each of these possible explanations is what a scientist calls a **hypothesis**. To be a possible explanation, any hypothesis must be supported by all the **evidence** that you have on the subject. Some of the above hypotheses may seem to you to provide more satisfactory explanations than the others for the observation that the yield is smaller when crop plants are not weeded (see Table 5). However, they could all be correct.

Scientists making observations, in an attempt to add to our knowledge on any subject or to obtain evidence that may lead to the solution of a problem, are engaged in scientific research and this common-sense method of working is called the **scientific method**. Scientists also carry out experiments so that they can collect evidence related to a particular problem. Each **experiment** is an attempt to **test** one hypothesis. The conditions under which the experiments are performed must always be standardised so that if necessary the experiment can be repeated under essentially similar conditions.

Many great discoveries in biology have been made in simple investigations. You can repeat many of the experiments described in this chapter with the inexpensive equipment illustrated in the diagrams (see Figs. 39–43).

The Discovery of Photosynthesis

In 1771 Joseph Priestley, a British chemist who was one of the discoverers of oxygen, experimented with plants and animals in closed containers (see Fig. 39). He knew that burning a candle in air made it unsuitable for the support of animal life, but he discovered that green plants restored to this air the property of supporting either combustion or animal life. He was surprised to find that whereas an animal would soon suffocate in a closed container (Fig. 39B), a green plant could live for many months.

In 1779 Jan Ingenhousz, a Dutch physician who had read about Priestley's observations, placed the green parts of bean plants in a sealed container overnight. On the following morning the air in the container immediately extinguished a candle; but after a few hours in sunlight the air again supported combustion.

As a result of these investigations, and those of later students of the effects of living organisms on the composition of the atmosphere, we now know the explanation for the observations of Priestley and Ingenhousz. (1) Oxygen is used and carbon dioxide produced in combustion and in the respiration of most plants and animals. (2) Carbon dioxide is used and oxygen produced by green plants in sunlight.

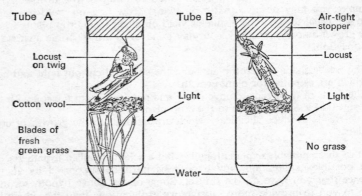

Fig. 39. Investigations, similar to those of Priestley, on the effects of living organisms on the composition of the air in a closed container.

In 1860 Sachs, a German botanist, demonstrated that the mass of green leaves increases, and starch is formed, when these leaves are exposed to sunlight.

Investigation: *test for starch.* Starch stains blue-black with iodine solution and the presence of starch in leaves which have been exposed to sunlight can be demonstrated by this simple test.

1. Boil the leaf in water for 30 s. This kills the tissues, stops enzyme controlled reactions (see p. 92), and makes the cell walls more permeable.
2. Place the leaf in methanol (methylated spirit) in a test tube.
3. Heat the tube in a water bath on a hot-plate. Do not use a bunsen burner because the flame may ignite the alcohol vapour. Chlorophyll from the leaf will dissolve in the alcohol, leaving the leaf white or pale yellow.
4. Soften the leaf again in boiling water.
5. Cover the leaf with a few drops of iodine solution. If starch is present in the leaf it will be stained blue-black.

When a plant is kept in the dark the starch in its leaves is converted to sugars, which are exported from the leaves to other parts of the plant (see Fig. 98). When there is little or no starch in the leaves, we say that they have been destarched.

In many plants the first organic molecules produced in photosynthesis are converted into starch which accumulates in the leaves. This is why leaves increase in mass while photosynthesis is taking place (Fig. 40): there is an increase in the amount of organic matter they contain.

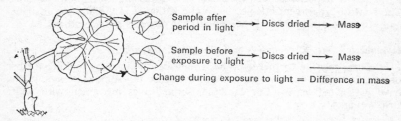

Sample after period in light ——→ Discs dried ——→ Mass

Sample before exposure to light ——→ Discs dried ——→ Mass

Change during exposure to light = Difference in mass

Fig. 40. Method by which Julius Sachs, in 1860, measured the increase in mass of leaf tissues exposed to sunlight.

Simple Experiments on Photosynthesis

Hypothesis: *that light is essential for photosynthesis*

1. Destarch the leaves of a plant by keeping the plant in the dark for two or three days. Then keep the plant in the dark but remove one leaf and test it for starch to confirm that the leaf has been destarched.
2. Remove the plant from the dark and place a stencil over both surfaces of one leaf (see Fig. 41A) so that light is unable to enter the covered part of the leaf.
3. Place a similar stencil, made of transparent material, over another leaf of the same plant (Fig. 41B). This will serve as what scientists call a **control**: the leaf is covered but light is not excluded.
4. Place the plant in the sunlight for a few hours.
5. Label the leaves that are covered with the stencils so that you know which is which; and then remove them from the plant and test them for starch.

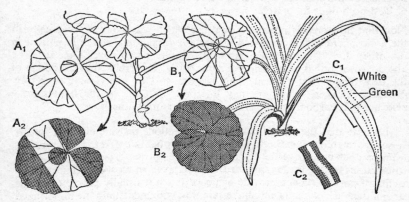

Fig. 41. Photosynthesis occurs only in parts of the leaf which (A and B) are exposed to light and (C) contain chlorophyll.

Note that starch is present in the parts of one leaf that were not covered by the black stencil and in all parts of the other leaf that were covered with a transparent stencil. Because starch is produced only in parts that were exposed to the sunlight, this experiment provides evidence which we may interpret in terms of the hypothesis—evidence that light is essential for photosynthesis. The control experiment enables us to check that it is the absence of light, and not some other effect of the stencil, that prevents photosynthesis.

Hypothesis: *that chlorophyll is essential for photosynthesis*

Evidence relating to this hypothesis may be obtained by making further observations. The leaves of most plants are green but some cultivated plants have variegated leaves. For example, some leaves are green with white stripes (Fig. 41C).

1. Make a drawing of a leaf and mark the green and white parts by labelling this drawing (as in Fig. 41C).
2. Place the plant in the sunlight for a few hours and then remove this leaf from the plant and test it for starch.

You will find that starch is present in the green parts but not in the white parts. This observation provides evidence in support of the hypothesis that photosynthesis is confined to the green parts of the leaf.

Hypothesis: *that carbon dioxide is essential for photosynthesis*

1. Destarch the leaves of a plant. Test one leaf for starch to check that no starch is present.
2. Place a disc from one leaf of this plant in an atmosphere that is without carbon dioxide (tube X in Fig. 42).
3. As a **control** experiment place another disc from the same leaf in an atmosphere that contains carbon dioxide (tube Y in Fig. 42).
4. Mark the tubes so that you know which is which.
5. Expose both tubes to sunlight for a few hours.
6. Test both discs for starch.

Note that no starch is present in the disc which was exposed to sunlight in the atmosphere which contained no carbon dioxide but starch is present in the other disc. The control experiment enables us to check that it is the absence of carbon dioxide, and not some other factor related to the design of the experiment, that prevents photosynthesis. This experiment, therefore, provides evidence which we may interpret in terms of the hypothesis— evidence that carbon dioxide is essential for photosynthesis.

Also note that the results of these investigations provide evidence which causes us to think that the hypotheses are probably correct. However, the evidence does not prove the hypotheses to be correct. There may be other explanations for the results obtained. This happens in most experiments. The results of an experiment provide evidence but not usually proof. Consider each of these experiments and make sure that you understand the importance of the controls. Every experiment should be associated with an appropriate control experiment: and they should be performed together.

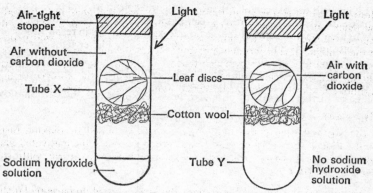

Fig. 42. Photosynthesis occurs only if the air contains carbon dioxide.

Hypothesis: *that the gas evolved by green plants in sunlight is oxygen*

If some green pond weed is placed in a beaker of pond water and covered with a glass funnel any gas excreted by the plant can be collected in an inverted test-tube of pond water. The gas displaces the water (Fig. 43) and when enough gas has been collected it can be tested by inserting a glowing wooden splint into the tube. Oxygen relights a glowing splint. However, even if the splint is relit this does not prove that the gas is pure oxygen. It proves only that the gas contains a lot of oxygen (more than 30 per cent by volume).

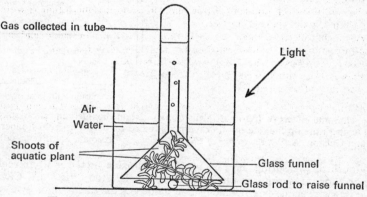

Fig. 43. Collecting the gas given off by an aquatic plant.

What Happens in Photosynthesis

Factors Affecting the Rate of Photosynthesis

In addition to internal factors that influence the rate at which photosynthesis takes place, such as the distribution of chloroplasts in the leaf (Fig. 41C) and stomatal opening and closure (Fig. 119), there are many external influences.

Living cells use oxygen all the time, in their respiration, and produce carbon dioxide. In the dark, therefore, green plants excrete carbon dioxide. At very low light intensities some of the carbon dioxide produced in respiration is used in photosynthesis and less is excreted. At a slightly higher light intensity the rate of respiration is the same as the rate of photosynthesis. At this point, called the **compensation point**, all the carbon dioxide produced in respiration is used in photosynthesis and there is no gaseous exchange. As light intensity increases further the rate of photosynthesis also increases and carbon dioxide

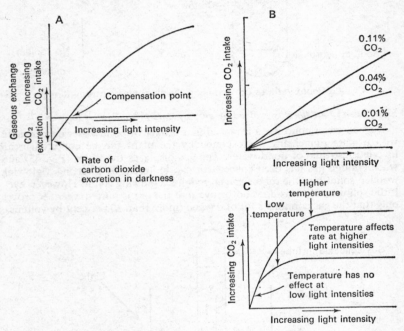

Fig. 44. Some effects of (A) light intensity, (B) carbon dioxide concentration, and (C) temperature on the rate of photosynthesis (based on diagrams from Bonner, J., and Galston, A. W., *Principles of Plant Physiology*, Freeman, San Francisco).

is absorbed. Measuring the rate of carbon dioxide intake is a convenient method for measuring the rate of photosynthesis. Study Fig. 44A. Clearly, light intensity is one external factor that influences the rate of photosynthesis.

Study the results of a second investigation (Fig. 44B). Note that with a very low concentration of atmospheric carbon dioxide, a maximum photosynthetic rate is obtained at a relatively low light intensity. With a higher carbon dioxide concentration a higher light intensity is necessary before a maximum photosynthetic rate is obtained. We can conclude that the carbon dioxide concentration of the atmosphere is another external factor that influences the rate of photosynthesis.

Study the results of a third investigation (Fig. 44C). At low light intensities, light limits the rate of photosynthesis but the rate is not affected by temperature. Since the rate of all chemical reactions is influenced by temperature we might conclude that photosynthesis is not a chemical reaction. However, at higher light intensities the rate of photosynthesis may be limited by the amount of carbon dioxide in the atmosphere (Fig. 44B) but also by temperature (Fig 44C). On the basis of this evidence scientists concluded that photosynthesis includes a part that is not dependent upon temperature (a **photochemical reaction**) and a part that is dependent upon temperature (a **chemical reaction**).

Experiments on the Mechanism of Photosynthesis

In 1880 Engelmann illuminated the chloroplast of *Spirogyra* with a narrow beam of light and used bacteria in the water as biological indicators of oxygen concentration (Fig. 45). The bacteria concentrated in regions of high oxygen concentration. He demonstrated (1) that oxygen concentration during photo-

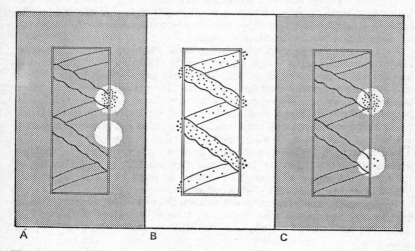

Fig. 45. Engelmann's observations on the distribution of bacteria next to a cell of *Spirogyra* (other cells of filament not included in diagram): A in dark with two white spotlights; B in light; C in dark with spotlights of red (above) and green (below) on the chloroplast.

synthesis is highest next to the chloroplast (Fig. 45B), and (2) that oxygen is evolved when a chloroplast is illuminated with white light (Fig. 45A and B) or red light (Fig. 45C) but not when it is illuminated with green light (also Fig. 45C), which is not absorbed by the chlorophyll. Engelmann concluded that light is absorbed by **chlorophyll** in the **chloroplast** and used in photosynthesis.

Our knowledge of the mechanism of photosynthesis is based upon experiments with radioactive isotopes. Isotopes are alternative forms of the same element which differ in mass but not in their chemical properties. Some isotopes of some elements are radioactive because they are unstable. For example, ^{14}C carbon atoms emit energy and matter as they break down to the more stable ^{12}C isotope which has a smaller mass.

When the green alga *Chlorella* is supplied with water containing marked oxygen $H_2^{18}O$ the oxygen evolved during photosynthesis contains marked $^{18}O_2$ molecules. However, when *Chlorella* is supplied with $^{14}CO_2$ the marked carbon ^{14}C is present in the molecules of sugar formed during photosynthesis.

The mechanism of photosynthesis is summarised in **two reactions**. Light is involved in the splitting or photolysis of water.

(1) **Light reaction** $2H_2O \longrightarrow 4H + O_2\uparrow$

                                                        $\downarrow$

(2) **Carbon assimilation** $CO_2 + 4H \longrightarrow (CH_2O) + H_2O$
                                                                          sugar

Ecological Importance of Photosynthesis

The green plants that you see every day, and many smaller organisms including *Chlamydomonas* and *Spirogyra* (Fig. 27) and some bacteria (p. 57), have the green pigment chlorophyll and are able to capture some of the energy of sunlight and use this in photosynthesis.

In photosynthesis light energy is converted to chemical energy. The second law of thermodynamics is that energy can be converted from one form to another but it cannot be destroyed. The world gains energy from sunlight and loses energy as reflected light and heat. The energy captured by green plants is used by the plants themselves in the intake of nutrients (p. 185) and in the synthesis of sugars and other organic molecules including: (1) the lipids, proteins and vitamins used in cell maintenance and growth; (2) starch, which is a storage material (see p. 184); and (3) the cellulose of plant cell walls. These organic molecules are the source of materials and energy used by animals (see p. 91) and by saprobionts (see Fig. 53, p. 96). Directly or indirectly, the energy of sunlight, captured in photosynthesis, is the only source of energy available to living organisms.

Photosynthesis involves **carbon assimilation** as well as **energy capture**. All the carbon atoms present in the organic molecules of living organisms (see Fig. 53, p. 96) were derived directly or indirectly from the carbon dioxide of the atmosphere. (*See also* Interdependence of all Organisms, p. 120.)

Day and Night

The energy of sunlight, captured in photosynthesis, is the basis for all life on Earth. But sunlight affects living organisms in many other ways. Because of the rotation of the world, organisms live in alternating conditions of night and day; and day-length (and so the length of the night) varies in different latitudes and at different times of the year. Differences in day-length result in regular variations not only in light intensity but also in the temperature of the land and sea, and in the temperature and water content (humidity) of the atmosphere.

The land and the water, and the air, are heated in sunlight and they lose heat at night. Since most organisms are on or just below the land surface, or near the surface of lakes or the sea, these temperature fluctuations affect their lives. The temperature of the air varies more between night and day than does the temperature of the soil; and the temperature of the seas is even less variable. Animals, by moving, avoid extreme temperatures.

The body temperature of a bird or mammal is maintained at a high and constant level (see p. 235). They are called **homeotherms**. All other animals (called **poikilotherms**), like all plants, change in temperature as the temperature of their environment changes. The rate at which chemical reactions proceed in their bodies changes as the body temperature changes (following the changes in the temperature of their environment); the rate of a chemical reaction being doubled by a rise in temperature of 10 °C, and halved by a fall of 10 °C.

Four Seasons

In all parts of the world there are seasonal differences in day-length, temperature and rainfall. Differences in the distribution of plants and animals (see *Biomes*, p. 121) are due, in part, to each organism's ability to thrive in or to withstand the variations which occur in its environment.

Seasonal changes in the form and functioning of the organisms that live in any place (see Figs. 16 and 17) are to be understood as adaptations to the seasonal changes in the amount of light and heat energy from the sun available in that place.

Test Questions

1. Name the structure, present in some plant cells, in which photosynthesis takes place.

2. Name the green pigment in this structure.

3. Name two metallic elements which are essential for the synthesis of this pigment in the cell.

4. What is the source of the energy used in photosynthesis?

5. List three ways in which you consider the leaves of flowering plants are adapted as organs in which photosynthesis takes place.

6. Describe how you would demonstrate that there is no photosynthesis in the absence of one raw material.

7. In an investigation (similar to the one illustrated in Fig. 43) the gas collected in an inverted test tube, on different days, was analysed. The results were as follows:

	Light	Percentage by volume		
Day	intensity	Carbon dioxide	Oxygen	Nitrogen
1	Very low	5	14	80
2	Low	0	22	78
3	High	0	44	66
4	Low	0	28	72
5	High	0	37	63

(*a*) An oxygen concentration above 30 per cent will relight a glowing splint. On what kind of day are you likely to obtain such a high concentration of oxygen if you repeat this experiment? (*b*) Why do you think the oxygen concentration varies so much in the samples of gas collected? (*c*) Why do you think there was carbon dioxide in the sample on day 1 but not on the other days? (*d*) Why must there be a gap between the edge of the funnel and the bottom of the beaker?

10

ANIMAL NUTRITION

Except for the unicellular plants, most of which float in the surface waters of lakes, rivers or the sea, green plants live fixed in one place by a holdfast (many algae), by thread-like processes (mosses and liverworts) or by roots (ferns and flowering plants). Plants are able to survive in one place. There they absorb inorganic molecules and mineral ions, and manufacture organic molecules—that is to say, they make their own food. Animals, in contrast, cannot make their own food. They eat plants, or animals that have eaten plants, or they absorb organic molecules directly from their environment.

Animals that eat plants are called **herbivores**. Those that eat animals are called **carnivores**. And those that eat both plant and animal food are called **omnivores**. Like those plants that lack chlorophyll (see *Fungi*, p. 39), animals that absorb organic molecules directly from their environment can live only in places where suitable nutriment is available; either inside a host organism (see *symbiosis* and *parasitism*, Chapter 12) or in the decaying remains of organisms (see *saprobionts*, Chapter 11).

Movement and Feeding

Herbivores and carnivores, as they feed, consume the food materials available in one place. Herbivores feed and move as they graze. Most carnivores move before they capture their prey. This movement makes possible food capture. In most active animals movement and feeding are closely associated. Indeed, movement and feeding are the characteristics by which we can most easily distinguish animals from plants—that is to say, most plants are fixed in one place and most animals move from place to place. Most animals feed and digest things whereas most plants do not (but see Fig. 165, p. 272).

Feeding Mechanisms

An *Amoeba* feeds by enclosing suitable food organisms in food vacuoles. Taking food into a food vacuole is called **ingestion** or **feeding** (see p. 59). *Hydra* extends its tentacles through the water like the threads of a fishing net. The holding of the prey by nematocysts on the tentacles is called food capture. The tentacles carry the food to the mouth, the mouth opens and the prey organism is ingested. Here, food capture comes before feeding. There are many other organisms that, like *Amoeba* and *Hydra*, consume the organisms upon which they feed in one piece.

Filter Feeding

Some animals feed on organisms which are so much smaller than themselves that many food organisms can be consumed at the same time. The herring, pilchard and anchovy, for example, are fishes that filter microscopic animals (plankton) from the surface waters of the sea (Figs. 46 and 73). Cockles, mussels and oysters are filter-feeding molluscs.

Feeding on Fluids

Some animals consume only fluid food. The house-fly will feed on milk, which provides a complete diet (see *Rearing house-flies*, p. 21). They also pour saliva on to solid food, such as sugar, which dissolves in the saliva and is then ingested. The proboscis of a house-fly (see Fig. 12) is expanded at its tip and has many narrow channels which take up fluids by capillarity (just as when a narrow-bore glass tube is placed in a beaker of water, the water rises in the tube). The fluid is then sucked from these tubes, through a food groove (Fig. 12), to the mouth.

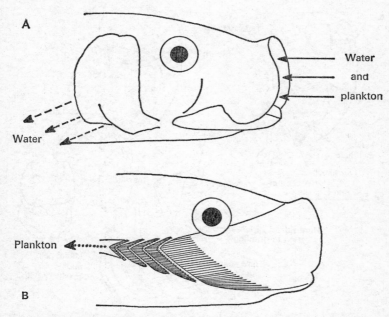

Fig. 46. Filter feeding mechanism of the herring: (A) water with microscopic animals in suspension enters the mouth; (B) right side of head removed to display the gill slits of the left side. The gill rakers project from the gill bars and cover the gill slits. Water passes between the gill rakers and then over the gills. Microscopic animals, retained in the pharynx, pass into the oesophagus.

A mosquito has mouthparts which fit together, forming a tube, like a hypodermic needle. This punctures the skin of a mammal. Saliva is pumped into the wound through one channel (Fig. 60). The saliva contains a chemical that stops the blood from clotting (an anti-coagulant). The blood, mixed with saliva, is then sucked into the mouth through another channel (Fig. 60).

Aphids (green-flies) feed on plant juices. Their mouthparts form a hollow tube which is forced through the surface tissues of a plant into deeper lying fluid-filled tubes in which food materials are carried from one part of the plant to another. These fluids are then ingested.

Biting and Chewing

Grasshoppers and locusts are pests because they feed on grasses and other growing plants (including crops). Beetles in stored grain are pests because they eat the grain. Palps on the mouthparts test the texture of the food and its chemical characteristics; just as when you eat you know what the food feels like and you are aware of its taste and smell. The food held near the mouth is cut by the sharp-edged maxillae and ground between the hard ridged surfaces of the mandibles, and then it is ingested.

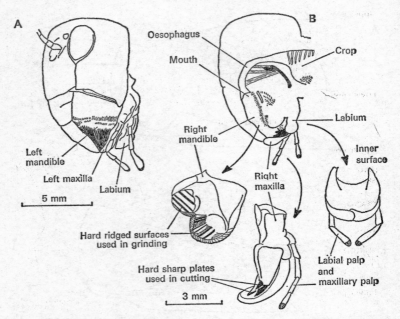

Fig. 47. Mouthparts of a locust *Locusta migratoria*: (A) view of head from left side; (B) head cut in half and mouthparts removed for display (at a higher magnification).

Mammals also bite and chew their food. The teeth of a young mammal, called the milk teeth, are replaced by a second set of teeth (the permanent dentition). People eat a variety of foods and have different kinds of teeth. We recognise, by their shape and position: **incisors** (used in cutting); **canines** (used in holding); **premolars** (used in shredding); and **molars** (used in grinding). However, there are no molars in the milk dentition. Other kinds of mammals have the same kinds of teeth but there are differences which are appropriate to their different diets (see Fig. 48). A dog's incisors cut and its canines hold living prey. Its carnassial teeth are used in shredding and its molars in crushing: as with a nutcracker, the mechanical advantage is greatest near the angle of the jaw. The incisors and canines of a sheep's lower jaw, and the tongue, are used in cropping vegetation against a hard pad of skin on the upper jaw.

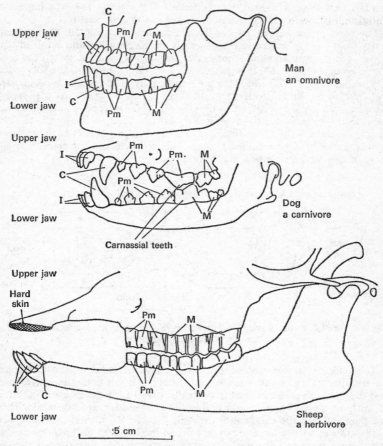

Fig. 48. The teeth of a man, a dog and a sheep (viewed from left side of skull).
I = incisor; C = canine; Pm = premolar; and M = molar.

There are no incisors or canines in the upper jaw and in both jaws there is a gap with no teeth (a diastema) through which the tongue is extended and used in grazing. Ridges on the premolars and molars form an effective grinding surface.

The Alimentary Canal and Digestion in Man

The **mouth** is the opening into a cavity, the buccal cavity (Fig. 50), which is the first part of the alimentary canal or food passage; the tube which leads from the mouth to the anus. Food is taken into this tube through the mouth (ingestion). As it passes along, this food is broken down physically and chemically (digestion) and the soluble food molecules are absorbed (absorption). The indigestible part passes out (egestion) through the anus. As in all animals that have a mouth, the **nutrition** of mammals involves ingestion, digestion, absorption (and assimilation, see p. 91) and egestion.

The parts of the alimentary canal are represented in Fig. 50. In the **buccal cavity** solid food is broken into smaller pieces, by chewing, and is mixed with saliva—the slightly alkaline secretion of the salivary glands. When the food is swallowed (see Fig. 50) it is pushed back by the tongue and the soft palate is raised, closing the opening into the nasal cavity. The trachea is constricted and covered by the epiglottis; and the food passes along a narrow tube, the **oesophagus,** a small quantity at a time (see Fig. 49). The food eaten in one meal accumulates in the **stomach** where it is mixed with acid gastric juices, secreted by glands in the wall of the stomach. As a result, the contents of the stomach may be more fluid than the food eaten. The stomach acids probably also kill most of the bacteria present in the food eaten.

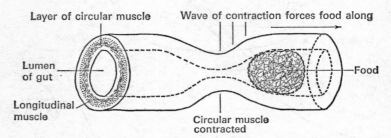

Fig. 49. Peristalsis: the waves of contraction of the circular muscle in the wall of the gut move the food along.

The pyloric sphincter closes the opening from the stomach to the duodenum, the first part of the **small intestine,** but after about an hour this valve opens and the stomach contents start to pour through—a little at a time. Secretions of the liver, stored and concentrated in the gall bladder, are called bile. These are pumped into the duodenum through the bile duct. And alkaline juices pass in through the pancreatic duct. In man the bile duct and pancreatic duct join before opening into the duodenum. Other juices, intestinal juices, are secreted by glands in the wall of the intestine. As a result of all these secretions, the contents of the small intestine are more fluid even than the contents of the stomach.

The soluble parts of the food are chemically digested, in the buccal cavity, stomach and small intestine. Chemical digestion is aided by the contraction of muscles in the wall of the alimentary canal which (1) mix the food fragments with the digestive juices, and (2) move this mixture along the alimentary canal (see Fig. 49).

Some chemicals (alcohol and some other drugs) are absorbed by the epithelial cells of the stomach but the absorption of food molecules takes place into the epithelial cells of the small intestine. The surface area of the epithelial lining is very large because: (1) the small intestine is a long coiled tube; (2) there are many finger-like processes, about 1 mm long, called villi (see Fig. 111B); and (3) there are about 1000 microvilli, 1μm long (Fig. 111C),

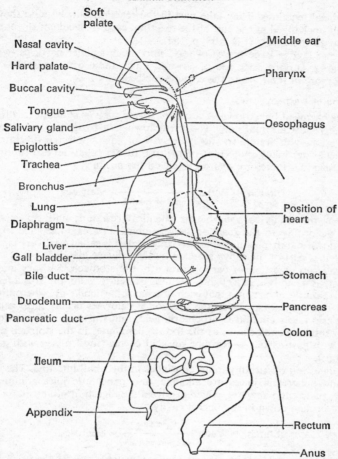

Fig. 50. Digestive system and respiratory system of a man. Not to scale. Complete arrow = passage of food. Dotted arrow = passage of air.

on each cell. As a result of absorption, the intestinal contents become less and less fluid as they pass along.

In the **large intestine** there is a further absorption of fluid and the contents of the rectum (the last part of the large intestine) may be very dry faeces. These accumulate in the rectum and are passed out, through the anus, from time to time. This voiding of faeces is called defaecation or egestion.

Digestion and Absorption

The chemical breakdown (digestion) of starch begins in the buccal cavity. The saliva contains an enzyme called salivary amylase. **Enzymes** are organic catalysts which, like the inorganic catalysts used in industrial processes, speed up chemical reactions. They take part in the reaction but, because they are liberated unchanged at the end of the reaction, each molecule of the enzyme can be used repeatedly (Fig. 108, p. 184).

Chewing breaks large pieces of food into much smaller particles (with a much larger surface area, see p. 58) and mixes these with the saliva. This exposes more of the food to the enzyme molecules.

Digestion of Carbohydrates

In the chemical breakdown of a carbohydrate such as starch, the starch is called the substrate molecule. The breakdown is a hydrolysis—a chemical combination with water. In the hydrolysis of each molecule of starch (a polysaccharide) many molecules of maltose (a disaccharide) are produced. In this reaction, therefore, maltose is called the product.

$$\text{Starch} + \text{Water} \xrightarrow[\text{amylase enzyme}]{\text{Salivary}} \text{Maltose}$$

Each enzyme catalyses a particular chemical reaction; and enzymes are named according to the reaction they catalyse. For example, this enzyme breaks down starch (chemical name = **amylose**). It is called a salivary amylase because it is part of the saliva secreted by the salivary glands.

There is no digestion of carbohydrates in the stomach. Salivary amylase acts best, as a catalyst, in a slightly alkaline or neutral solution. It is a feature of the action of all enzymes that each one has a particular pH (the optimum pH for this enzyme) at which the reaction it catalyses occurs most rapidly. The gastric juices contain hydrochloric acid, and this is why the action of salivary amylase soon ceases as the food accumulates in the stomach and is mixed with gastric juices—forming an acid **chyme** (food mixed with gastric secretions).

The digestion of carbohydrates continues in the small intestine. The intestinal and pancreatic juices are alkaline, and pancreatic juice contains an enzyme, pancreatic amylase, which catalyses the digestion of any starch that was not broken down in the buccal cavity.

$$\text{Starch} + \text{Water} \xrightarrow[\text{amylase enzyme}]{\text{Pancreatic}} \text{Maltose}$$

Intestinal juice contains the enzyme maltase, which catalyses the breakdown of maltose to glucose (a six-carbon or hexose sugar).

$$\text{Maltose} + \text{Water} \xrightarrow[\text{maltase}]{\text{Intestinal}} \text{Glucose}$$

Intestinal juice also contains enzymes which are essential for the digestion of other carbohydrates. For example, the enzyme lactase catalyses the digestion of milk sugar (another disaccharide).

$$\text{Lactose} + \text{Water} \xrightarrow[\text{lactase}]{\text{Intestinal}} \text{Glucose} + \text{Galactose}$$

Digestion of Proteins

The chemical breakdown of protein molecules starts in the stomach and continues in the small intestine. The gastric protease (pepsin) works best in an acid medium and the intestinal protease (trypsin) in an alkaline medium. The breakdown products of the digestion of proteins are amino acids.

$$\text{Proteins} + \text{Water} \xrightarrow[\text{proteases}]{\text{Gastric and intestinal}} \text{Amino acids}$$

Digestion of Lipids

The chemical breakdown of lipids (fats and oils) starts in the small intestine. Bile is pumped from the gall bladder after the chyme starts to pass from the stomach into the duodenum. Bile contains salts which, like soap, emulsify fats—that is to say, the large fat or oil droplets, when mixed with bile, are broken into very small droplets. The enzyme lipase (secreted by the pancreas) further emulsifies lipids. Also, it splits some of the fat and oil molecules (triglycerides, see p. 56) into smaller molecules:

$$\underset{\text{(triglycerides)}}{\text{Lipids}} + \text{Water} \xrightarrow[\text{lipase}]{\text{Pancreatic}} \underset{\text{monoglycerides}}{\overset{\text{Diglycerides}}{\text{and}}} + \text{Fatty acids}$$

Absorption of Food Molecules

Note that the small molecules, resulting from the digestion of foods that contain large carbohydrate, protein and lipid molecules, are: (1) sugars; (2) amino acids; and (3) diglycerides, monoglycerides and fatty acids. These are absorbed by the epithelial cells that line the small intestine (see Fig. 111, p. 186).

The food ingested also contains (4) mineral salts which are absorbed from the intestine as mineral ions, and (5) organic molecules called vitamins which are present in the diet in small amounts and are absorbed without digestion (see *Balanced diet*, p. 193). (6) Drinking water, and water present in the food ingested, is absorbed in the small intestine. This absorption of water continues in the large intestine but the faeces always contain some water.

The incorporation of all the materials **absorbed** by the cells of the intestine into the materials of the body is called **assimilation**; that is to say, once absorbed, these molecules and ions become part of the body tissues or part of the body fluids (blood plasma, tissue fluid and lymph, see p. 215). They are used in a great variety of chemical reactions involved in respiration, in cell maintenance and repair, and in cell growth and reproduction.

Investigation: *the digestion of starch by salivary amylase*
1. Wash out your mouth with warm water.
2. Chew a clean rubber band to stimulate the flow of saliva.
3. Mix the saliva with a little warm water in your mouth and then collect about 4 cm³ of this mixture in a test-tube.
4. Pour half of this into another test-tube. Boil this for 10 seconds. Allow this to cool. Draw 1 cm³ into a clean syringe.
5. Draw 1 cm³ unboiled water/saliva mixture into another clean syringe.
6. Draw 1 cm³ 0.5 per cent starch solution into each syringe.
7. Hold the syringes upside down so that the contents mix; and then test the mixture from each tube, separately, at one-minute intervals, by adding one drop to one drop of iodine solution on a spotting tile.
8. Record your observations. What do you conclude?

Investigation: *the effect of pH on the action of salivary amylase*

1. Collect 8 cm³ saliva/water mixture in a clean test-tube, as in the previous investigation. Label this tube: *enzyme*.
2. Boil half of this saliva/water mixture in another test-tube (for 10 seconds). Allow to cool. Label: *boiled enzyme*.
3. Number six clean test-tubes (1 to 6) with marking ink. Add 5 cm³ buffer solution to each tube: tubes 1 and 2 with pH 4 buffer (acid); tubes 3 and 4 with pH 7 buffer (neutral); and tubes 5 and 6 with pH 9 buffer (alkaline).
4. Add 5 cm³ 0.5 per cent starch solution to each tube.
5. Add 1 cm³ boiled enzyme to each of the even-numbered tubes. Shake the tubes. These are the **controls**.
6. Add 1 cm³ unboiled enzyme to each of the odd-numbered tubes. Shake the tubes.
7. If possible, keep all six tubes in a water bath at 37 °C.
8. After 20 minutes, add a drop of iodine solution to each tube. Record your observations. What do you conclude?

Investigation: *the effect of temperature on the action of salivary amylase.* Plan this investigation yourself. What effects of temperature do you observe?

Note. When you have written your conclusions from these three investigations, look at the comments at the end of this chapter.

Test Questions

1. When you look at a skull from one side you can see the teeth in the upper and lower jaws, and the number of teeth of each kind (visible from this side), can be represented as a dental formula. The llama, for example, has a dental formula: i $\frac{1}{3}$, c $\frac{1}{1}$, pm $\frac{3}{2}$, m $\frac{3}{3}$. There is also a diastemma.

(*a*) What kind of food do you think llamas eat? (*b*) Look at Fig. 48 and then write the dental formulae for a man, a dog and a sheep. (*c*) How do the canines of a herbivore differ from those of a carnivore? (*d*) What is the term we use for an animal that eats plants and animals?

2. (*a*) Draw a diagram of the alimentary canal of a man. Label the oesophagus, buccal cavity, liver, pancreas, large intestine, stomach and small intestine. (*b*) Use the following letters to label. on your diagram: A the structure in which bile is produced; B the region in which fat is digested; C the region from which the products of digestion are absorbed; D a region in which acid is secreted and mixed with the food; E a gland which secretes a digestive juice.

3. Describe briefly how some plants digest food.

Comments on the Investigations Included in this Chapter

1. The amount of starch gradually decreases in the tube which has not been boiled. There is no change in the other tube. You may conclude that saliva contains something, which is destroyed by boiling, that takes part in the digestion of starch. All enzymes are proteins and proteins are denatured by boiling. This is why enzymes are not effective as catalysts after they have been boiled.

2. Tube 1 is the most acid, tube 4 is neutral, and tube 7 is the most alkaline. Saliva is neutral or slightly alkaline and salivary amylase acts most rapidly under these conditions. Each enzyme works most rapidly at a particular pH (the optimum pH for this enzyme).

3. The rate of a chemical reaction doubles for each rise of 10 °C but proteins are denatured at high temperatures. You might expect the optimum temperature for salivary amylase to be about body temperature.

11

SAPROBIONTS

Saprobionts are organisms which obtain their nutriment (food molecules) by absorbing the organic molecules that are available in their environment when, after death, the bodies of other organisms decay. Indeed, by digesting organic matter, saprobionts contribute to the process of decay.

Yeast: A Unicellular Fungus

The yeast that you can buy for making bread or beer is an almost solid thick paste or a coarse dry powder. Prepare a suspension of yeast in sugar solution (see p. 181). If you have a microscope, examine a drop of this suspension.

Yeast is a unicellular fungus (Fig. 51A). Like other fungi (see p. 39) it is without chlorophyll, the pigment which gives the green colour to other plants,

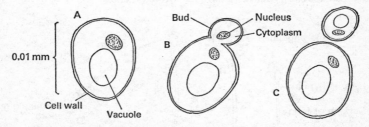

Fig. 51. Yeast *Saccharomyces*: (A) single cell; (B) budding cell; (C) new cell produced by budding.

and its thin cell wall does not contain cellulose (the main constituent of most plant cell walls). Yeast is abundant in many places on land. Yeasts are present, for example, on the surface of soft fruits such as grapes.

In wine-making, yeast washed from the skins of the grapes mixes with the other ingredients: water, grape juice and sugar. The yeast absorbs sugars and other food molecules from the grape juice; and the yeast cells grow and multiply by budding (Fig. 51B). In budding, the nucleus divides. An outgrowth containing one nucleus enlarges and separates, adding to a chain of cells or breaking away.

In the presence of oxygen the yeast uses sugars in its respiration, as a source of energy:

$$\text{Sugars} + \text{Oxygen} \longrightarrow \text{Carbon dioxide} + \text{Water} + \text{Energy}$$

As a result all the oxygen in the fluid is used, but the yeast continues to obtain energy from the sugars:

$$\text{Sugars} \longrightarrow \text{Carbon dioxide} + \text{Ethanol} + \text{Energy}$$

93

The fermentation stops *either* when the sugars are used completely *or* when the alcohol is so concentrated that it kills the yeast. The alcohol in wine and beer is ethanol (ethyl alcohol) and the release of energy from sugars, in the absence of oxygen, is called **anaerobic respiration** (or alcoholic fermentation).

In bread-making, yeast is mixed with water and sugar. Later, this fluid is mixed with flour to produce dough. Because of thorough mixing by the baker there is oxygen in the dough and, when it is left to stand in a warm place (at about your body temperature), the yeast respires aerobically. The carbon dioxide given off causes the dough to rise. The baker then kneads the dough, mixing it thoroughly and introducing more air, and then places it into tins or on trays. He leaves it to rise again, due to further aerobic respiration and the production of more carbon dioxide, before baking the bread. In the oven the bread continues to rise for a short time until the heat kills the yeast. The small holes in bread, which give it an open texture, are due to the carbon dioxide produced in the respiration of the yeast.

A Bread Mould: *Rhizopus*

If bread is left in a warm damp place, such as a closed container in a kitchen, it soon goes mouldy. The mould lives on and just below the surface but is first conspicuous as small circular grey-white patches.

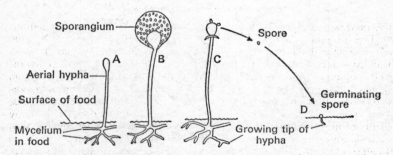

Fig. 52. Life-cycle of a mould *Rhizopus*: (A) developing sporangiophore; (B) sporangium (about 75 μm diameter) containing spores; (C) spores released; (D) a spore germinating on a suitable food develops into a new mycelium.

Rhizopus, like other fungi, is without chlorophyll. It is a common saprobiont in soil. It may also cause the rotting of stored fruit and grain, and is a common bread mould. Spores of *Rhizopus*, carried in air currents, may be deposited on bread. Here they germinate if the surface is moist. The tubular outgrowth that penetrates the surface of the bread is called a **hypha**.

The tip of the hypha secretes enzymes. The organic molecules in bread are digested, outside the hypha, and then the products of this digestion (the smaller food molecules, see p. 91) are absorbed by the hypha. The hypha grows at its tip and branches and becomes a mass of threads called a **mycelium**. At the surface of the bread some erect hyphae project into the air (Fig. 52). These aerial hyphae are unbranched. They are called **sporangiophores** because each of them bears, at its tip, a spore case or **sporangium** containing **spores**.

All the hyphae of the mycelium, and the aerial hyphae, have a wall outside the surface membrane and a large central vacuole. Many nuclei share the same cytoplasm (Fig. 28A)—that is to say, the hyphae are not divided into cells. Such a non-cellular arrangement in which a number of nuclei share the same cytoplasm is called a syncytium. The streaming of the cytoplasm carries food materials, absorbed at the tips of the hyphae, to all other parts of the mycelium.

A cross-wall forms between the sporangium and the stalk of the sporangium. Within the sporangium many spores are formed, each with several nuclei and some cytoplasm and a spore wall. The wall of the sporangium breaks open and the spores are released. So the organism, which grew from a spore, produces many **spores**. Some are carried by the wind; and some on the bodies of flies and other animals. Any spore deposited on a suitable food soon germinates and forms a new mycelium. In this way, *Rhizopus* obtains food, grows, reproduces and its spores are dispersed to places where the organism may obtain nutriment, grow and reproduce.

As with other organisms, the form of *Rhizopus* is different in each stage of its life cycle. The form at each stage is adapted to its place in the life cycle: the mycelium is concerned with **nutrition** and **growth**; the sporangiophores with **reproduction**; and the spores with **dispersal** and **survival**.

The Role of Saprobionts in Decay

The presence of saprobiotic fungi and bacteria in the soil can be demonstrated by providing them with a suitable nutrient medium (see p. 100). Some micro-organisms in the soil will grow. These are the ones that can use the food molecules in this medium in these particular conditions of pH and temperature. If a different food medium was provided, containing different nutrients or having a different pH, or if the soil was incubated at a different temperature, the conditions would be suitable for the growth of other micro-organisms. A great variety of bacteria and fungi live in the soil. Which ones grow in any nutrient medium depends upon which organisms were present as spores in the soil sample, and the precise conditions of their environment.

Because of the part they play in the decay of dead organisms and faeces, saprobionts in soil and water are essential to the life of all other organisms.

The Carbon Cycle

Carbon, from carbon dioxide in their environment, is assimilated by green plants in photosynthesis. This carbon is then part of the organic molecules of the green plant.

$$\text{Carbon dioxide from air} + \text{Water} \xrightarrow{\text{Light}} \text{Sugars in plants} + \text{Oxygen}$$

Animals absorb carbon-containing molecules after digesting either plants or other animals that have fed on plants.

In the respiration of plants and animals, carbon from these organic molecules is returned to the atmosphere as part of carbon dioxide molecules:

$$\text{Sugars in plants or animals} + \text{Oxygen} \longrightarrow \text{Carbon dioxide} + \text{Water} + \text{Energy}$$

When plants and animals die, saprobionts contribute to their decay. Organic molecules are digested and absorbed by saprobionts. Some of the carbon-containing molecules are used in respiration, adding carbon dioxide to the atmosphere, and some are incorporated in the structural and storage molecules of the saprobionts.

When saprobionts are eaten by animals they are digested and the organic molecules absorbed are either used in respiration or incorporated in the structural and storage molecules of the animal.

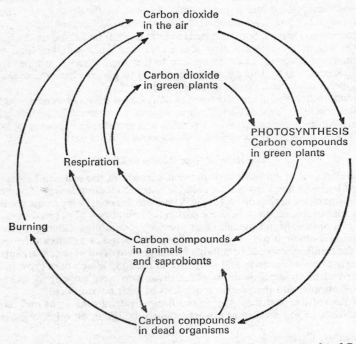

Fig. 53. The carbon cycle (simplified from Barrass, R., *Biology: Food and People*, Hodder & Stoughton, London).

These processes—(a) photosynthesis in green plants; (b) the use of carbon-containing molecules in the nutrition of organisms that have no chlorophyll; and (c) the respiration of all organisms—contribute to the circulation of carbon in nature. This can be represented in a diagram as a **carbon cycle** (Fig. 53). Also, in burning timber and fossil fuels carbon-containing molecules are completely oxidised and carbon dioxide is returned to the atmosphere.

The Circulation of Mineral Elements in Nature

Plants absorb mineral ions. Some of these are incorporated in organic molecules; others are present as ions in solution in the cell fluids. The organic molecules produced by green plants and the mineral ions present in the plants are the food materials required by animals (see p. 91). When plants and animals die, and when undigested food is egested by animals, these same kinds of food materials are available to saprobionts. The excretions of animals also include mineral ions which may be absorbed by green plants or by saprobionts.

The only source of mineral ions is by solution from rocks, but once absorbed by living organisms the supply of mineral ions in any place depends upon the circulation of these ions in nature, from one organism to another, and upon the loss of ions from some organisms and their absorption by others (see *Mineral cycle*, Fig. 54).

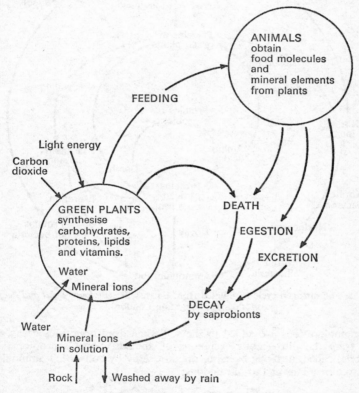

Fig. 54. The circulation of mineral elements in nature (simplified from Barrass, R., *Biology: Food and People*, Hodder & Stoughton, London).

The Nitrogen Cycle

Amino acid molecules, from which proteins are formed, contain nitrogen, an essential element in all living organisms. Unlike the mineral elements considered above, nitrogen is not present in rocks. Its presence in soil is a result of the activities of living organisms.

Plants absorb nitrogen-containing ions from the soil or from the water in which they live, and use these in the synthesis of proteins. Animals eat plants or they eat other animals that have fed on plants, and so obtain protein molecules from plants either directly or indirectly. The amino acids from dead organisms are absorbed by saprobionts and used in the formation of new proteins.

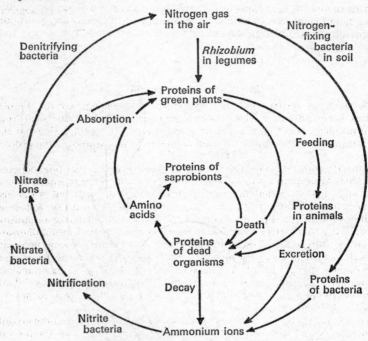

Fig. 55. The nitrogen cycle (simplified from Barrass, R., *Biology: Food and People*, Hodder & Stoughton, London).

Ammonium ions are added to the soil when dead organisms decay and also from the nitrogenous excretions of animals. Some saprobiotic soil bacteria, called **nitrifying bacteria**, obtain energy by converting ammonium ions to nitrite ions and to nitrate ions:

$$\underset{\text{ammonia}}{NH_3} + \underset{\text{oxygen}}{2O_2} \longrightarrow \underset{\text{nitrate}}{NO_3^-} + \underset{\text{water}}{H_2O} + H^+ \text{ Energy}$$

Nitrates are absorbed by green plants.

Other soil bacteria are called **de-nitrifying bacteria** because they break down nitrate ions and, as a result of their activities, nitrogen gas is returned to the atmosphere. The amount of nitrogen available to living organisms is reduced by **de-nitrification**. However, de-nitrification is offset by the activities of other saprobiotic soil bacteria which absorb nitrogen gas from the soil atmosphere and use it in the production of nitrogen-containing compounds. When these

nitrogen-fixing bacteria die and decay, nitrogen-containing compounds are added to the soil. Other nitrogen-fixing bacteria live in swellings called root nodules which are formed by leguminous plants (see p. 102).

The circulation of nitrogen from the atmosphere, in the bodies of living and dead organisms, in chemicals in solution in the soil water, and back to the atmosphere is called the **nitrogen cycle** (Fig. 55). Apart from the activities of nitrogen-fixing bacteria, nitrogen and oxygen combine in the atmosphere during lightning discharges, forming nitrous and nitric oxides which dissolve in rain and so are added to the soil.

Studying Micro-organisms

The study of micro-organisms was called **microbiology** by the French scientist Louis Pasteur in 1882. Twenty years earlier he had extracted from the atmosphere small particles that he was unable to distinguish from the spores of moulds. He went on to demonstrate their importance in the process of decay.

By this demonstration he disproved what most people at that time believed to be true. More than 2000 years ago, Aristotle studied the reproduction of fishes and concluded that most fishes developed from eggs but some just appeared in mud and water. By the beginning of the 18th century, following the discoveries of the first microscopists, it was clear that larger organisms do not just appear from nowhere. However, until the work of Spallanzani later in the 18th century and of Pasteur in the 19th century, many biologists believed that some living organisms could arise spontaneously from non-living matter—for example, in rotting meat and other foods—by spontaneous generation or **abiogenesis**. People knew that like begets like but they did not know that living things come only from living things; that is to say, they are formed only by biogenesis.

Lazaro Spallanzani (1729–99), an Italian scientist, observed that the growth of living organisms in sealed containers was prevented by heating the food to a high temperature; and in 1810 Francois Appert started the commercial bottling of fruit in France. He placed the food in clean jars, corked them and then raised the temperature to 100 °C. Note that the containers were sealed, as in Spallanzani's experiments, and some people who still believed that abiogenesis was possible argued that the absence of growth was due to the absence of fresh air. Others suggested that heating the air in the jars had destroyed some *vital principle*, spoiling it for the purpose of spontaneous generation.

Pasteur, in his experiment, boiled broth in a swan-necked flask and then allowed the broth to cool slowly. The flask was not sealed (see Fig. 56) but, even in the presence of air and suitable food, micro-organisms did not arise from nowhere. The broth did not go bad. However, contamination was possible when he broke the neck of the flask. Then the spores of bacteria could fall into the broth from the air, and the broth soon went bad. Because of the shape of the swan-neck, spores were not able to fall into the broth until the neck was broken. Pasteur concluded that living organisms arise only from pre-existing organisms.

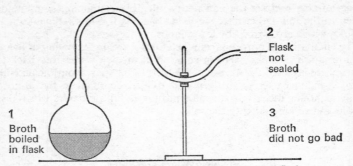

Fig. 56. Pasteur's experiment with a swan-necked flask.

All methods of **food preservation** depend upon the prevention of decay. Saprobionts cause decay in stored foods, as in other environments, and decay can be prevented only if the food is stored either without micro-organisms or in conditions which prevent their growth and reproduction (see Table 11).

Table 11. Methods of preserving food.

Canning and bottling	Organisms in the food are killed by cooking at high temperatures. The containers are sealed while they are still very hot and this prevents contamination*.
Refrigeration	Temperature kept so low that any organisms in the food respire very slowly. They do not grow or reproduce.
Dehydration	Drying fish and meat in the sun until their water content is very low. Freeze-drying of food products in industry.
Osmotic dehydration	Salting increases the osmotic potential of the fluid in which the food is stored and so water is extracted from any micro-organisms present. Addition of sugar in jam-making has the same effect. Drying fruit in the sun removes water and so increases the concentration of sugars in the fruit.
Sterilisation	Milk heated to 140 °C for 2 s kills micro-organisms; then the containers are sealed to prevent contamination.
Pasteurisation	Milk heated to 62 °C for 30 min or to 72 °C for 15 s and then cooled rapidly. This kills pathogenic bacteria but does not kill all bacteria.
Preservatives	Suspending meat and fish in the smoke of a wood fire adds toxic chemicals to their surface. In other processes chemicals are added to food (e.g. acetic acid and sulphur dioxide). These kill micro-organisms but at the low concentrations used are not harmful to man.

Note. Food bottled at home must be properly washed and stored in clean properly sealed containers, and then properly sterilised, or it may be contaminated by *Clostridium botulinum*, a bacterium that causes food poisoning.

Investigation: *micro-organisms in soil.* Prepare Petri dishes with sterile nutrient agar (see p. 52). Mix some soil with about the same volume of distilled water. Pour the mixture on to a plate of nutrient agar. Leave this for 30 s. Pour away the soil and water. Replace the lid of the Petri dish. Secure and label the dish (see p. 53). Incubate the plate upside-down at about 25 °C or at room temperature. Bacteria from the soil will multiply and produce colonies.

Investigation: *micro-organisms in milk.* To estimate the number of bacteria in 100 cm³ milk, shake the milk and then add 1 cm³ milk to the surface of a nutrient agar plate in a Petri dish. To do this, raise the lid of the dish as little as is necessary. Gently lower the lid. Tilt the plate from side to side to spread the milk evenly. Secure and label the Petri dish (see p. 53). Incubate the plate upside-down at about 25 °C (or at room temperature). Each bacterium will grow and reproduce and give rise to a separate colony. About a week later, count the colonies. This is your estimate of the number of bacteria in your sample from the 100 cm³ milk at the time that you took the sample.

Test Questions

1. State (*a*) **one** way in which the nutrition of a saprobiotic fungus is similar to that of a green plant, and (*b*) **two** ways in which they differ in their modes of nutrition.

2. Make a list of the missing words in the following statements:

(*a*) Yeast reproduces by ——.
(*b*) —— make possible the rapid and widespread dispersal of saprobiotic fungi such as *Mucor.*
(*c*) There are no fishes in rivers which contain large amounts of sewage because bacteria in the water use up all the ——.
(*d*) The gas —— ——, that causes bread to rise, is produced in the —— respiration of yeast.

3. Draw a simple diagram to represent the circulation of a named element in nature.

4. Name **four** different methods by which people preserve foods and state why each of these methods is effective in preventing the food from going bad.

5. How would you estimate the number of bacteria in a glass of water?

12

LIVING TOGETHER

One kind of **biotic association** is social behaviour between members of the same species (see next chapter). Another kind, the close association of members of different species, is the subject of this chapter.

Symbiosis

When two different kinds of organisms live together and when they both benefit from their association, the relationship is called symbiosis.

Micro-organisms and Ruminants

Some mammals, including sheep, cattle and goats, are called ruminants. Bacteria and protists live in the sac-like first chamber of the stomach (the rumen), in symbiotic association with their host. They live in the rumen, where food is always present, and so obtain both shelter and food. They (1) make amino acids and vitamins from other molecules present in the food consumed by the host, and (2), unlike their host, they have a cellulase enzyme and can break down the cellulose cell walls of plants to sugars (see p. 56). As a result, the food eaten by the host is (1) made more nutritious, and (2) when the food passes on to the next parts of the alimentary canal, the plant cells and the micro-organisms are digested.

The food added by feeding balances that lost to the next chamber of the stomach. The micro-organisms are cultured and harvested continuously.

Leguminous Plants and *Rhizobium*

Legumes (Family Leguminosae, including peas, beans, lucerne and clover) have swellings or **nodules** on their roots (Fig. 5). These swellings are caused by a bacterium called *Rhizobium* which enters the cells of a young root from the soil. It then receives nutrients from the cells of the host plant and grows and multiplies. The cells of the host also multiply, producing a nodule of plant cells infected with the bacteria.

In this symbiotic association *Rhizobium* fixes nitrogen from the soil atmosphere. The cells of the legume cannot fix nitrogen unless they are infected by *Rhizobium*; and *Rhizobium* can do so only when it is living in the cells of a legume. This association, therefore, benefits both organisms. It also benefits all other organisms by adding to the amount of nitrogen circulating in nature (see p. 98); and leguminous plants, in cultivation, add to the nitrogen content of the soil (see p. 126).

Parasitism

Mosquitoes settle on a host animal and feed on its blood (see Fig. 60, p. 107). Head and body lice live on their host and feed on its blood. These insects are called **ectoparasites** (Gk. *ektos* = outer). Some parasitic plants live on the surface of their host but have parts that are permanently within the host (see Fig. 57). Many other parasites live inside their host and are called **endoparasites** (see Figs. 58 and 59).

The term **host** is used in relation to both symbiosis and parasitism. The rumen micro-organisms are symbionts and the ruminant is their host animal. The *Rhizobium* in root nodules are symbionts and the legume is their host plant. Similarly, a parasite is an organism that lives on or inside its host.

Symbiosis is a relationship in which both the symbiont and its host benefit from the association.

Parasitism is a relationship in which the parasite benefits in some way from the association but the host does not; and the host may be harmed or even killed by the activities of the parasite.

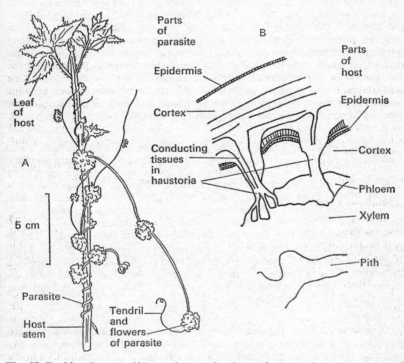

Fig. 57. Dodder *Cuscuta*: (A) growing on the shoot of a host plant; (B) section of part of the host's stem with haustoria from the dodder penetrating the cortex (based on Barrass, R., *Biology: Food and People*, Hodder & Stoughton, London).

However, it is not possible to draw a hard and fast line between symbiosis and parasitism because there are many different ways in which organisms of different species may live together in close association and we do not always know if the relationship is beneficial to both.

Mistletoe: A Partial Parasite

The mistletoes are perennial stem parasites of trees. *Viscum album* is common on apple and pear trees in Europe. The female plant has sticky semi-transparent berries which are carried by birds. The birds may wipe them from their beaks on to the bark of trees. The growing root of the seedling penetrates the bark of the host tree. However, the leaves and stem of the mistletoe contain chlorophyll. The parasite is not completely dependent upon its host for food. Other mistletoes parasitise conifers and damage many forest trees to such an extent that they are of no use for timber.

Dodder

The different species of dodder (*Cuscuta:* Fig. 57) are all annuals. They are parasitic on other flowering plants, including hops, clover and lucerne. If the seedling contacts a suitable host, the parasite's root withers as its shoot grows up and entwines the host stem. Processes called **haustoria** grow into the host until the conducting tissues of the parasite and host are continuous with one another. Water, mineral nutrients, sugars and other materials then pass from the host to the parasite. The shoot is thread-like, with long internodes and small scale-like leaves. However, chlorophyll is present and the parasite is not, therefore, completely dependent upon its host for food. One dodder plant may produce more than 600 metres of stem in one growing season and it has very large numbers of flowers and seeds. This increases the chances of some seeds germinating next to a suitable host.

Lice

Head lice and **body lice** (*Pediculus humanus*) are very small insects, about 2.5 mm long, that live on the surface of the skin of people. They feed on blood and cause irritation, but may also transmit epidemic typhus, relapsing fever and trench fever if they move from an infected person to someone who is not infected. The eggs of *Pediculus*, called nits, are fixed to hairs close to the skin. If a person has lice, you can see the eggs if you look closely. One female may lay 300 eggs. In this way a heavy infestation is produced.

Anyone can have lice. They pass from one head to another when people are close together; for example, when two children are reading the same book. People can also be infected with lice (and with ringworm, p. 107) if they use other people's hair brushes or combs, or use their towels and pillowcases, or try on their hats and clothes. If one person in a family or school has lice, others are likely to have them.

Tapeworms

Tapeworms live in the intestines of vertebrate animals, including farm animals, pet animals and people. Each tapeworm has a **scolex**, a knob-like structure with hooks and suckers which is embedded in the wall of its host's intestine. There is then a cylindrical part which flattens into the tape. This tape hangs in the lumen of the intestine surrounded by the digestive juices and partially digested food of its host. The tape is made up of a large number of pieces, called **proglottids**, joined end to en⌐.

Proglottids are produced in the region of proliferation next to the scolex. Each new proglottid, therefore, separates the scolex from the last-formed proglottid. Once formed, the proglottids start to develop and grow. The smallest proglottid is next to the scolex, the next one is a little larger, and so on; so that the tape gradually widens away from the scolex (see Fig. 21A). The oldest proglottid is the one furthest from the scolex.

A tapeworm has no digestive system but it lives in the food digested by its host. Food molecules in the host's intestine are absorbed not only by the epithelial cells of the host's intestine, but also by the epithelium of the parasite's skin. Many of the food molecules which would otherwise provide

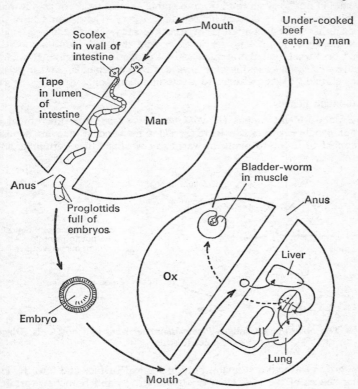

Fig. 58. Life cycle of the beef tapeworm *Taenia saginata* (based on Barrass, R., *Biology: Food and People*, Hodder & Stoughton, London).

nourishment for the host are absorbed by the parasite. As a result, the host is weakened by the presence of a tapeworm in its intestine. This is why tapeworms are of veterinary and medical importance.

Fully formed proglottids, packed with embryos, pass out with the host's faeces. These embryos may infect another vertebrate host (see Fig. 58) called the **intermediate host**, in which they develop into a bladder-worm in a muscle. People may be infected when they eat insufficiently cooked meat containing bladder-worms. Cattle may be infected if there are tapeworm embryos in the sewage sludge spread on farm land.

There are many diseases that people can catch from their pets. Some animals—particularly tortoises, terrapins, monkeys and birds (parrots, parakeets and budgerigars)—should not be kept in any home. With other pets, such as dogs and cats, there is less risk but children are most likely to be affected. To reduce the chances of infection, animals should be trained not to dirty lawns, paths or childrens' play areas. Pets should be kept out of parts of the house where young children crawl or where people may walk bare-foot. They should not be given food from the table at meal times, or be allowed to lick children, or to feed from household crockery. They should have their own dish that is washed apart from other crockery. Their beds and bedding should be kept clean. Any vomit or excreta dropped indoors should be burned or buried, and the area should be properly disinfected. Even when they are well, after touching pets always wash your hands. And if pets are ill they should be taken at once to a veterinary surgeon.

Potato-blight Fungus

The potato-blight fungus (*Phytophthora infestans*), like other fungi (see Fig. 52), produces spores which are carried in the wind. If these are deposited on the leaf of a potato plant, in warm wet weather, they germinate and a

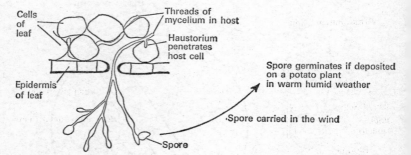

Fig. 59. The potato-blight fungus *Phytophthora infestans* and host cells. Diagram not to scale.

hypha grows through a stomatal pore in the leaf surface and into the intercellular spaces of the leaf. Here the hypha grows and branches, forming a mass of tangled threads (a mycelium, see p. 51). Projections from the hyphae into the cells of the leaf (see Fig. 59) are called **haustoria**. These secrete enzymes, which digest the host's cells, and absorb food molecules. This kills the host's cells and the leaf turns brown near each point of infection.

The parasite begins to produce **spores** (Fig. 59), which may infect other plants or may be washed into the soil where they infect the tubers (potatoes). A whole crop may be destroyed. Indeed, the potato-blight fungus was the principal cause of famine in Ireland in 1845, and in the next ten years or so more than a million Irish people died of starvation and of diseases favoured by the weakened body.

There are many other kinds of plant-parasitic fungi. These are called blights, moulds, smuts and rusts. Great economic losses are caused by many of the fungi that attack crop plants. One of the problems of any cultivation is that by growing many plants of the same kind together, we create conditions which favour the spread of diseases from plant to plant. The study of plant diseases is called **plant pathology** (see also p. 109); and the diseases are usually controlled by the use of fungicides or by growing crops that are resistant to fungus diseases.

Fungi also cause diseases of animals; for example, the so-called ringworm, a skin disease of people, is caused by a parasitic fungus. The infection is passed from one person to another when people wear other people's hats or use their pillows, brushes and combs, or use public shower baths.

The Malarial Parasite

Plasmodium, the malarial parasite, is a protist that lives in the liver epithelial cells and in the red blood corpuscles of infected people. When a person has malaria, the parasites absorb nutriment and destroy the infected cells. Malaria is caused by the regular release of the parasites' waste products into the blood of the host, every 24 hours or every 48 hours. These cause the periodic fevers characteristic of the different forms of malaria; and more people die of malaria than from any other cause.

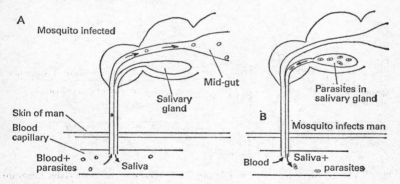

Fig. 60. Mosquito feeding on man: (A) ingests malarial parasites; (B) transmits malaria when it feeds again.

Mosquitoes, of the genus *Anopheles*, may ingest *Plasmodium* when they suck blood from someone who has malaria (Fig. 60A). When they next feed, the mosquitoes may inject parasites into the blood of another person. This is likely to happen because, before they feed, mosquitoes inject saliva into the wound. The saliva contains an anticoagulant, which prevents the blood from clotting, and this enables the mosquito to suck up the blood. But if the mosquito is infected with *Plasmodium*, these parasites will be injected with the saliva (Fig. 60B). This is the only way in which malarial parasites can pass from one person to another.

Quinine and many synthetic drugs have been used in the treatment of malaria (see p. 273). However, if contact between people and mosquitoes can be reduced there is less chance of infection. In places where there is malaria, people should sleep only under mosquito nets. Residual insecticides are also used on the inside walls of houses in an attempt to kill those mosquitoes that are most likely to bite people. The larvae and pupae of mosquitoes are aquatic (see Fig. 61) and control operations usually include (1) the drainage of standing waters to reduce the number of breeding sites, and (2) the introduction of minnows (mosquito-eating fish) into the water as a method of biological control (see p. 134).

Trypanosoma, another protist, causes sleeping sickness of people and a disease of cattle called nagana. These diseases are confined to Africa, south of the Sahara desert, and *Glossina*, the tsetse fly, is the intermediate host. Like the *Anopheles* mosquito, *Glossina* feeds on blood and transmits the trypanosomes from one mammal to another.

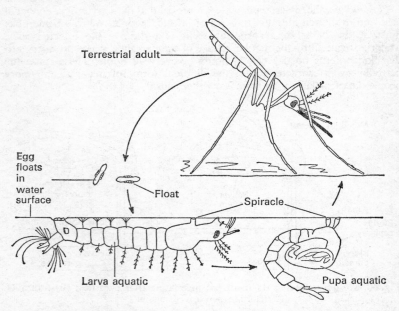

Fig. 61. Life cycle of *Anopheles* mosquito (based on Barrass, R., *Biology: Food and People*, Hodder & Stoughton, London).

Bacteria that cause Diseases

Many parasitic bacteria cause diseases of plants and animals. They live in the cells or body fluids of their host and absorb food materials from their environment. The waste products of the bacteria, excreted into the body of their host, are poisonous (toxic) and are therefore called **toxins**. It is the toxins that cause diseases and the host's responses to the toxins are the **symptoms** (or signs) of the disease caused by bacteria of a particular kind. Some of the diseases of people, caused by parasitic bacteria, are typhoid and paratyphoid fever, bubonic plague, diphtheria, cholera, leprosy, tuberculosis, whooping cough, tonsillitis, pneumonia and tetanus.

Saprobiotic bacteria in the buccal cavity contribute to the **decay of teeth,** especially if people do not clean their teeth properly after meals or if they eat sweets between meals.

Ill health or death is caused by other saprobiotic bacteria that cause **food poisoning**. Cooking destroys bacteria but it does not necessarily destroy the toxins that they excrete. *Salmonella* toxins are not destroyed by cooking and they cause food poisoning, which sometimes results from eating reheated meat dishes. The toxins produced by *Clostridium*, a soil bacterium, are fatal even in very small amounts. However, both *Clostridium* and the toxin it produces are destroyed by boiling food for 15 to 20 minutes. In commercially canned or bottled foods, proper attention to cleanliness and complete sterilisation prevents food poisoning. Inadequately processed home-preserved foods are the most usual cause of trouble.

The potato-blight fungus occupies an important place in the history of plant pathology. In 1846 Berkeley in England and de Bary in Germany demonstrated that the blight of potatoes was always associated with the presence of the fungus *Phytophthora* (see p. 106). This was the first convincing evidence that a micro-organism could cause a disease. Before this, people thought that the rotting of the crop was due to some other cause such as unfavourable weather.

Pasteur, in 1866, investigated a disease of silk-worm moth caterpillars, which were reared in large numbers in France for silk production, and he was the first to demonstrate that bacteria could cause a disease of animals. In 1876 Koch, in Germany, isolated a bacterium from animals that were suffering from anthrax. He cultured this bacterium on a nutrient jelly. He also stated four things that scientists must do if they wished to prove that a particular kind of bacterium is the cause of a particular disease.

1. They must be able to isolate the bacterium from all organisms investigated that have the disease.
2. They must isolate the bacterium and maintain it in pure culture (with no other kind of organism present to contaminate the culture).
3. They must check that when bacteria from this pure culture are injected into a healthy host organism, they cause the host to develop symptoms of the disease.
4. They must then isolate the bacterium from such infected hosts and maintain it again in pure culture.

Pasteur isolated and cultured anthrax bacteria in his laboratory. He found that this bacterium was weakened when it was maintained in a laboratory culture at too high a temperature. He demonstrated dramatically in 1881 that when the weakened bacteria were injected into sheep, a process called **inoculation**, the sheep did not suffer from anthrax. More than this, these sheep recovered from this disease after being infected later with normal (un-weakened) anthrax bacteria. The first inoculation, with weakened bacteria, had given them an **immunity** to anthrax. On the other hand, the sheep in a control experiment were not inoculated with weakened anthrax bacteria and they all died after being infected with normal anthrax bacteria.

People who have suffered from a disease caused by bacteria, such as whooping cough, may afterwards have an immunity to that disease: they do not usually suffer from it twice. Artificial immunisation, with dead or weakened bacteria, as in Pasteur's experiment with anthrax in sheep, also results in an acquired immunity. This technique has been used to prevent many diseases and it has saved many lives. However, only people who have been immunised against a particular disease are protected.

The skin is a barrier which prevents most bacteria from entering the body. Wounds destroy this barrier and provide one means of infection. Wounds and scratches should therefore be cleaned, treated with an antiseptic and then covered with a clean dressing. The ability of people to transfer a disease from a patient who is suffering from the disease to a previously healthy person was demonstrated by Semmelweis in 1846. By hand-washing and rinsing in chlorinated lime solution, he reduced the death rate from a fever in the maternity hospital in Vienna from 7 per cent to 1.2 per cent without knowing the cause of the disease.

The use of disinfectants, the introduction of **antiseptic** surgery by Lister in 1867, the demonstration by Pasteur and Koch that bacteria may cause diseases, and the introduction of the technique of immunisation, were all great advances in medical science. The application of the results of these investigations has dramatically reduced the number of deaths from infectious diseases.

Bacteria may also enter the body through the mouth. Many of these are killed by the digestive juices but food poisoning is caused by toxins produced by saprobiotic bacteria which have grown and multiplied in food that has not been properly stored. Food should be covered to keep away house-flies, which may walk on rotten food in dustbins, on faeces on the ground, and then on food on your table. Dustbins should be covered. Sewage should be treated before disposal so that it is not a danger to health. And **foods** should be kept clean, cooked in clean utensils and either eaten fresh or properly preserved (see Table 11). People who handle food should make sure that their hands are clean, especially after emptying the bladder or bowels, and they should not touch their mouths or other parts of their body. **Water** should not be used for drinking or for washing food, unless it is known to be clean and fit to drink. Otherwise, the water should be boiled for 20 minutes.

Another method of infection is through close bodily contact, especially in sexual intercourse (see p. 248). The **venereal diseases** (syphilis, gonorrhoea and urethritis) can be caught only from an infected person and, therefore, they can be passed on only by an infected person. Apart from other considerations (see p. 249), this is one good reason why sexual intercourse should not follow a casual encounter but should be part of a lasting relationship.

In 1928 Alexander Fleming, a British microbiologist, observed the mould fungus *Penicillium* growing as a contaminant in a culture of bacteria. He noticed that there was a clear area around the fungus where no bacteria were growing. He concluded from this observation that the fungus must be excreting something which inhibited the growth of bacteria. Fleming's observation, and his understanding of its possible importance, led to the discovery of **penicillin**, a chemical that was named after the fungus. Penicillin is called an **antibiotic** (Gk. *anti* = against; *bios* = life) because it kills bacteria. Other antibiotics are now known. They are extracted, purified and then used, like penicillin, as tablets or by injection, in the treatment of people who are suffering from diseases caused by bacteria, for which previously there was no cure.

Viruses

Viruses (0.3 to 0.01 μm diameter) are the smallest organisms. They have a core of nucleic acid (either DNA or RNA, see p. 151) and a protein coat. Each kind of virus grows and reproduces only in the cells of an appropriate host organism—that is to say, they are all parasites. They are of great economic importance because many of them cause diseases. Virus diseases of people include the common cold, influenza, yellow fever, poliomyelitis, smallpox, measles and rabies. Virus diseases of farm animals include rinderpest (cattle plague), foot and mouth disease of cattle, sheep and pigs, and myxomatosis of rabbits. Viruses also cause diseases of crop plants, including maize streak and swollen shoot of cocoa.

Different viruses are transmitted from host to host in different ways. Common cold and influenza viruses are dispersed in the air when people suffering from these diseases breathe out and sneeze, and then they are breathed in by other people. Yellow fever is transmitted by the bite of the *Aedes* mosquito. Some virus diseases of plants are transmitted by aphids.

Edward Jenner observed that people who had suffered from cowpox did not catch smallpox. In 1798, nearly a hundred years before Pasteur's work on anthrax (see p. 109), Jenner produced an immunity to smallpox by taking matter from a cowpox pustule and introducing this into people through small punctures in their skin. Jenner did not know what caused the disease; nor did he understand the reason for the success of this treatment (called **vaccination**; L. *vacca* = a cow). Indeed, no one knew of the existence of viruses until 1898.

We now know that people suffer from a number of diseases caused by viruses—for example, chickenpox and measles—and those who recover have an acquired immunity to these diseases. People can also be immunised against these common diseases of childhood. Poliomyelitis is now a less common disease of childhood—mainly due to the use of vaccines developed by Salk and Sabin which have saved many lives. Influenza, however, still leads to many deaths; usually from secondary bacterial infections.

Investigation: *the spread of disease.* Prepare Petri dishes containing sterile nutrient agar (see p. 52).

1. Gently wipe a clean finger across the surface of one plate. Secure and label the dish (see p. 53).
2. Ask someone who has not washed their hands recently to wipe one finger on the surface of another plate. Secure and label the dish.
3. Catch a fly and keep it in another Petri dish until it has walked over the surface of the agar. Secure and label the dish.

Incubate all the Petri dishes upside-down at about 25 °C (or at room temperature). Examine them after about a week. What do you conclude about the ways in which disease-producing bacteria could be spread? *Read the note on safety on p. 53.*

For further information, see *The Use of Micro-organisms in Schools* (Education Pamphlet 61, HMSO, London).

Test Questions

1. Make a list of the words needed to complete the following paragraph:

The swellings on the roots of —— plants are called —— ——. These are the result of a —— association between the bacterium —— and the host plant, in which —— gas is used in the synthesis of proteins. This process, called —— ——, increases soil fertility.

2. (*a*) What is a parasite? (*b*) Name a parasite that you have studied. (*c*) Explain how this parasite remains in contact with its host and how new hosts are infected. (*d*) How is a knowledge of a parasite's life cycle useful in control operations?

3. Drone honey bees live in the nest constructed by the workers, and they consume food collected by the workers. State two reasons why biologists do not consider the drones to be parasites.

4. Explain the importance, in medicine, of the following: (*a*) disinfectants; (*b*) antiseptics; (*c*) immunisation; and (*d*) antibiotics.

5. (*a*) Name a bacterium that is useful to man. Why is it of economic importance? (*b*) Name a protist that is harmful to man, and name a disease that it causes. (*c*) Describe the structure of a named fungus that is useful to man. Where does it live in nature, and for what purpose is it used by people?

6. Which one of the words A to G do you associate most closely with each of the words *a* to *f*:

A	poliomyelitis	*a*	host
B	photosynthesis	*b*	chlorophyll
C	parasite	*c*	Salk
D	toxins	*d*	Jenner
E	penicillin	*e*	Fleming
F	vaccination	*f*	bacteria
G	haustoria		

7. When animals are imported they may be kept for a time in quarantine; and when people have certain diseases they may be kept in an isolation hospital. How do a country's quarantine regulations and the isolation of patients contribute to the health of its animals and people?

13

SOCIAL BEHAVIOUR

The close association of animals of the same species does not necessarily involve social behaviour. Animals may be crowded because they are sharing a limited resource: for example, there may be many biting flies on the one host. Similarly, if an insect lays many eggs in one place the larvae will be crowded when they hatch from the eggs. Such aggregations of animals of the same species do not involve social behaviour. When locusts live close to one another they are different in structure and physiology from solitary locusts (see p. 25) and locusts in a swarm move together: they respond to one another but this is not usually considered to be social behaviour. What then is social behaviour?

Social behaviour involves some or all of the following: (1) recognition of other members of the species; (2) tolerance of other members of the species; (3) cooperation; (4) division of labour, which may be associated with differences in form (see *Polymorphism*, p. 117); and (5) the construction of a nest or home.

Social Behaviour in Insects

Rearing Jewel Wasps *Nasonia* (also called *Mormoniella*)

The male, which is about 2.5 mm long, has a green head and short wings. The female, which is about 3 mm long, is blue-black and has long wings. This difference in form between the male and female is called **sexual dimorphism** (see Fig. 63). The female lays its eggs in the puparia of house-flies (see Fig. 12). The larvae consume the pupa of the house-fly; in this way jewel wasps reduce the number of house-flies. The larvae develop into pupae, inside the puparium of the house-fly, and later the adult wasps bite a hole in the puparial case and emerge.

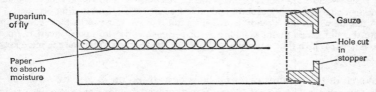

Fig. 62. Culture tube (7.5 cm × 2.5 cm) for jewel wasps. Write the date on the paper when the wasps are introduced and again when they are removed, as a record of the days when eggs have been laid.

Jewel wasps, reared in the laboratory in house-fly puparia, can be kept throughout the year (Fig. 62). They are useful for studies of behaviour. Courting, mating, preening, feeding and egg-laying can be observed at any time. The insects seem to behave normally in the laboratory, and if a good

113

magnifying glass or a low-power microscope is used, this close-up study of insect behaviour is like the use of binoculars in bird-watching.

A small observation cell can be constructed from a glass ring (11 mm diameter × 4 mm deep) to which half a microscope slide is fixed as a roof. Place the insect on a white card and cover it with the observation cell. When you study behaviour there is so much to see that you will need to repeat your observations if you wish to prepare an accurate record.

Investigation: *courtship in jewel wasps.* In courtship the male chases the female and moves to the courtship position (Fig. 63A). Here the male's fore-legs beat upon the female's head; there is a slight pulsing of the male's wings; the male's antennae sweep to the sides and then down, and then the male nods its head between the female's antennae. These movements are repeated in a definite sequence.

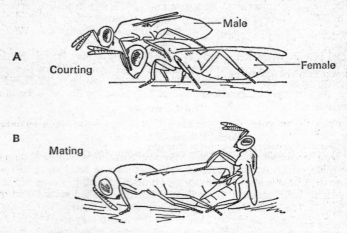

Fig. 63. Jewel wasps: (A) courtship position; (B) mating position.

A female which has not previously mated lowers its antenna (see Fig. 64U1) as the male's head is raised. The male moves backwards. The shape of the female's abdomen changes, making mating possible (see Fig. 63B), and mating occurs.

A female which has already mated does not mate in most of its later courtships. Note the difference in the female's response each time the male's head is raised (see Fig. 64M1). In the continuing presence of the female's antennae the male keeps on courting.

Which of the features of social behaviour listed on p. 113 are observed in this courtship? The social interaction involved in courtship makes mating possible and provides an observer with an opportunity to study how animals **communicate.**

By dissecting jewel wasp pupae from house-fly puparia, you can place them in separate glass tubes and so obtain males and females that have had no previous contact with one another. In this way you can observe mating in the female's first courtship. Note: (1) this **complex** sequence of movements is (2) performed **perfectly** by animals that (3) have had **no opportunity to learn**. Such behaviour, usually called **instinctive behaviour**, is (4) **inherited**, and is

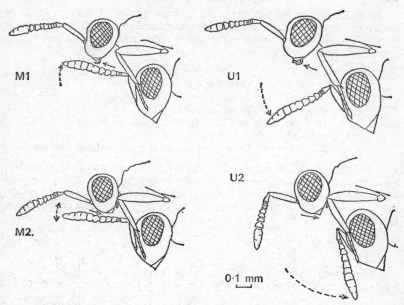

Fig. 64. Some of the courtship movements of jewel wasps: M = female that has already mated; U = unmated female (based on Barrass, R., Rearing jewel wasps and their use in teaching biology, *Journal of Biological Education*, **10**, 119–26).

(5) as **characteristic of the species** as are anatomical and other physiological features.

Social Life in Bees

In nature honey-bees (*Apis mellifera*) build nests in sheltered places—for example, in hollow trees. The beekeeper provides a hive so that he can keep the bees where he wants them, and so that he can remove honey and look after the bees without disturbing them. Up to 40 000 bees may live in one hive.

For most of the year all the bees in the hive are females. One female, which is larger than the others, is called the **queen**. The other females are **workers**. They feed the queen by regurgitating food. They also lick a substance from the surface of the queen. This queen substance contains a chemical which prevents the ovaries of the worker females from developing. As a result, only the queen lays eggs.

All the fertilised eggs develop into females. Unfertilised eggs develop into males, the **drones**, and this development without fertilisation is called **parthenogenesis**. This is most unusual. The eggs of most organisms do not develop unless they are fertilised. A young queen leaves the hive with many drones, and mates in the air. Sperm is stored in the reproductive system of the queen in a sperm sac. This is why the queen can continue to lay fertilised eggs, and so produce more workers, even when there are no males in the hive.

The difference in the size, structure and physiology of the two kinds of female (the queen and the workers) can be related to their different roles in the life of the colony. The queen lays eggs. The workers do different things, according to their age:

Age in days	*Workers' activities*
1 to 3	Cleaning
3 to 10	Nursing
10 to 16	Building comb
16 to 20	Building comb and storing honey
20 to 27	Guarding nest entrance
27+	Collecting nectar and pollen from flowers

This division of labour is not rigid. Bees do more than one thing each day; but they stop other activities once they start to leave the hive. Then they feed on nectar which is regurgitated when they return to the hive, and collect pollen which is stored between long hairs on their hind legs (see *Pollen basket*, Fig. 65).

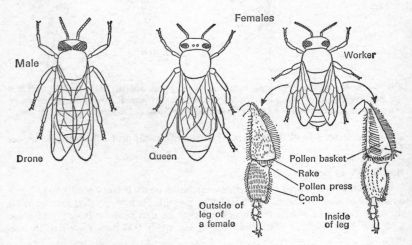

Fig. 65. Honey bees *Apis mellifera*: drone, queen and worker; with drawings of the structure of one hind limb of a worker.

As well as feeding the queen, the food regurgitated by the bees returning to the hive is shared by the younger workers inside the hive. As a result of this **food sharing** all bees in the hive have a distinctive colony odour. Bees from other hives have a different odour and they are attacked if they approach the wrong nest entrance. Only bees with the same colony odour can enter.

The younger workers prepare hexagonal cells (the comb). Some cells contain only stored food. In other cells, called the **brood-comb**, the queen lays eggs (one per cell) and the workers feed the developing larvae with pollen and nectar.

Life in a home, nest or hive is possible only if the members of any society are able to find their way back to the home whenever they move away. When a bee leaves the hive it **navigates** by flying at an angle to the sun. On the return flight it makes use of this information about the angle of the sun even though it is now flying in the opposite direction. Bees also use landmarks as an aid to their route-finding.

On returning to the hive the bee **dances** on the vertical comb in the dark. Other bees follow the dancing bee. In this way they are aware of the scent of the food collected. They also receive information about the source of the food.

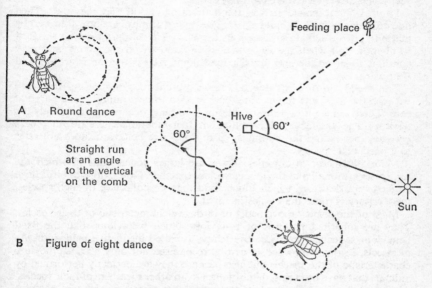

Fig. 66. Dances of the honey-bee *Apis mellifera*.

A round dance (Fig. 66A) indicates that the food is near the hive. A figure of eight dance (Fig. 66B) indicates that the flowers are further away; and the angle of the straight line of the dance to a vertical line indicates the angle at which the food is to be found with respect to the sun. If the dancing bee moves its abdomen rapidly from side to side this waggle dance also indicates that the food is not too far away. The less it waggles the further the food is from the hive. In these ways, information is conveyed about the direction, distance and odour of the food collected. If one bee finds a good source of food other bees are quickly **recruited** to the same food source.

Social life in honey-bees has all the characteristics listed on page 113: (1) mutual recognition which results from food-sharing; (2) tolerance of other members of the colony but not members of other colonies; (3) cooperation, which involves (4) a division of labour and (5) life in a nest and the defence of the nest. The division of labour is supported by polymorphism (Gk. *poly* = many; *morphe* = form), the three forms being the queen, the workers and the drones.

Social Behaviour in Birds and Mammals

Territory and Bird Life

Many birds occupy a nesting area or territory. The male sings in its territory and keeps away other males by singing (an auditory display), by posturing (visual display) or by attacking them. But usually there is no fighting. We can determine the boundaries of territories by noting the area from which each male drives away neighbouring males.

Later, when a female arrives, the male displays and they may pair. Then one or both of the birds build a nest. The male's displays are now followed by mating and the female lays eggs in the nest. The birds may take turns at incubation and when the eggs hatch the parents feed the young and may continue to sit on the nest, especially at night. The young birds are fed and kept warm.

The social life of birds depends upon mutual recognition and tolerance between the male and female, and cooperation in nest-building and parental care. There is also a division of labour. The male occupies and defends the territory. The female may play a major part in incubation. There are differences between species and this summary of reproductive behaviour does not refer to a particular species.

Many birds nest in colonies. These are larger social units in which the territories are small and the nests are close together. Other kinds of birds have larger territories from which much food may be collected. In such species, the territory is more than a nesting area.

Most of the **display** movements of birds are characteristic of their species. They are inherited patterns of behaviour. Such behaviour, like the fixed behaviour sequences in insect courtships, is called instinctive behaviour. As in insects, instinctive responses can be recognised not only because they are characteristic of the species but also because they are perfectly performed by animals that have been raised in isolation from other members of their species. Also the behaviour is stereotyped: a succession of movements and postures always follow one another in the same order.

The song of birds is also characteristic of each species. Birds reared in isolation will sing this same song. Singing, like visual displays, is instinctive behaviour. However, with experience, a bird may add to its song. Some birds copy phrases from the songs of other species of birds—that is to say, their singing is a mixture of instinctive and learned behaviour.

Much of the reproductive behaviour of birds is characteristic of their species, but the importance of **learning** is indicated by their recognition of their partner and by remembering the nest site. Some birds even pair for life and may use the same nest-site year after year. Similarly, all members of each species eat similar foods but young birds learn from their parents, and thereafter may prefer certain foods and so teach their own young to do the same.

Learning and Social Behaviour in Mammals

Many mammals occupy and defend a territory. They also adopt postures and make movements which are characteristic of their species. But the behaviour of mammals, more than that of birds, is modified by experience.

The social life of mammals depends upon a mixture of inborn responses and learned behaviour.

Parental care is a characteristic feature of the life of all mammals (see p. 250) and in people the **family group** is the basic unit of social life: the father and mother and their children living in a home, sometimes with their parents and other relations. We recognise other kinds of larger social groups by such names as school, tribe, community and nation. In each of these, is there tolerance, cooperation and division of labour?

Investigations

1. Observe birds of one species throughout the year and keep a record of their activities in each of the seasons. If you find nests, do not collect the eggs. Make observations from a distance so that you do not disturb the parent birds. Remember to note the date each time you record your observations.
2. If you have the opportunity to study mice, observe their behaviour when they are placed in a clean cage. Note the use of materials in the construction of a nest. What part do the male and female play in parental care?

Test Questions

1. What are the characteristics of instinctive behaviour? Explain how insects can communicate with one another.

2. Write a concise essay on life in a honey-bee colony.

3. Most kinds of birds sing, and each species has a characteristic song. Explain two ways in which the song is of value to the species.

14

THE INTERDEPENDENCE OF ALL ORGANISMS

Apart from the associations between members of different species (Chapter 12) and the social interactions between animals of the same species (Chapter 13), all the organisms in any place depend upon one another. For example, note how different organisms are involved in the carbon cycle (Fig. 53), in the circulation of mineral elements in nature (Fig. 54) and in the nitrogen cycle (Fig. 55). Living organisms also affect and are affected by their environment.

The complex interactions between all land-living organisms, the climate and the soil, are represented in Fig. 67. Heat, cold and rain all weather the soil. They also affect the rate at which plants and animals grow. These influences are represented by the three arrows that extend away from the word *Climate* in the diagram. The cover of vegetation acts like a blanket and has a

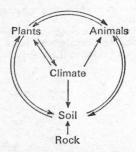

Fig. 67. Interdependent basic components of an ecosystem (based on Eyres, S. R., *Vegetation and Soils: a world picture*, Edward Arnold, London).

moderating effect on the temperature and water content of the air near to the ground. The roots of plants help to break up the soil, and the bodies of dead plants and animals decay and become part of the soil, as do the faeces and urine of animals. All this decaying organic matter which makes soil black is called **humus**. The chemicals present in the soil water are dissolved from the rock particles and from the decaying organisms and faeces. The growing plants provide a variety of places in which animals live. Many animals eat plants and affect both the growth of individual plants and the development of plant communities. Rabbits, for example, by eating the seedlings of trees and shrubs, prevent bush encroachment and so help to maintain grasslands. The term **ecosystem** refers to all the living organisms in any place, and to their interactions with one another and with their physical environment.

Ecological Succession and Soil Formation

On land, the first plants to grow on a bare rock surface are flat encrusting plants called **lichens**. Each lichen is an alga and a fungus living in a symbiotic association. By breaking up the rock and holding the small rock particles together, the lichens start the process of soil formation. They colonise bare ground. With the animals that live in the water held by the lichen and the rock particles, they form a **pioneer community**.

Because of their part in soil formation, lichens help to create conditions in which other plants can live: first plants with rhizoids (mosses, see p. 39) and then plants with roots that require a deeper soil (ferns and seed-bearing plants, see p. 39). As a result, the pioneer community is replaced by an association of plants and animals that could not have lived on the bare rock surface. All these organisms play a part in **soil formation**.

The plants living in one place at any time form a plant association. These plants and the animals living with them form a **biotic community**. The process of change, in which the pioneer community is replaced by a succession of different biotic communities, is called **ecological succession**. The process is complete, perhaps after hundreds of thousands of years, when a community has developed which is not replaced by another later community. This final stage in the succession is called a **climax** community.

The climax community is named according to the most conspicuous plants present. The climax vegetation is associated with a fully developed soil. The climax vegetation and its characteristic soil type is the stable condition that always develops in a particular climate. In some parts of the world this is grassland; in other parts it is open woodland; and in other places it is dense forest, etc. These world regions are named according to the climax vegetation that grows in areas with different climates. Different animals are associated with these different types of vegetation. Each region is called a **biome**: an area in which a characteristic association of plants and animals live together.

When people consider using the land in a new way—for cultivation, ranching and forestry, or for building roads, houses and factories—it is important that they should realise how long the process of ecological succession has taken. When the climax vegetation is removed the animals associated with it are lost, and neither can be replaced quickly. Furthermore, if forests are removed or if grassland is destroyed—for example, by **deforestation** and **overgrazing**—the soil particles are no longer held together by plant roots. Then the soil, formed over thousands of years, may be washed or blown away. This loss of soil is called **soil erosion**.

The Structure and Properties of Soils

Even a handful of fresh soil is an ecosystem—in which organisms interact with one another and with their physical environment. A study of the structure and properties of soils, therefore, provides a basis for our understanding of the conditions in which many organisms live. Also, soil maintenance and soil improvement for agriculture depends upon an understanding of the characteristics of different soils.

If a sample of fresh soil is placed in water, bubbles of air rise to the surface. More air rises if the soil is broken with a stirring rod. If this soil is thoroughly shaken with water and then allowed to stand, any particles that are lighter than water will float. The heaviest particles will sink most rapidly and settle on the bottom of the container. Other particles that are heavier than water will settle: first the heavier and then the lighter particles. This is a simple demonstration of the fact that soil contains air, rock particles of different sizes and also material that is lighter than water.

If a soil sample is thoroughly shaken with distilled water, filtered and then the filtrate evaporated to dryness, a residue is obtained of chemicals that are dissolved in the water from the soil.

If another sample of fresh soil is kept in a warm dry place it will lose weight. It will smoke and lose more weight if it is heated in a crucible, with the lid on, until it is no longer black. These changes are due (1) to the evaporation of water and (2) to the combustion of organic matter. Only rock particles and ash remain.

Small Rock Particles

The properties of soils are determined by the kind (or kinds) of rock from which they were formed, and by the size of the small rock particles present in the soil. Some soils, called **sedimentary soils**, lie above the parent rock from which they were formed. Other soils, called **alluvial soils**, are in places where rock particles have been deposited by the wind or by water.

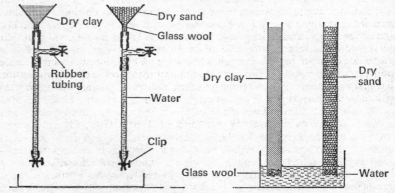

Fig. 68. Porosity and permeability of soils.   Fig. 69. Water rising through clay or sand by capillarity.

Soils which have large rock particles (mostly above 0.02 mm diameter) are classified as **sandy soils**; **clay soils** have very small rock particles (mostly less than 0.002 mm diameter); and **loam** has particles of intermediate size mixed with some sand and clay.

In the apparatus illustrated in Fig. 68, dry powdered clay is placed in one funnel and an equal volume of dry sand in the other. The funnels must be the same size and the tubes must be the same length and diameter. When the clips at the bottom of the tubes are opened, the tube below the sand drains more rapidly than the tube below the clay, indicating that sand is more permeable to air (more porous) than is clay. If the same funnels of dry clay and dry sand are held over beakers, and an equal volume of water is poured into each funnel, the clay retains more water than the sand. Also, the clay drains more slowly than the sand.

Sandy soils contain more air than do clay soils, drain quicker, and retain less water. As a result, these three soil types (sand, loam and clay) are different habitats in which different kinds of organisms can live.

Soil Water

Clay in soils helps to retain water. Water is also absorbed by the dead organic matter in soil. The water and humus help to hold the small rock particles together.

The amount of water in soil depends upon rainfall and upon the lie of the land, as well as upon the amount of humus in the soil and the size of rock particles.

Water percolates through the soil and through permeable rocks but accumulates on impermeable rocks. The surface of this underground water is called the **water table**. Plant roots absorb water from the soil and this water may be replaced (if not by rainfall) by the upward movement of water in the soil. If a glass tube is placed in water, in a beaker, the water rises in the tube above the water level in the beaker. The narrower the bore of the tube the further the water rises. Similarly, if two wider tubes are used, one filled with sand and the other with clay (Fig. 69), water rises more quickly in the sand than in the clay but rises further in the clay than in the sand. This is because the particles in the clay are close together (as are the walls of a narrow capillary tube). The force that draws water upwards is called **capillarity**: it is due to water molecules adhering to surfaces.

The water-retaining capacity of soils is due to its humus content, since humus acts like a sponge, but also to capillary forces between the small rock particles. These capillary forces also cause the small particles of rock and humus to hold together.

Table 12. Differences between sandy and clay soils.

	Sandy soils	Clay soils
1	Easy to work (light soil)	Hard to work (heavy soil)
2	Mostly large particles	Mostly small particles
3	Retain little water	Easily waterlogged
4	Particles fall apart easily	Particles hold together
5	Drain rapidly	Drain slowly
6	Large air spaces	Poor aeration
7	Retain heat	Do not retain heat
8	Mineral salts easily washed away	Mineral salts retained

Living Organisms in Soil

Soil is a mixture of (1) small rock particles, (2) water, (3) chemicals in solution, (4) air spaces, (5) humus and (6) living organisms. In short, it is an ecosystem (see p. 120). Many millions of micro-organisms may live in a cubic centimetre of soil (bacteria, fungi, algae, protists, nematodes, mites and small insects). Soils also contain earthworms, slugs, large insects, centipedes, woodlice, millipedes, small mammals and plant roots.

The living and dead organisms in soil contribute to its structure, aeration and drainage. **Earthworms**, for example, feed on soil and digest the organic matter it contains. They burrow in the soil, contributing to soil aeration and drainage. They pull vegetable matter into their burrows and leave worm casts on the soil surface. In this way they mix the different components of soil and contribute to the formation of aggregates of organic and inorganic matter.

Effects of Cultivation on the Soil

Clay Soils

Clay soils, because their particles are so small, are easily waterlogged. Wet soils contain very little air because the air is displaced by water. In the absence of air humus decays very slowly and incompletely, releasing organic acids. The soil water is acid, therefore, and this preserves the humus, further reducing the rate of decay.

Clay soils may be broken up and improved for agriculture by adding sand and/or slaked lime. The lime neutralises the acids and also causes the small clay particles to bind together, forming larger particles. This improves the aeration and drainage of the soils. The land may also be improved by the construction of additional drains.

Sandy Soils

Sandy soils, on the other hand, have large particles. Water is not retained. They are well aerated and humus decomposes rapidly. Nutrients are easily washed away. Such soils may not hold enough water to support the growth of crop plants and they may be deficient in dissolved salts.

Sandy soils may be improved by the addition of clay and humus, which contribute to the retention of water and nutrients.

Conservation of Water

Ploughing along the contours, or constructing terraces, reduces the rate of water loss. Water conservation by these methods, or the provision of extra water by irrigation, may make cultivation possible in sandy soils which otherwise would contain too little water.

It is also desirable, especially on hillsides, that grassland and woodland should be preserved because, after rainfall, they regulate the rate at which water drains away. Overgrazing and deforestation result in the loss of soils on hillsides, the silting of reservoirs, and frequent flooding in the lowlands.

Conservation of Nutrients in the Soil

Plants remove nutrients from the soil. When the plants die and decompose these nutrients are returned to the soil (see Figs. 54 and 55). But when a farmer removes a crop and sends it to market the nutrients in the crop are not returned to the soil. Also, chemicals in the rock particles are dissolved only very slowly. The farmer may balance the loss of nutrients by adding manure to the soil. The manure also improves the soil texture by increasing the humus content.

The chemicals removed as a result of cropping can also be replaced by the addition of **fertilisers** to the soil. We know, from the work of Sachs and Knop (see p. 17), that plants require calcium, potassium, magnesium, nitrate, phosphate and sulphate ions. The first successful fertilisers were produced by Lawes, who also established the Rothamsted Experimental Station, in Britain, where science is still applied to agricultural improvement. Most farmers add fertilisers to their land, as soluble salts, according to the condition of the land and the needs of the crop plants they are growing. If these are to be used by the crop plants they should be applied when the crop is growing, for if they are applied too soon they may be washed away before the crop starts to grow.

In temperate and tropical climates heavy rainfall may wash away mineral salts. This is called **leaching**. In the tropics irrigation may have the opposite effect. If most of the water added to the soil is lost by evaporation, salts accumulate in the soil and may harm the crop. In any climate the excessive use of fertilisers may be harmful.

The Advantages of Crop Rotation

When farmers grow different crops on the same ground in successive years, until it is time for each plot to be used again for the first crop in the sequence, this is called crop rotation (Fig. 70). The advantages of this method of farming are as follows:

1. Different plants extract nutrients from different depths and one soil layer is not depleted year after year. Also, the deeper rooted plants absorb nutrients that have leached from the surface layers and return these into circulation.

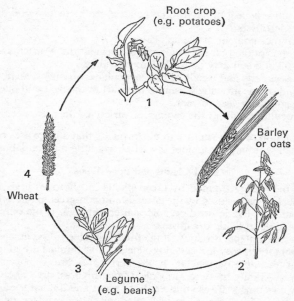

Fig. 70. Crop rotation: crops grown in the same soil in successive years in a four-course rotation (as indicated by arrows) (based on Barrass, R., *Biology: Food and People*, Hodder & Stoughton, London).

2. Different plants require different amounts of each essential nutrient and the same nutrients are not in greatest demand every year.
3. Parts of the different plants are not harvested and these add to the humus content of the soil.
4. The soil is left bare for shorter periods between the harvesting of one crop and the planting of the next. This reduces the leaching of nutrients and the loss of soil by erosion.

5. A varied crop production reduces the accumulation of those weeds, pests and diseases which thrive in only one crop of the sequence.

6. If one crop in the sequence is a legume or a mixture of grasses and legumes, the nitrogen content of the soil is increased while the crop is growing (see p. 102).

When animals are also kept on the farm, in what is called **mixed farming**, their faeces add to the humus content of the soil and this helps to maintain soil structure and fertility. Also, some crops are used as fodder for the animals and many of these can be grown when the soil would otherwise be without vegetation.

Some Harmful Effects of Monoculture

When only one kind of plant is grown in the same soil, year after year, this is called monoculture. This method of agriculture has many disadvantages:

1. The nutrients lost in harvesting the crop can be made good only by the addition of fertilisers.

2. The humus content of the soil is low.

3. For much of the year the soil is without vegetation. Nutrients are washed from the soil and soil may be washed or blown away.

4. Diseases, pests and weeds of the particular crop may remain in the soil from the end of one growing season to the start of the next and may accumulate in the soil from year to year.

5. Monoculture reduces the ecological variety of the area.

The attraction of monoculture to the farmer is that a large area of land can be cultivated with large machines but with very little manual labour.

Food Chains and Food Webs

Part of the energy trapped by green plants in photosynthesis is used by these plants and part is used by the animals and non-green plants which either feed on plants or live in dead organic matter. Sunlight is the only source of energy available to living organisms.

Because green plants produce all the food available to the other organisms in any community, they are called **producers**. The animals are all **consumers**. Those that feed only on vegetation, the herbivores, are primary consumers. Those that feed only on other animals, the carnivores, are either secondary or tertiary consumers. Those that eat both plant and animal food, as we do, are omnivores. They cannot be classified as either primary or secondary consumers, since they are both.

Because green plants produce organic food molecules from inorganic materials they are also called self-feeders or **autotrophs**. All other organisms depend upon the autotrophs for food molecules and are called **heterotrophs**. Many of the interactions between the organisms in any place are concerned with feeding. They are called feeding relationships (or trophic relationships) and can be represented in a diagram either as a food chain or as a food web. The following words and arrows represent a **food chain**:

$$\text{green plant} \xrightarrow{\text{eaten by}} \text{rabbit} \xrightarrow{\text{eaten by}} \text{man}$$

This is clearly an oversimplification since green plants and rabbits are eaten by other things. The sun is the only source of energy and in Fig. 71 the arrows represent the flow of energy through different kinds of living organisms. This looks more complicated than the food chain but it is still an oversimplification of the interactions that are involved in feeding and energy flow in a biotic

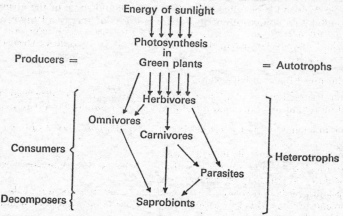

Fig. 71. Flow of matter and energy through organisms (simplified from Barrass R., *Biology: Food and People*, Hodder & Stoughton, London).

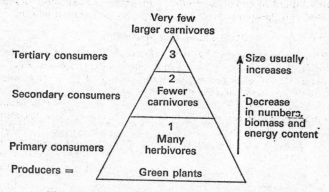

Fig. 72. Pyramid of numbers, biomass and energy.

community. A more accurate picture is obtained if we try to construct a **food web** to represent which organisms in a community are consumed, and which organisms they are consumed by (see Fig. 73).

Another method of representing the feeding relationships in a natural community is the **pyramid of numbers** (Fig. 72). The producers, primary consumers and secondary consumers are represented at different levels in the pyramid. The producers will support a certain number of primary consumers, and these provide food used by a smaller number of secondary consumers. Note also that the mass of living matter (the so called **biomass**) decreases: a lot of vegetation supports a large number of primary consumers (with a total mass much less than that of the vegetation) and there are fewer secondary consumers (with a total mass which is less than that of the primary consumers). Two reasons for these changes in biomass at successive levels in the pyramid are that some food is not digested by the animals and some of the absorbed food is used as a source of energy. There is a **loss of energy** all the time as heat.

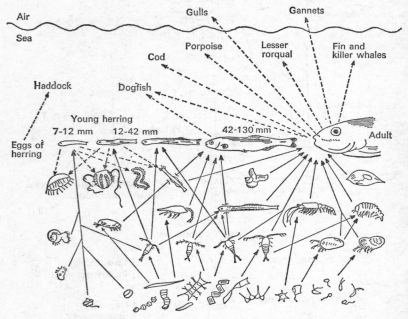

Fig. 73. A food web. Each arrow means *eaten by*. The complete and broken lines indicate the place of the herring *Clupea harengus* in the food web (based on Barrass, R., *Biology: Food and People*, Hodder & Stoughton, London).

If the numbers of one species increase this may mean that more food is available to another species. If in turn the numbers of this second species increase, feeding on the first species, the numbers of the first species are likely to decrease. There will then be less food available to the second species, and the numbers of this species might be expected to decrease. When, in any system, an increase in A causes an increase in B which, in turn, causes a decrease in A (negative feedback), which in turn, results in a decrease in B which, in turn, allows an increase in A (positive feedback), etc., there is said to be a **feedback** interaction between A and B. Because of such positive and negative feedback mechanisms, the numbers of the two species in a community may vary and yet remain fairly constant over many years. A food web is much more complex: it involves many more interactions and these might be expected to smooth out the fluctuations in numbers. As a result of these complex interactions the numbers of each species, in any community, probably remain fairly constant from year to year. These ideas are expressed in the terms **ecological equilibrium** and the **balance of nature**.

The place of each kind of organism in a community is called its **ecological niche**. No two kinds or organisms in the community occupy quite the same place—that is to say, no two species have quite the same way of life. Every species occupies a place in the community, to which it is adapted, which is distinct from that of any other species.

Interdependence of all Organisms

Some interactions between the organisms in one community are represented in Fig. 73; and some interactions between all organisms and their environment are represented in Figs. 53, 54, 55 and 67. These interactions are an indication of the interdependence of all organisms in any community. Moreover, all the communities of the world and therefore all organisms in the world interact. We are part of this world ecosystem.

More than this, the relatively constant composition of the earth's atmosphere depends upon the activities of all living organisms. The amount of oxygen in the atmosphere is reduced and the amount of carbon dioxide is increased by the respiration of plants and animals. On the other hand, the amount of oxygen in the atmosphere is increased and the amount of carbon dioxide reduced by photosynthesis in sunlight in those organisms that have chlorophyll. The amount of nitrogen in the atmosphere is increased by the activities of denitrifying bacteria and reduced by the process of nitrogen fixation (see Fig. 55).

Such constancy as exists in each community, and in the world as a whole, is the result of an **ecological equilibrium** or balance between the activities of all living organisms.

Investigations

1. *Study the characteristics of a habitat* (for example, a woodland, or grassland, or waste ground, or a pond). Describe the habitat. Use the techniques described in this chapter and investigate the structure and properties of the soil. Prepare **maps** of the distribution of different kinds of plants and of the places where you see different kinds of animals. Keep a **written record** of what each kind of animal eats and construct food chains and a food web.

2. *Select one organism* and find out as much as you can about it. Study its life cycle. Make regular **measurements** of its size, and the size of its parts, so that you can accurately describe the way it grows. Record the date and time when you write each observation so that you know, for example, how long it takes for a bird to build a nest or to rear its young. **Count** things and record, for example, how many fruits are produced by one plant or how many seeds each fruit contains. To help you to concentrate on the things you examine, **describe** them carefully in writing and make accurate drawings.

3. *Sampling techniques.* It is not possible to study the whole of any habitat in detail. Nor is it possible, with many plants, to study all the flowers or fruits of one plant. We therefore take **samples**. For example, we might study every plant in a square 25 cm × 25 cm; and we might compare such squares in different parts of the habitat. If we wanted to know something about the leaves of a tree we might start

by studying the leaves of one branch, and we might compare this branch with other branches on the same tree.

Test Questions

1. Name three animals and three plants which you have studied in a named habitat. Explain how these organisms are adapted to their ecological niche. What do the animals eat and how do they obtain their food?

2. Rabbits eat green plants. Foxes eat rabbits. People eat green plants and they also eat rabbits. Rabbit fleas live in the nests of rabbits and feed on the rabbits' blood. When all these organisms die, saprobiotic bacteria obtain nutriment from the dead organic matter. Draw a simple diagram to represent the flow of energy through these organisms. Which of the organisms are (*a*) producers; (*b*) primary consumers; (*c*) decomposers; (*d*) omnivores; and (*e*) parasites?

3. What is humus? Explain how and why gardeners try to increase the humus content of their soil.

4. Which of the following is a definition of an ecosystem: (A) a method ecologists use for solving problems; (B) organisms interacting with one another and with their physical environment; (C) a handful of sterilised soil; or (D) a food web which represents the trophic relationships between many of the organisms living in any community?

5. Write a concise essay on the ecology of an area you have studied. Use effective subheadings to emphasise each aspect of your answer.

15

PEOPLE—PEOPLE—PEOPLE

The number of each species of animal present in a community varies from year to year but these fluctuations are rarely so great as to result in either underpopulation, which might reduce the chances of successful breeding, or overpopulation, when some essential resource might be exhausted.

Animals may be killed by heat, cold or flooding, by disease, by one kind of animal preying upon another, and by fighting between animals of the same kind. People are killed by the same things that kill other animals. However, the numbers of an animal species present in a community may be determined, if other conditions are favourable, by their need for some resource other than food. For example, an animal may require the shelter provided only by certain types of vegetation, or it may nest only in tall trees, or it may breed only in a territory of a certain size. Or mature males and females may be able to breed successfully only if other breeding pairs are nearby: the social stimulation appears to be essential. All these different factors may influence the size of different animal populations. What limits the size of human populations?

Population and Food Supply

By wearing clothes and living in a home people isolate themselves from extremes of heat and cold. The first people hunted and gathered fruits and other plant foods. Their numbers, as with other animals, were probably limited by the amount of food available.

When people started to cultivate the land, to grow crops and to provide food for grazing animals, they increased the amount of food available near their homes. In different parts of the world people bred different kinds of cereals by selecting productive wild plants and improving them: wheat in the Middle East; rice in Asia; millet in Africa; oats and barley in Europe; and maize in South America. These grains could be stored throughout the year, and from year to year. **Agriculture** and the storage of grain increased the amount of food available and helped to ensure that the food supply was maintained in seasons when crops were not growing and in years when the harvest failed.

The different food crops and farm animals developed from wild plants and animals in pre-history, are still the main sources of food consumed by people today. Most of our food comes from a few kinds of food plants: rice, wheat, maize, sugar-cane, sugar-beet, potato, sweet potato, cassava, beans, coconut, bananas (plantains) and ground nuts.

In the 19th and 20th centuries the results of biological research have been applied in agriculture and, as a result, the yields from these crop plants have been increased by the use of fertilisers to improve soil fertility, by plant breeding to improve crop plants, and by using plant growth substances to promote plant growth (see *Plant hormones*, p. 226). Yields from farm animals have been increased by animal breeding and as a result of our better understanding of their food needs.

Increased crop production has resulted from improved methods for the control of weeds, parasitic fungi and insect pests. The control of parasites which cause diseases of farm animals has resulted in increased milk and meat production. And the amount of food available to people has been further increased by reducing losses of stored food due to decay caused by saprobiotic fungi and spoilage caused by insects and rodents.

World Population Growth

It took more than two million years for the population of the world to reach 1000 million, in about 1800, but only one hundred years for the world population to reach 2000 million, in about 1900. Then in sixty years another thousand million people were added (3000 million in about 1960); and in fifteen years another thousand million (4000 million in about 1975). Each thousand million is being added in a shorter time and by the end of this century there may be 6000 million people.

Population growth, at the rate at which this has taken place in the 19th and 20th centuries, has two basic causes: (1) the prevention and cure of many diseases; and (2) increased food production.

As a result of disease control many people who would previously have died in infancy and childhood survive and have children. Since 1881, when Pasteur immunised sheep with weakened anthrax bacteria and so caused them to develop an immunity to anthrax, the technique of immunisation has been developed and used in the prevention of many of the diseases caused by bacteria which used to kill many people. Since 1897, when Ross discovered malarial parasites in the *Anopheles* mosquito, mosquito control and the development of anti-malarial drugs has resulted in the eradication of malaria in some places and a reduction in the number of deaths from malaria in many other places. Since 1928, when Fleming concluded that the fungus *Penicillium* must produce a chemical that is toxic to bacteria, antibiotics have been produced and used to cure many of the diseases caused by bacteria.

Population growth started in pre-history and continued despite the ravages of disease and deadly quarrels. Improvements in the prevention and cure of disease have recently contributed to the more rapid growth of population. However, without agricultural improvement over the last two hundred years and man's efforts in bringing more land under cultivation, no population growth would have been possible. Furthermore, for as long as food is available, more people are likely to survive. They will not necessarily be better fed. Unfortunately, though increasing food production allows more people to survive it does not prevent world food shortages.

Man's Influence on the Environment

The more people there are in the world the more effect they have on their environment.

Increasing the area of land under cultivation has resulted in a decrease in the area covered by natural grasslands, forests (see p. 121) and other kinds of vegetation. By agriculture, more than in any other way, people have altered the appearance of much of the earth's surface.

Only a limited number of people can be employed on the land in food production, and fewer still if agriculture is mechanised. Population growth has been made possible not only by increases in food production but also by the growth of towns and cities where people who could no longer work on the land have been employed.

As towns and cities grow, more and more of the surrounding countryside is covered by houses and shops, factories and warehouses, places of entertainment and recreation, roads and railways. This progressive change in land use is called **urbanisation**. One result is that, as populations grow, less land is available for food production.

Many of man's activities result in **pollution** of the environment. The faeces and urine of animals do not accumulate in nature. They are quickly used by saprobionts because there is a natural balance between the activities of different kinds of organisms. In towns and cities, however, a clean environment is maintained only with adequate means of sewage disposal.

Many industries produce harmful chemicals. Factories burning coal and other fossil fuels may produce smoke and colourless fumes containing sulphur dioxide. These irritate the surface of the lungs and are harmful to health (see p. 177). They are also harmful to the life of other organisms. For example, lichens have been called pollution monitors (or biological indicators) because they grow best in unpolluted air and the more the air is polluted the less they grow. Some factories release fluorine and heavy metals into the air. These settle on the soil and vegetation. They are toxic to some plants and are absorbed by others without killing them. In this way grazing may be made unsuitable for farm animals and crops may be unfit for human consumption, so that farming has to stop in these places.

The fluid effluent from factories must be controlled and tested to ensure that it does not contain poisons and that it is released a little at a time rather than in separate large quantities. Small amounts of an effluent poured into a river may be made harmless by being diluted. By treating effluents and by effective sewage disposal the harmful effects of people on the environment can be kept to a minimum.

Another source of pollution is agriculture. When fertilisers and other chemicals are used on farm land or sprayed on crops, the farmer cannot control the rate at which these are washed into streams, rivers and lakes. With intensive agriculture, based on the increased use of fertilisers, more mineral ions are washed away. This kind of pollution favours the growth of algae. When the algae die they are decomposed by saprobionts. As a result the oxygen in the water may be used completely. Then most animals in the water die. These changes in streams, rivers and lakes are called **eutrophication**.

Pesticides (including weed-killers and insecticides) are used in attempts to kill organisms that are harmful to man's interests. We should prefer to do this without killing beneficial organisms at the same time. For example, insecticides may kill the natural parasites and predators of the pest insects as well as the pests themselves. They also kill beneficial insects in the soil, which play a part in the decomposition of humus, and they kill honey-bees and other insects that are essential for the pollination of some crop plants.

Another problem in the use of pesticides is that qualities which are desirable if we wish to kill as many pests as possible may be undesirable in other ways. For example, an insecticide that is not quickly broken down is a persistent toxic chemical. It will continue to be effective as an insecticide for some time after it has been sprayed on a crop (to kill a crop pest) or on the inside walls of houses (to kill mosquitoes, see p. 107). However, persistent chemicals may accumulate in the bodies of other organisms, especially in animals that come later in a food chain, if at each stage the organisms consume other organisms that contain the persistent chemical. At these higher concentrations the insecticide may be harmful to other organisms as well as to the insects against which it was used.

This problem of **accumulation**, with concentrations increasing at each stage in a food chain, occurs with some of the chemicals present in effluents. Radio-active materials and heavy metals such as mercury persist in the environment and may accumulate in food chains, with the result that the dilution of an effluent does not provide a solution to all pollution problems. Foods which contain high concentrations of toxic chemicals may be unfit for human consumption.

Other ecological problems may follow the deliberate or accidental intro-duction of plants or animals to places where they did not occur previously. In Australia, for example, the prickly pear cactus *Opuntia* made vast areas of pasture unproductive. The cactus had been introduced from South America and it was successfully controlled by introducing a moth called *Cactoblastis* from South America. The moth caterpillars feed on the cactus. This is an example of **biological control**: the use of one organism to reduce the numbers of another. Both organisms continue to live side by side. The weed is not eliminated completely but after the initial introduction of *Cactoblastis* there is no further expense. Another advantage of biological control is that the environment is not contaminated by potentially harmful or harmful chemicals. Each country has regulations which are intended to reduce the number of harmful plants and animals imported either deliberately or as contaminants of other cargoes.

Conservation

The word conservation means different things to different people. To a biologist **nature conservation** means the maintenance of natural communities so that a variety of organisms can live in their natural surroundings with little interference from people. Considering the world as a whole, as an eco-system, **conservation** is the wise use of resources in an attempt to minimise the harmful effects of people upon other organisms and upon the land, rivers and seas.

In clearing the land for agriculture, people destroy natural communities (see p. 121). As a result of bad farming people have already destroyed some of the previously fertile areas of the earth's surface. Two thousand years ago the Mediterranean lands were much more fertile than they are today. In other parts of the world, desert encroachment makes land unproductive. Man is the **desert maker.** Much more land is lost each year than is claimed by bringing desert soils into cultivation or by extending shore-lines.

People were hunting and fishing before the development of agriculture; and people have continued with these activities. But with the growth of populations and the development of more effective weapons, large wild mammals have been **eliminated** in many places. In other places wild mammals are conserved and cropped. They are both a source of food and a tourist attraction, and therefore a source of revenue.

Similarly, the seas were once thought to contain so many fishes that their numbers could not be much reduced by fishing. But with improvements in fishing techniques and with boats from many nations competing to remove more and more fish from the same seas, overfishing has taken place in many fisheries. **Overfishing** is the removal of so many fish in one year that the same number cannot be taken in the next.

Urbanisation makes land unproductive. People in towns and cities also make demands upon the surrounding land; building roads, canals, railways, ports and airports. They make demands upon nearby and upon distant lands as sources of food and the raw materials used in industries and to further the process of urbanisation, and as places where they can relax and enjoy themselves in recreation. These great accumulations of people make conservation impossible in the area they cover; and they make more difficult the conservation of any part of the world's surface.

People compete with other living organisms for food and for a place in which to live. We are the most destructive creatures that have ever lived on this planet and, with the production of 200 000 extra people every day, the conservation of natural resources becomes more and more difficult. This is a major problem facing mankind. How can people conserve other organisms, the soil, and other resources, so that the world remains fit for human life?

Legislation may help. Laws concerning the output of wastes from factories help to reduce such things as smoke production and the release of harmful chemicals. By law certain areas may be set aside as nature reserves or national parks in an attempt to reduce the impact of people. Attempts are also made, by international agreement, to conserve stocks of fishes and whales—for example, by allowing fishing only in certain seasons or by banning the catching of certain species.

Education is important, to let as many people as possible know of the need for conservation—and that population growth makes conservation more difficult. The problem of population growth has been tackled, in some countries, by legislation and education. In India, for example, legislation was introduced to make available the means by which people could limit the size of their families (see p. 248), and there was also an advertising campaign with such slogans as 'One or two children is enough'.

In planning for the future, population increase should not be accepted as inevitable. We should not try to fit as many people as possible into the world but to accommodate fewer, healthier people leading a better life. Moreover, because of the interdependence of all organisms, we should not plan only for people. People cannot exist by themselves.

Test Questions

1. (*a*) What do you understand by the slogan 'Save waste paper—save a tree'? (*b*) What is meant by recycling and how can this practice contribute to the conservation of resources?

2. Give specific examples of the harmful effects of man's activities on the environment. How could these effects be reduced?

PART 3: CELLS AND ORGANISMS

16

CELL STRUCTURE AND FUNCTION

The invention of the microscope enabled biologists not only to observe very small organisms for the first time (see p. 46) but also to look at the details of the structure of larger organisms. They found that large organisms, as different as a flowering plant and a mammal, have essentially similar components. Each component is called a cell.

The word cell was used by Robert Hooke, a British microscopist, in the 17th century for the empty spaces he observed in thin sections of cork. But we now use the word **cell** for a unit of life. In 1839 two German scientists Schleiden and Schwann stated the **cell theory**: that living organisms are either single cells or they are aggregations of cells—that is to say, they are either unicellular or multicellular, the cell being regarded as a fundamental unit of living matter. If this theory is correct, you should be able to see cells by preparing material from the body of any organism and examining this with a microscope.

Investigation: *examining the pulp of a tomato fruit*

1. Place a drop of the soft pulp from immediately below the skin of a ripe tomato on a microscope slide.
2. Mix this with a drop of distilled water.
3. Lower a cover-slip on to this fluid (see Fig. 25).

Examine your preparation under the low power and then under the high power of a microscope. Note the cells floating in the fluid and the red pigment in spherical structures within each cell.

Investigation: *examining the epidermis of an onion leaf.* Each scale of a bulb is the swollen base of a leaf (see Fig. 18A).

1. Remove one of these leaves from an onion and break it so that you can peel off the delicate skin.
2. Place a small portion of this skin (the *Epidermis*, see p. 154) on a microscope slide in a drop of water.
3. Add a cover-slip and examine your preparation.

Make a similar preparation but this time mount the epidermis not in water but in a solution of iodine. The iodine is absorbed by some structures in the cells. You can therefore see these structures in this preparation (Fig. 74A).

Investigation: *examing cells from the inside of your cheek*

1. Gently scrape the inside of your cheek with a clean spatula or with the handle of a spoon.
2. Wipe the saliva from the spoon on a microscope slide and add a drop of distilled water.
3. Lower a cover-slip on your preparation.

Examine this preparation with the microscope properly adjusted (see p. 47) and then use the substage diaphragm to reduce the amount of light. In an unstained preparation this should help you to see more than would otherwise be possible. Now take another similar preparation but this time, instead of distilled water, add a drop of methylene blue. This stains the cytoplasm blue and the nucleus a deeper blue, and so makes it easier for you to distinguish the nucleus from the cytoplasm (Fig. 74B).

Most cells and cell parts are transparent but microscopists use stains to help them to distinguish different structures. Different **stains** are absorbed by different parts of the cell because they combine with different chemicals in

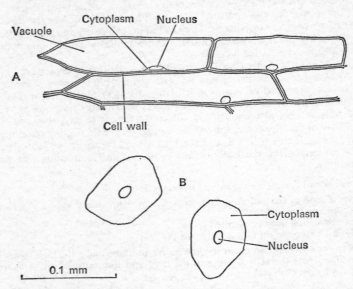

Fig. 74. Cells of plants and animals: (A) cells of epidermis of an onion bulb; (B) epithelial cells from buccal cavity of man.

the cell. Therefore, stains help you not only to study the different parts of cells but also to recognise some of the chemicals that are present in cells and between cells (see *Cytology* and *Histochemistry*, Table 13, p. 144).

Measurement with a Microscope

A ×3 objective with a ×10 eyepiece makes things appear 30 times larger and wider than they would if you viewed them without a microscope at a distance of 25 cm. Similarly, a ×20 objective with a ×10 eyepiece magnifies things 200 times. A microscope also enables you to estimate the dimensions of objects.

1. Place a plastic millimetre rule on the stage of the microscope.
2. Use the low-power objective and obtain a well-defined image. Measure the diameter of the field of view. For example, with a ×3 objective and a ×10 eyepiece the field might be 10 mm diameter (= 10 000 μm).
3. To determine the diameter of the field with a ×45 objective and the same eyepiece, first divide 45 by 3 (= 15) and then divide 10 000 by 15 to give 666 μm = diameter of field of view.

Knowing the diameter of the field under low or high power, you can esti-mate the dimensions of anything that you examine or of any of its parts. With more expensive microscopes, with a mechanical stage, it is possible to make accurate measurements.

Whether or not you are using a microscope, always mark a scale on your drawings as part of your record of your observations.

Differences between Plant and Animal Cells

1. **Plant cells have a cell wall** outside the cell membrane of every cell. The cell wall is of **cellulose** (a polysaccharide, see p. 56 and p. 142) which is secreted by the cell. Animal cells do not have a cell wall.

2. The cytoplasm of one plant cell is continuous with that of the adjacent cells through small pores in the cell walls. These cytoplasmic connections are represented in Fig. 76. In contrast, the cytoplasm of one animal cell is sepa-rated from that of the next by the membranes of the two cells. There are no cytoplasmic connections between animal cells.

3. Much of the space in many plant cells is occupied by a **large central vacuole**. A watery solution, called **cell sap**, is enclosed by the **vacuolar mem-brane**. Animal cells do not have a vacuole. This is why most animal cells are smaller than most plant cells.

4. Plant cells contain **plastids**. In parts of the plant exposed to light the cells contain green plastids—the chloroplasts. These are green because they contain the green pigment chlorophyll which absorbs the light energy used in photosynthesis. Animal cells do not have chlorophyll and they cannot carry out photosynthesis.

5. Animal cells have two **centrioles**, just outside the nuclear membrane (see Fig. 79). The cells of most plants do not have centrioles.

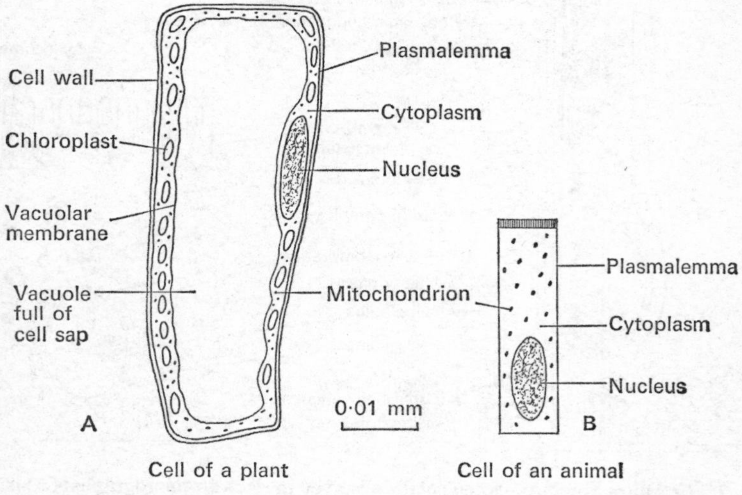

Fig. 75. Cell structure: (A) a palisade parenchyma cell from the leaf of a flowering plant; (B) an epithelial cell from the intestine of a mammal.

Similarities between Plant and Animal Cells

Plant and animal cells have many common features (see Fig. 76).

The **plasmalemma** (surface membrane) is the outermost part of the cytoplasm. It therefore covers surface organelles such as cilia and flagella. Anything entering or leaving the cell passes through this outer cover, which also prevents many things from entering or leaving the cell. The membrane is therefore both a link and a barrier between the cell and its environment. It helps to maintain the constant composition of the cell.

Cell fluids. Much of the cell is an aqueous solution of ions and small molecules. This fluid is the medium in which the chemical reactions of the cell proceed and it contains the small molecules which are the raw materials used in these reactions. It also contains both large and small molecules produced in many reactions.

Mitochondria are present in the cytoplasm of the cells of all protists and in the cells of all multicellular organisms: that is to say, they are present in all eucaryotic cells (see Table 7, p. 35). Like the chloroplasts (which occur only in plant cells), but unlike other organelles, the mitochondria have a double membrane. There is a smooth outer membrane and a folded inner membrane next to the fluid of the inner chamber. The mitochondria are concerned in respiration in the controlled release of energy from sugars and other organic molecules (see p. 182).

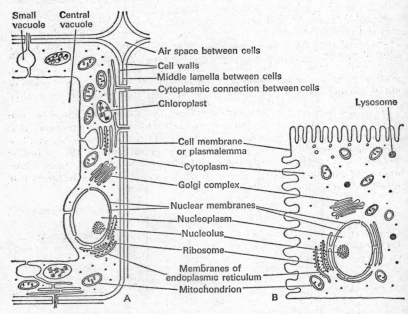

Fig. 76. Cell ultrastructure—some details observed in electron-micrographs: (A) part of one cell of a flowering plant; (B) part of one cell of a mammal. Diagram not to scale.

The endoplasmic reticulum is made up of sheets of interconnected membranes in the cytoplasm. These membranes and the small structures associated with them (the **ribosomes**, see Fig. 76) are the places where proteins are synthesised from amino acids.

The Golgi complex, another arrangement of membranes, is the place in the cell where cell products accumulate. For example, in cells which produce secretions, the materials accumulate in the Golgi complex before they are secreted. Secretions are materials formed in the cell which are then passed out of the cell, such as the materials that form the plant cell wall.

The lysosomes contain enzymes in an inactive form. These enzymes may be activated after they have passed out of the cell, as in digestive secretions (see p. 90), or they may be activated in the cell where they destroy part or all of the cell. Lysosomes may also be involved in the absorption and storage of materials. Each lysosome has a single membrane.

The nuclear membrane, sometimes called the nuclear envelope, encloses the nuclear material. Anything entering or leaving the nucleus must pass through this membrane which helps to maintain the identity of the nucleus and the cytoplasm. However, note that it is a double membrane, continuous with the endoplasmic reticulum, and there are pores in the nuclear membrane. Through these pores the fluid of the cytoplasm is continuous with that of the nucleus. All parts of the cell outside the nuclear membrane are called cytoplasm and everything inside is called the nucleus. The nuclear membrane is usually considered to be the outermost part of the nucleus.

The nucleus, like the rest of the cell, is mostly a watery fluid. Long threads called **chromosomes** (not included in Fig. 76) are suspended in this fluid. Each one is composed of many long molecules of protein and many long molecules of DNA (deoxyribonucleic acid, see p. 149). The nucleus controls the activities of the cell. The **chromosomes** carry information, stored in DNA molecules, which makes possible this control (see p. 151). The **nucleolus,** within the nucleus, is a concentration of RNA (ribonucleic acid, see p. 151).

Fig. 76 includes details from electron-micrographs which cannot be seen in a living cell. They are too small to be seen with a light microscope. It is possible that they do not exist in living cells and that they are the result of the methods used in preparing cells for electron-microscopy. We cannot be certain, therefore, that living cells have lysosomes, folds on the inner membranes of their mitochondria, an endoplasmic reticulum, pores in the nuclear membrane, or a Golgi complex.

Division of Labour in a Cell

Each part of the cell is concerned with a particular activity. We say that there is a division of labour between the parts; and the life of the cell depends upon the proper functioning of all its parts.

Part of cell	*Function*
Plasmalemma	A barrier and a link between the cell and its environment
Cell fluids	The bathing medium in which chemical reactions proceed
Mitochondria	Centres of energy release

Part of cell	Function
Endoplasmic reticulum and ribosomes	Protein synthesis
Golgi complex	Accumulation of materials before secretion
Lysosomes	Breakdown of cell parts, or of whole cell, or of materials outside the cell
Nucleus	Control of cellular activity

Table 13.   Some studies made possible by the invention of the light microscope.

Subject	Things studied
Bacteriology	Bacteria
Cytogenetics	The cellular basis of inheritance
Cytology	Cell structure and function
Embryology	The development of a cell into a multicellular organism
Histochemistry	Chemicals in cells and tissues
Histology	Tissues
Microbiology	Microscopic organisms

Test Questions

1. Prepare a fully labelled drawing of a plant cell.
2. Which of the following are not present in the cells of animals: (A) a nucleus; (B) a cell wall; (C) a cell membrane (plasmalemma); (D) plastids; (E) mitochondria.

17

CELLS AND TISSUES

Unicellular organisms grow and then divide. Bacteria, for example, in suitable food and at a favourable temperature will double their size in 30 minutes and then divide. From one cell, two are formed in 30 minutes and four in 60 minutes. Doubling every 30 minutes, their numbers increase: 1 to 2, 2 to 4, 4 to 8, 8 to 16 and so on. At this rate of multiplication, how many would there be after 24 hours? This is why a colony of bacteria, large enough for you to see it, can develop very quickly (see p. 52).

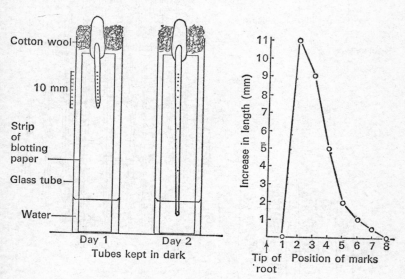

Fig. 77. Growth of a young root of a broad bean *Vicia faba*.

When unicellular organisms divide the two cells separate. From one individual two are produced (see p. 61). Many multicellular animals start life as a single cell (the fertilised egg). When this cell divides the two cells that are formed do not separate; and when these two cells divide the four cells so formed hold together. By repeated division a multicellular organism is produced.

In the growth of a flowering plant, from a seed, the seedling grows at the shoot tip (producing new leaves and axillary buds at intervals on the stem) and at the root tip (see Fig. 77). If you examine a thin slice cut along the length of the root tip (see Fig. 78) you will see that the cells differ in size and shape and that the smallest are near the tip. Such thin sections may be cut

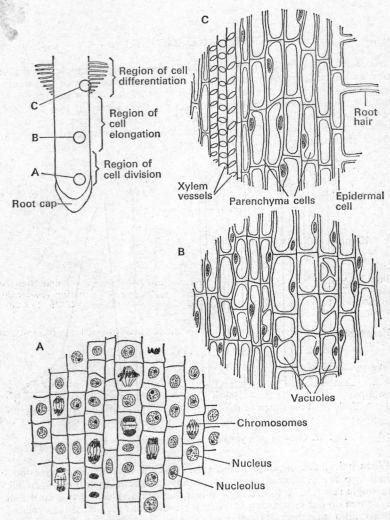

Fig. 78. Root tip of a flowering plant (longitudinal section): (A) cells growing and dividing; (B) cells elongating as large vacuoles are formed; (C) cells in different positions developing in different ways (differentiating). Diagram not to scale.

with a microtome, an instrument like a bacon slicer. Another way to prepare cells for microscopic examination is to make a squash preparation.

Investigation: *preparing a squash of a root tip of an onion.* Rub any loose material from the base of an onion (or other bulb) and then place the bulb on a jar full of water so that the base of the bulb is about 1 mm above the water. The roots that grow from the base of this bulb (or the root tips of a bean seedling) may be used for a squash preparation.

1. Cut off a root tip (about 1 cm long) and place it in a watch glass containing equal volumes of concentrated hydrochloric acid and absolute alcohol. Leave this for 5 to 10 min.
2. Transfer the tip to another watch glass containing 45 per cent glacial acetic acid. Leave for 5 min.
3. Place the tip on a microscope slide and cover it with a drop of acetic orcein (or propionic orcein).
4. Cut the tip in half, and then into quarters, and keep on cutting until you have many long strips.
   Do not let your preparation dry. If necessary add another drop of stain.
5. Place a cover-slip on your preparation.
6. Fold blotting paper (or filter paper) into a thick pad. Place this over the cover-slip. Place one thumb on the pad and then press on this gently with your other thumb.

Acetic orcein stains the chromosomes of cells which are dividing or just about to divide but it does not stain other parts of these cells. In your preparation, you can see many cells (outlined by their cell walls).

1. You cannot see chromosomes in all the cells.
2. All the cells in which you can see chromosomes are together in the region just above the root tip.
3. All the cells in which you can see chromosomes have the same number of chromosomes.
4. This number of chromosomes is an even number.

If you repeat this squash preparation, with the root tip of any other plant, you will make these observations.

The correct explanation for these observations is as follows:

1. It is possible to stain chromosomes only in cells which either are about to divide or are dividing.
2. All the dividing cells are together in the region just above the root tip.
3. All the cells of one plant have the same number of chromosomes.
4. If you find one chromosome that has a particular size and shape, you can find another that is the same size and the same shape. The chromosomes differ in size and shape but there are two of each.

Cell Division

The cell division which results in more body cells being produced, in the root tip for example, is called **mitosis**. The sequence of events in mitosis is essentially the same in the cells of plants and animals (see Fig. 79), except that the cells of animals do not have a cell wall and the cells of most plants do not have centrioles. The chromosomes cannot be stained until just before the cell divides. They are called chromosomes (Gk. *chroma* = colour; *soma* = body) because they can be stained during cell division.

1. At the start of mitosis the chromosomes can be stained. They are long

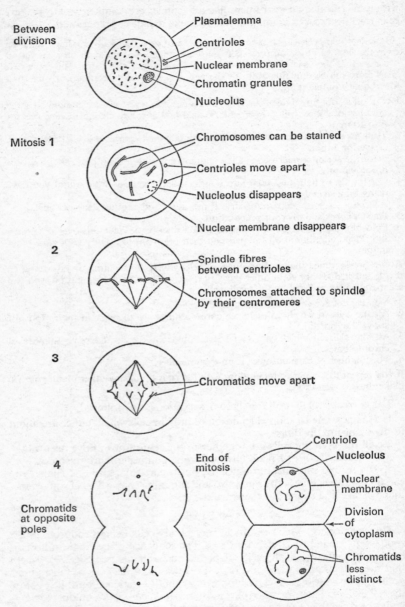

Fig. 79. Mitotic division of an animal cell. Diagram not to scale.

thin structures. They gradually become shorter. Pairs of chromosomes can be recognised. The centrioles migrate, outside the nucleus until they are at opposite poles of the nucleus. The nuclear membrane disappears and so does the nucleolus. A spindle of fibres forms between the centrioles.

2. The chromosomes are arranged at the equator of the cell; and each chromosome comprises two chromatids.

3. The chromatids of each chromosome move apart, one **chromatid** to one pole of the cell and the other chromatid to the other pole. During this movement the chromatids appear to be attached by their centromeres to the spindle fibres.

4. The chromatids become longer until, once again, they cannot be stained. A nuclear membrane forms around each set of chromatids and a nucleolus is formed in each nucleus. Then the cytoplasm divides. In this way two cells are formed from one.

After a while one or both of the cells may divide again, but before this happens more cytoplasm is produced, a **duplicate** is formed of each chromatid, and the centriole is also duplicated. As a result, at the start of the next mitosis, each chromosome comprises two chromatids and there are two centrioles—as at the start of the last mitosis.

In plant cells, after nuclear division, each new cell secretes a cell wall which divides the cytoplasm about equally between the two new cells.

The result of repeated mitotic cell division, in both plants and animals, is that all the cells of a multicellular organism have an **identical** set of chromosomes.

Mechanism of Chromosome Duplication

Each chromosome includes long molecules of nucleoprotein. Each long protein molecule acts as a carrier for **deoxyribonucleic acid** (DNA) molecules. Each nucleic acid molecule is a chain of nucleotides (Fig. 80A): with deoxyribose sugars, linked by phosphoric acid molecules, and with either a purine molecule (adenine = A; or guanine = G) or a pyrimidine molecule (thymine = T; or cytosine = C) attached to each sugar.

In any organism, there are always equal numbers of A and T; and always equal numbers of G and C. This is what we would expect if these molecules always occur in pairs (Fig. 80B); and this line of reasoning led Watson and Crick to suggest in 1953 that the long molecule of DNA comprises two chains wound around one another and forming a **double helix** (Fig. 80C).

The duplication of the DNA molecule is thought to take place in the following way. The spiral unwinds (Fig. 80D) and the linkages A–T and G–C are broken (Fig. 80E). Where an A is exposed a T is added from the nuclear fluids; and where a T is exposed an A is added. In the same way an exposed G can link only with a C, and an exposed C only with a G. The unwinding of the double helix, therefore, in the nucleus which contains the necessary raw materials, is accompanied by the construction of two new chains (Fig. 80F). These two chains are identical. They are also replicas of the unwinding double helix that formed the templates for their construction.

This copying of the nucleic acid molecules is the basis for the duplication of the nucleoproteins, and therefore for the duplication of chromatids between the end of one cell division and the start of the next. This results in all the

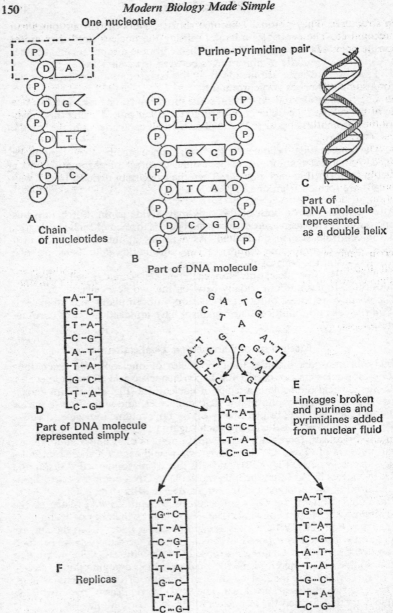

Fig. 80. The DNA molecule: (A to C) structure; (D to F) method of duplication (or replication). Key to symbols: D = deoxyribose sugar; P = phosphate; A and G = purines; T and C = pyrimidines.

body cells of a multicellular organism having the same number of chromosomes; and the set of chromosomes in one body cell is identical with the set in any other body cell.

Control of Activity in the Cell

The DNA molecules of the chromosomes are thought to provide templates upon which **ribonucleic acid** (RNA) is formed. Ribonucleic acid molecules pass into the cytoplasm where they become part of the **ribosomes**. In each ribosome, RNA is associated with about the same amount of protein. It seems likely that the long RNA molecules of the ribosomes act as templates upon which amino acids are assembled in definite sequences in the formation of each protein. Enzymes are proteins, and the chromosomes of the nucleus probably control the activity of their cell by controlling the production of different enzymes—with each enzyme concerned in only one chemical reaction in the cell (see p. 184).

Differentiation

Different Kinds of Cells in a Flowering Plant

Cell division occurs near the shoot tip, where new leaves are produced as the stem grows longer, and near the root tip. In the root tip, new cells on one

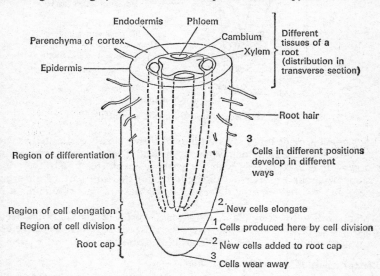

Fig. 81. Tissues in a root tip of a flowering plant.

side of the region of cell division develop into root cap cells. These are worn away and they act as a lubricant as the root tip pushes through the soil. New cells formed on the other side of this region of cell division have elastic walls and they increase in length due to the absorption of water (see p. 157). This is what pushes the root tip through the soil.

Cells in different positions, after enlarging, develop in different ways. We say that they **differentiate.** Many of those at the surface develop long projections called root hairs which grow between the soil particles and greatly increase the area of root surface in contact with the soil. These are epidermal cells. The thin-walled cells just inside the epidermis, with air spaces between them, are the parenchyma cells of the cortex.

Each kind of cell is associated with similar cells as part of a **tissue.** For example, the epidermal cells form one tissue (the epidermis) and the parenchyma cells form another (parenchymatous tissue).

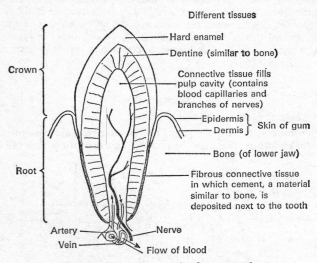

Fig. 82. Tissues in a tooth of a mammal.

Each **organ** is made up of several kinds of tissue, closely associated as part of one structure and functionally **interdependent.** The root is an example of an organ—that is to say, as with the parts of a cell (see p. 63), there is a division of labour between the different tissues that are part of an organ (see Fig. 81) and between the different organs that are part of one plant or animal.

The body of a flowering plant comprises: (1) cells, (2) the cell walls which are secreted by the cells and (3) air spaces. Because the cell walls are permeated by a watery solution, the cells live in a fluid environment.

Different Kinds of Tissues in a Mammal

The body of a **mammal comprises:** (1) cells, (2) materials secreted by the cells and (3) fluids which bathe the cells. In some tissues the cells are close together and in others they are separated by fluid or solid materials.

Each part of the body of a mammal is made up of various kinds of tissues (see Fig. 82, for example). The kinds of tissues in animals are different from those of plants but, as in the root of a plant, the tissues which form part of an organ work together. There is a division of labour between them:

1. Epithelial tissues cover surfaces and line tubes. They always provide protection and in some parts of the body materials pass through them into or out of the body.

2. Connective tissues support other tissues.

3. Muscles contract.

4. Nerves conduct nerve impulses.

5. Blood-forming tissues are places in which blood corpuscles and blood platelets are formed.

Investigation: *cutting thin sections of plant material for microscopic examination.* Hold a cylindrical root or stem vertically and cut thin horizontal slices. These slices are called transverse sections. Use a single-edged razor blade. Cover the cut surface with water and keep a water film along the edge of the blade, so that as you cut thin sections they float on the water. Transfer these sections to water in a watch-glass. Mount one section on a microscope slide in a drop of water (see Fig. 25). Mount another section in a drop of iodine solution. Note how the stain helps you to distinguish different kinds of cells and different parts of cells.

Investigation: *examination of prepared slides of thin sections of plant and animal material.* The cell walls are the most conspicuous structures in most sections of plants. Different kinds of cells have cell walls which contain different chemicals that can be distinguished by using different stains. Similarly, cytologists usually stain the tissues of animals with two dyes. One of these stains the nuclei and the other the cytoplasm. Animal cells do not have a cell wall. In stained preparations the nucleus is usually the most conspicuous part of the cell. Because there is no cell wall it is usually impossible to see clearly the limits of any one cell.

Test Questions

1. Make a list of the words needed to complete the following paragraph:

The chromosomes in the ―― control the activities of the cell. They are composed of ―― and deoxyribonucleic acid molecules. In some way the chromosomes control the production of ribonucleic acid molecules which pass into the ―― where they are a constituent of the ――. These provide templates upon which ―― ―― are assembled in the synthesis of proteins, including the ―― that make possible chemical reactions at the relatively low temperatures of living cells.

2. Which of the terms A to C is used for each of the things listed in *a* to *e*:

A	organ	(a)	mammal
B	organism	(b)	epithelium
C	tissue	(c)	root
		(d)	flowering plant
		(e)	parenchyma

3. Draw labelled diagrams to represent the sequence of events in the mitotic division of a plant cell that has two pairs of chromosomes.

18

SUPPORT IN A FLOWERING PLANT

The submerged parts of aquatic plants are supported by the water, and the roots are supported by the soil. But air offers little support and the aerial parts of terrestrial plants are supported by many of the tissues of the shoot, as well as by the roots which provide anchorage and resist stresses to which the shoot is subjected.

Supporting Tissues of the Plant Body

The Epidermis

The epidermis is a skin that covers and protects internal tissues (see Figs. 83 and 84). It is a barrier between the plant and its environment and also a link with the environment.

In the epidermis that covers the stem and leaves there are two types of cells. Most of the cells are packed closely together, with no air spaces between them, and their outer walls have a thick waxy cuticle. There are spaces between some pairs of epidermal cells, called **guard cells**, and through these

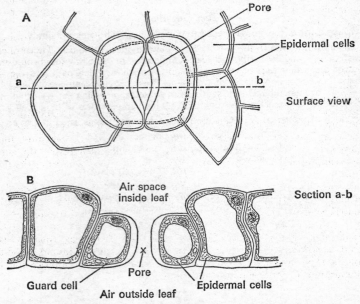

Fig. 83. Epidermal cells of a flowering plant: (A) surface view and (B) vertical section (a–b). Diagram not to scale.

spaces (called **stomata**) the air outside the plant is continuous with the air spaces inside. There is some loss of water through the cuticle of the epidermal cells, unless the air outside is saturated with water vapour, but most water loss is through the stomata.

If the loss of water from the aerial parts of the plant is more rapid than the intake of water from the soil, the leaves wilt. If water loss continues the stem may also wilt. The occurrence of wilting, as a result of water loss, indicates the importance of water in providing support.

Parenchymatous Tissue

Except in woody plants, the parenchyma cells of the root and shoot form the main supporting tissues: the cortex of the root (Fig. 84); the cortex and pith of the shoot (Fig. 84); and the mesophyll of the leaves (Fig. 98, p. 172). If these parenchyma cells are full of water the plant body is firm and stiff but if they are not the plant wilts.

Tissues Providing Mechanical Support

The vascular bundles are threads in the shoot (Fig. 84). They link different parts of the plant.

Some cells in the **xylem** are arranged end to end. These lose their end walls, their cytoplasm and their nuclei, and form the long hollow tubes through which water, with mineral ions in solution, is carried through the root, up the stem, and through the veins of the leaves. The side walls of these xylem vessels are thickened by the addition of a rigid material, called **lignin**, and are described as lignified or woody. Like the hollow tubes used by builders for scaffolding, they are strong and they provide mechanical support.

Note the difference between the distribution of the xylem in the root and in the shoot. In the root the core of xylem resists the pull caused by the shoot blowing in the wind. In the stem the xylem is in separate strands which help to keep the shoot upright, in much the same way as guy ropes support a flagpole.

Food materials are carried in aqueous solution in the **phloem**, from the leaves to other parts of the plant. The **cambium**, sandwiched between the phloem and the xylem (see Fig. 84) produces more phloem and xylem cells as the plant gets bigger, providing more conducting tissues and more mechanical support. The cambium cells divide by mitosis and then the newly formed cells differentiate either as phloem or as xylem, according to their position.

In shoots that persist from year to year (those of shrubs and trees) the additional xylem formed in successive years is apparent in a cut stem as concentric **annual rings** of wood. As a shrub or tree grows, the addition of xylem provides more mechanical support. By counting the annual rings you can determine the age of a felled tree. Remember that these rings of rigid material, as seen in a cross section of the stem, are really cylinders. Like the scaffolding used by builders, they give the strongest construction possible for a given amount of a particular kind of material.

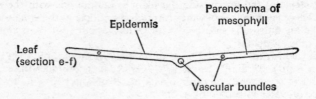

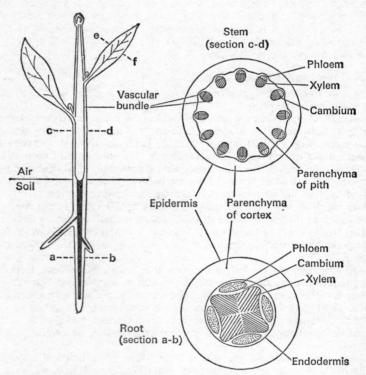

Fig. 84. Tissues that support the plant body: the epidermis; the parenchyma; the xylem core of the root; and the xylem strands of the vascular bundles of the stem and leaves.

Importance of Water in Supporting the Plant Body

Investigation: *water intake by osmosis.* A membrane which is permeable to water (solvent) but much less permeable to solute molecules is called a **differentially permeable membrane.** Water molecules pass through such a membrane from a less concentrated solution into a more concentrated solution. This movement of water molecules, through a differentially permeable membrane, is called **osmosis.**

Pure water is said to have a **water potential** of zero. And because solutes in water reduce its energy content, they give the solution a lower water potential (less than zero). Osmosis, therefore, is the result of the diffusion of water molecules from a region of higher to one of lower water potential.

When two solutions of sucrose in water, of unequal concentration, are separated by a differentially permeable membrane, water molecules diffuse from the less concentrated into the more concentrated sugar solution, increasing its volume (see Fig. 85) and so reducing the difference in concentration. The pressure in the sugar solution that forces the liquid up the glass tube is called **osmotic pressure**. The solution of sugar in the dialysis tubing, before water is added to the beaker, is said to have an **osmotic potential**. If you repeat this investigation with starch instead of sucrose you will find that there is no movement of water. This is because starch does not dissolve in water: it is as though there was pure water on both sides of the membrane. That is to say, there is no difference in water potential.

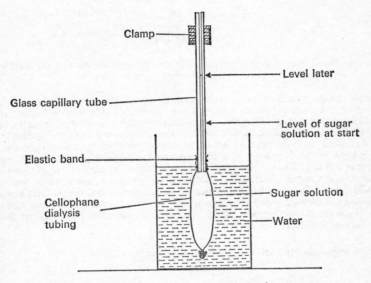

Fig. 85. Demonstration of osmosis and osmotic pressure.

Water Relations of Plant Cells

The cytoplasm of a plant cell acts like a differentially permeable membrane. It separates the watery solution in the vacuole, which contains dissolved salts and sugars, from the soil water imbibed by the cell wall (see Fig. 115). Because of the difference in water potential, water molecules diffuse from the soil and cell wall into the vacuole. However, there is a limit to the amount of water that a cell can hold. As water accumulates in the vacuole, the cell contents press more and more upon the cell wall. The wall has a certain elasticity but exerts a **wall pressure** that acts in the opposite direction.

As water enters the cell it dilutes the vacuolar fluids—and so the osmotic pressure decreases as the wall pressure increases. Water continues to enter the cell until the wall pressure equals the osmotic pressure. The cell is then **turgid**. It is the turgidity of the parenchyma cells that maintains the shape of leaves, and the loss of turgidity results in wilting. Water intake by the roots of plants is possible only (1) if water is present in the soil next to the root and (2) if the cells of the root are not fully turgid.

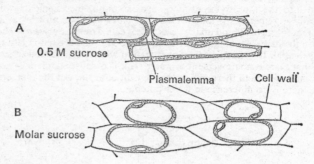

Fig. 86. Plasmolysis of cells from the inner epidermis of an onion bulb scale leaf.
Diagram not to scale.

Investigation: *measuring the osmotic potential of vacuolar fluids.* If a plant cell is immersed in a solution that has a lower water potential (that is, a more concentrated solution) than the fluid in the cell vacuole, water molecules will pass from the cell. The cytoplasm contracts until, as a result of the loss of water, the water potential of the vacuolar fluid is the same as that of the solution in which the cell is immersed. If the volume of the cytoplasm is so reduced that it no longer presses upon the cell wall, the cell is said to be **plasmolysed** (see Fig. 86). If separate pieces of tissue are immersed in a range of solutions of different concentration, the solution that just fails to cause plasmolysis (usually about 0.4 M sucrose) is the one that has a water potential (an osmotic potential) equal to that of the vacuolar fluids. Note that the vacuolar fluids of different cells differ in their osmotic potential (Fig. 86A): some are plasmolysed but others are not.

Test questions are included at the end of the next chapter.

19

SUPPORT AND MOVEMENT IN ANIMALS

Aquatic animals, like aquatic plants, are supported by the water in which they live. Terrestrial animals are supported by the soil upon which or in which they live; but the air offers little support. In all environments, multicellular animals are supported by their skins, by their skeleton and by the muscles which act upon the skeleton.

Contrasted with plants, which live in one place, animals are supported (by their skin and skeleton and muscles) not only when they are keeping still (in the maintenance of **posture**) but also as they move from place to place (in **locomotion**). Locomotion allows animals to live in a more constant environment than would otherwise be possible. They can avoid many of the hazards to which a static organism is exposed. Habitat selection, therefore, contributes to their survival. In most animals locomotion also precedes and may accompany feeding (see p. 84) which is essential for survival.

Support from Water

A *Hydra* (see Fig. 36, p. 67) is supported by the water in which it lives and also by the water in its enteron. Just as a balloon is rigid when it is full of air, and a plant cell is turgid when it is full of water, so a *Hydra* is rigid (or turgid) when it is full of water. Water cannot be compressed: it forms a **hydrostatic skeleton** upon which the muscles of the body wall act. When the muscle tails in the ectoderm contract the body shortens. If they contract on one side but not on the other, the body bends to one side. If the muscle tails of the endoderm contract, reducing the diameter of the enteron, the body becomes longer. Note that the muscle tails of the ectodermal and endodermal cells act upon the hydrostatic skeleton but they have opposite effects. The shape of the body at any time depends upon the water in the enteron and the state of contraction of muscle tails of the cells of the ectoderm and endoderm in different parts of the body. *Hydra* may keep still—with its body shortened or with its body and tentacles extended—or it may move by looping or somersaulting.

Earthworms have a delicate skin which is bathed by a thin covering of mucus. The skin is the outermost part of the body wall, just as the epithelium of the gut is the innermost part of the gut. In both the body wall and the gut wall there are layers of muscle. The muscles in the gut wall, when they contract, act upon the food in the gut and move it along as digestion proceeds. Note that between the body wall and the gut wall there are two fluid-filled cavities, one on either side of the body (see Fig. 87). When the muscles of the body wall contract they act upon these fluid-filled cavities. Contraction of the circular muscles reduces the diameter of the cavities and so makes them longer (making the worm longer) because the watery fluid they contain resists compression. Conversely, contraction of the longitudinal muscles increases the diameter of these cavities by making them shorter (and so making the worm shorter).

If you watch a worm moving over the soil surface you will see that each part of its body is first thinner and longer and then thicker and shorter. The fluid-filled cavities in each segment (see Fig. 87) maintain the earthworm's cylindrical shape. As in *Hydra*, the muscles act upon a **hydrostatic skeleton** and the circular and longitudinal muscles have opposite effects. As an earthworm moves over the soil, as certain segments become longer, the **chaetae** project from the skin in other segments. These provide anchorage when the longitudinal muscles contract and the segments shorten, pulling the body along.

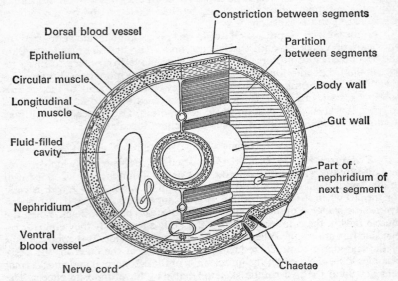

Fig. 87. Parts of one segment of an annelid worm. Diagram not to scale.

Support from Skins

Insects

The skin of an insect consists of a layer of epithelial cells and the cuticle secreted by these cells. The cuticle is both a surface cover and a skeleton. Because it covers the body, the cuticle is called an **exoskeleton**.

The outermost part of the cuticle is the epicuticle which, although very thin, has several layers including a **wax layer** which restricts water loss from the body. Below the epicuticle there is an exocuticle, and between this and the epithelial cells there is an endocuticle. The exocuticle and endocuticle contain long molecules of chitin, a flexible material, but in the exocuticle there are also molecules of a hardened protein and this makes the cuticle rigid. However, there are flexible parts of the cuticle in which there is no hard material. These **flexible membranes** allow the movement of one **rigid plate** relative to the next. All skeletons have both rigid and flexible parts.

Movement in insects and the maintenance of posture depend upon the rigidity of the exoskeleton which (1) supports and maintains the shape of the body, (2) provides firm surfaces to which muscles are attached and (3) has flexible parts which allow the movement of one rigid part in relation to another. Note that many skeletal parts are strong hollow cylinders and that the muscles work in pairs and pull on different parts of the skeleton. The contraction of one muscle of a pair has one effect, and the contraction of another muscle has the opposite effect: they are mutually antagonistic (see Fig. 88). In more complicated movements several muscles may be involved.

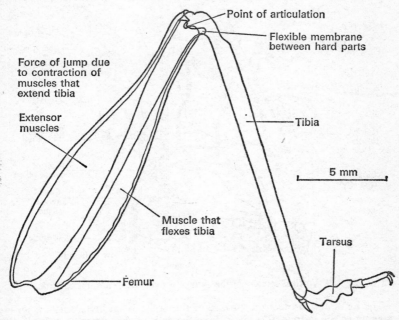

Fig. 88. Hinge joint between the femur and tibia of a hind leg of a locust (simplified from Albrecht, F. O., *The Anatomy of the Migratory Locust*, Athlone Press, London).

Skins of Vertebrates

The skin is the outermost part of any organism: the area of contact between the organism and its environment. Like the plasmalemma, which is the area of contact between the cell and its watery environment, the skin is both a link and a barrier. Some things pass through the skin and other things are kept out or in.

Members of the different classes of vertebrates can be recognised by their skins (see p. 29). In all vertebrate animals the skin allows movement but resists tension. It supports the body and helps to maintain its shape and therefore has a **skeletal function**.

The skin of a mammal (Fig. 89) is composed of two tissues: a surface epithelium (the epidermis) and a connective tissue part (the dermis). The **epidermis** is formed by the division of cells in the basal germinative layer. Recently formed cells, near to the germinative layer, are alive but they are gradually cornified and die. The outer dead cells, therefore, form a layer of tough cornified material which protects the internal tissues against: (1) mechanical damage; (2) the harmful effects of ultraviolet light; (3) bacterial infection; and (4) water loss by evaporation. The thickness of the epidermis is maintained because new cells are being formed all the time, and then cornified, and then worn away.

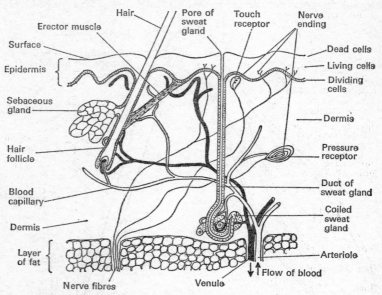

Fig. 89. Vertical section of the skin of a man. Diagram not to scale.

The hairs also protect the surface of the body. Each hair follicle is an in-pushing of the germinative layer. Like the cells of the germinative layer, the cells in the follicle continue to divide and (1) at the base of the follicle, where the cells of the hair papilla divide and the new cells are cornified, the hair grows longer; and (2) some cells of the sebaceous glands divide, producing cells which fill with a secretion called **sebum**. This sebum lubricates the hair follicle and the surface of the skin, and it has bactericidal properties.

The connective tissue of the dermis has a certain elasticity but it also resists stretching. The **dermis** (1) supports the epidermal structures (epidermis, hair follicles, sebaceous glands and sweat glands); (2) supports the many blood capillaries and nerves which run through it; and (3) with the epidermis **supports** and **protects** the internal organs and helps to maintain the shape of the body.

The Skeleton of a Mammal and Locomotion

The skeleton of a mammal comprises:

1. The cranium (or brain case) and the vertebral column (backbones);
2. The bones of the jaws (Fig. 48) and those of the middle ear (Fig. 136);

3. The sternum (or breast bone) and ribs (Fig. 90);
4. The pectoral (shoulder) and pelvic (hip) girdles; and
5. The bones of the fore-limbs and hind-limbs.

All mammals, like most other animals with backbones, have a skeleton that is composed of two materials: bone and cartilage. When the skeleton is first formed, in the embryo, it is composed entirely of cartilage; but most of the

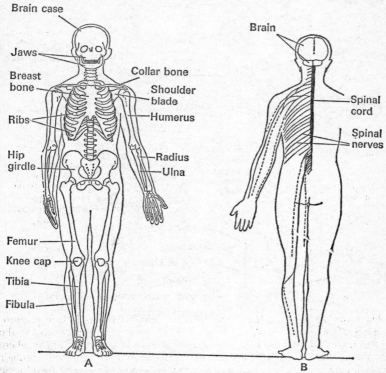

Fig. 90. (A) skeletal system; (B) nervous system of man (simplified).

cartilages are replaced by bone before a baby is born. Cartilage and bone are living tissues. The bones get bigger throughout childhood and in adolescence; and when a bone is broken the parts fuse if they are held together. Bone contains calcium salts and it is much harder than cartilage. Cartilage can be cut with a knife and has a certain flexibility; especially the cartilages that support the pinnae of your ears and the tip of your nose.

The bones and cartilages are inside the body—that is to say, they form an **endoskeleton**. This skeleton: (1) provides rigid surfaces to which muscles are attached, and together with the muscles; (2) supports the body; (3) supports and protects the more delicate tissues of the body; and (4) makes possible the maintenance of posture, the movement of parts with respect to one another, and the locomotion of the whole organism.

Locomotion of Mammals

As you know from crossing dry sand on foot, when we walk, run or jump, movement in one direction results from the pressure of our limbs acting in the other direction upon firm ground. If the ground is not firm we have difficulty in moving forward.

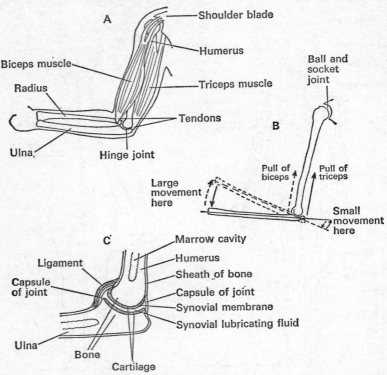

Fig. 91. Arm of a man: (A) arrangement of biceps and triceps muscles (simplified); (B) antagonistic action of these muscles; (C) arrangement of tissues in a section through the elbow joint (a synovial joint). Diagrams not to scale.

In the movement of one limb, (1) the bones are rigid levers, (2) the joints allow the movement of one bone in relation to another, (3) the muscles provide the pull which moves the bones, (4) the inelastic tendons, anchored in the muscle at one end and in the sheath of the bone at the other end, link the muscle to the bone, (5) the nerves of the limb make possible the co-ordinated contraction of different muscles in correct order, (6) the blood supply to the muscle provides the glucose and oxygen used in the provision of energy in the contracting muscle fibres and (7) the blood flowing from the muscle carries away carbon dioxide, a waste product of the respiration of the muscle fibres. The control of the movement of the limb depends upon all these parts working together.

Muscles exert their effect by contracting. Your biceps muscle bends (flexes) and your triceps muscle straightens (extends) your fore-arm. That is to say, these muscles have **antagonistic** (opposite) effects. They work as a pair (see Fig. 91B). The ulna moves upon the humerus at the elbow, and the elbow joint is called a **hinge joint** (Fig. 91A). The two bones are rigid levers and the ulna pivots upon the humerus like a seesaw. Note that the muscles move the ulna only a short distance near the pivot but the hand moves much further. You can feel the tendons near your elbow as you raise and lower your fore-arm. If you bend your arm through 90° at the elbow, how far does it move (*a*) 3 cm from your elbow, and (*b*) at your wrist?

The joint at the elbow is a **synovial joint** (Fig. 91C). The bones are not in contact. Both bones have a pad of cartilage, at the joint, and there is a lubricating fluid (synovial fluid) between the cartilages. Movement is possible but the joint is held in place by the joint capsule (which is continuous with the fibrous sheath of the bones) and by ligaments.

The shoulder joint is a **ball and socket joint**. Like the hinge joint it is a movable joint but movement is possible in more than one plane. Another type of joint is the **fixed joint**, at which no movement is possible: and this is not a synovial joint.

Locomotion of Other Animals with Backbones

Swimming of Fishes

The streamlined body of a fish offers little resistance as it moves through the water. The propulsive force, which results from the contraction of blocks of muscle along the sides of the body, is provided by the surface of the tail and tail fins pushing upon the water (force **a**, which is the resultant of forces **b** + **c** in Fig. 92C). The water is incompressible. The shape of its body prevents movement sideways, so the fish moves forward (**d** in Fig. 92C). The contraction of muscles on the left side of the body causes this side to press on the water. Then the contraction of muscles on the right side of the body presses this side against the water. The median and paired fins contribute to stability, by reducing pitching, rolling and yawing (Fig. 92D, E and F) and to movement up, down or straight ahead. A swim bladder (dorsal to the alimentary canal) provides buoyancy and, by regulating the amount of gas it contains, the fish can remain at the same level in the water with a minimum of muscular activity.

Locomotion of Birds

Birds differ from living reptiles not only in being feathered but also in the use of their fore-limbs in flight and the hind-limbs in walking, take-off and landing. The large wing-feathers greatly increase the surface area of the wings but add little to their weight. Other adaptations to flight include features of the skeleton (Fig. 93) and of the associated muscles. Many of the bones are hollow tubes. They are light-weight but strong and, especially where they are fused, they provide rigid girders which resist the stresses imposed in flight (especially on the fused thoracic vertebrae and on the breast-bone) and in take-off and landing (note the fusion of several vertebrae with bones of the hip girdle). When you eat a bird, most of the meat is from the breast and leg— the powerful muscles used in flying and walking.

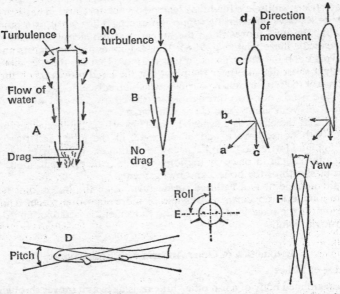

Fig. 92. Flow of water around (A) a rectangular and (B) a streamlined object; (C to F) swimming of a fish.

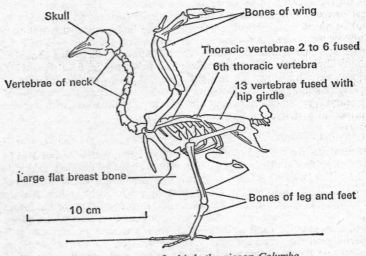

Fig. 93. Skeleton of a bird: the pigeon *Columba*.

In an aeroplane the forward thrust is provided by the engines, which provide thrust against the air. Lift is provided by the rigid wings fixed at an angle to the air-stream. However, the wings of a bird provide thrust as well as lift. They move down and back, pressing upon the air, and they have rigid and flexible parts. The bird flaps its wings and remains in the air or rises, and at the same time it moves forward. Air offers less resistance than does water but when a bird is in flight the body is streamlined and there is a smooth flow of air over the body and wings.

Investigations

1. Observe the locomotion of different animals. For example, observe fishes swimming in an aquarium; and observe the flight of different kinds of birds. Observe an earthworm moving over the surface of the soil. Note that some segments shorten as others are extended. Can an earthworm move over a sheet of glass? When you crawl, in which order do you move your limbs?

2. Examine a wing of a bird and note the arrangement of the feathers. Compare wing, contour and down feathers. If possible, examine these feathers with a microscope and see how the parts of a wing feather are hooked together, forming a rigid whole.

3. If you examine a prepared slide of a vertical section of the skin, remember that Fig 89 is a diagram. A section will cut through some structures but you will not see them all in one section.

4. Examine the skeleton of a mammal. Note the parts labelled in Fig. 90A.

Test Questions

1. Will plant cells placed in distilled water absorb water until they are (A) turgid; (B) plasmolysed; (C) dissolved; or (D) catalysed?

2. Draw large diagrams of transverse sections of a stem and a root of a herbaceous dicotyledonous plant. Label (A) epidermis; (B) parenchymatous tissue; (C) xylem; (D) phloem; and (E) cambium.

(*a*) Which of these tissues provide support?

(*b*) In which of these tissues would you expect there to be many cells in mitotic cell division?

(*c*) In which tissue are the cell walls composed of lignin as well as cellulose?

3. (*a*) Draw a large labelled diagram to represent the structures visible in a vertical section of the skin of a mammal.

(*b*) Which of the following statements are correct?

(A) The skin is a sense organ.

(B) The skin has skeletal functions.

(C) The skin is involved in temperature regulation.

(D) The skin is a barrier to infection.

4. (*a*) State four functions of the skeleton of a mammal. (*b*) Which of these are also functions of the exoskeleton of an insect? (*c*) Name one tissue in the stem of a flowering plant which has two of these functions; and state these two functions.

5. Draw a diagram of the bones of your arm, viewed from the side. Do not include your wrist and hand bones.

(*a*) Label the humerus, radius and ulna.

(*b*) Draw in the outlines of a muscle that flexes the arm and a muscle that extends the arm.

(*c*) Explain why many muscles work in pairs.

(*d*) What is the function of a tendon?

(*e*) The elbow joint is correctly described as (A) a hinge joint; (B) a ball and socket joint; (C) a synovial joint.

20

GASEOUS EXCHANGE

There is a constant exchange of materials and energy between living organisms and their environment. This is one of the ways by which we distinguish living from non-living things. An animal would soon suffocate in a closed container. We may conclude from this observation that the animal in some way alters the composition of the air. Joseph Priestley expected that plants would be affected in a similar way to animals and he was surprised to discover that plants in some way purified the air (see p. 75). He concluded that both animals and plants alter the air, but in different ways. We call the exchange of gases, between any organism and its environment, gaseous exchange.

Investigation: *carbon dioxide content of inspired and expired air.* In this demonstration (with the apparatus arranged as in Fig. 94), as you breathe gently through the mouth piece, you draw air in through the lime-water in tube A but force air out through the lime-water in tube B. Carbon dioxide makes lime-water cloudy. The lime-water in B turns cloudy before that in A, indicating that there is more carbon dioxide in the air you breathe out (expired air) than in the air you breathe in (inspired air). This is because carbon dioxide, produced in the respiration of all body cells, is excreted from the lungs (see p. 177).

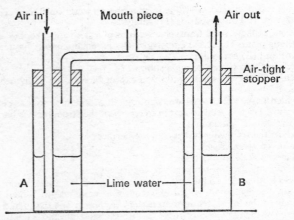

Fig. 94. Apparatus for comparing the carbon dioxide concentration of air breathed in through tube A, with that of air breathed out through tube B.

Investigation: *effect of a living locust on the carbon dioxide content of the air in a sealed tube.* If a locust is put in a sealed tube with lime-water (Fig. 95) the lime-water becomes cloudy. In a similar tube, without a locust, the lime-water remains clear. The experiment with the locust, and the control experiment in which there is no locust, provide evidence that the locust increases the carbon dioxide concentration of the atmosphere in the tube.

This investigation may be repeated with bicarbonate indicator solution in the tubes instead of lime-water. This is a **more sensitive** test (see next investigation) and is useful for investigations with small organisms which, in contrast to the effects of breathing in man (Fig. 94), cause slower changes in the composition of small volumes of air. However, pH may be affected by other things as well as changes in the concentration of carbon dioxide; so this test is **not specific** for carbon dioxide.

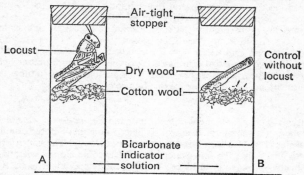

Fig. 95. Apparatus for studying the effect of a living locust on the carbon dioxide content of air in a sealed tube.

Investigation: *some effects of a fresh leaf on the composition of the air in a sealed tube.*

1. Rinse four test-tubes with distilled water and then with bicarbonate indicator solution.
2. Add 2 cm³ bicarbonate indicator solution to each tube and some cotton wool (see Fig. 96).
3. Cut discs of leaf from a plant. Place one disc in tube A and another in tube B. Leave tubes C and D, the controls, without a leaf disc. Seal the tubes with air-tight stoppers. Wrap tubes A and C in black paper.
4. Place the tubes side by side in the sunlight and keep a record of any colour changes in the indicator solution.

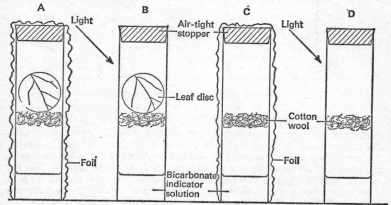

Fig. 96. Arrangement of glass tubes for a study of the effects of leaf discs on the composition of air: (A) in the dark; (B) in the light. C and D are controls.

An increase in the acidity of the indicator solution in tube A (due to the addition of carbon dioxide to the atmosphere in this tube) is indicated by a change from orange to yellow; and a decreased acidity in tube B (due to the removal of carbon dioxide from the atmosphere in this tube) is indicated by a change from orange to red or purple. The indicator solution in tubes C and D will not change colour.

The carbon dioxide concentration increases in tube A (in the dark) because carbon dioxide is produced in respiration and this cannot be used in photosynthesis. The carbon dioxide concentration decreases in tube B (in sunlight) because photosynthesis proceeds more rapidly than respiration at high light intensities. If the changes in tubes A and B are due to the presence of leaf discs in these tubes, you would expect no change in the colour of the indicator solutions in tubes C and D. Tubes C and D serve as **control experiments**, providing evidence that any changes in tubes A and B are due to the presence of leaf discs and not simply to other conditions of the experiment such as the presence or absence of sunlight.

Investigation: *effect of soil micro-organisms on the carbon dioxide content of the air in a sealed tube.* If a sample of fresh soil is placed in a small closed container with fresh lime-water (Fig. 97A) the lime-water becomes cloudy. The control (Fig. 97B) enables us to check that the lime-water does not become cloudy when any micro-organisms in the soil have been killed. Together, the experiment (tube A) and the control experiment (tube B) provide evidence which supports the hypothesis that micro-organisms in soil produce carbon dioxide in their respiration and excrete this gas into the atmosphere.

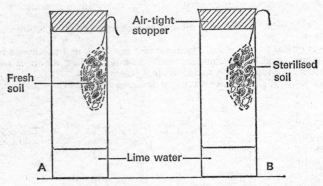

Fig. 97. Carbon dioxide production by micro-organisms in soil.

Investigation: *effect of germinating pea seeds on the carbon dioxide content of air in a sealed tube.* If 30 pea seeds are soaked in water overnight they will start to germinate. Put ten of these peas on one side for use in tube A. Rinse ten in disinfectant to kill any micro-organisms on the surface of these peas (for use in tube B). Boil the remaining ten for 10 min and then cool them (for use in tube C) so that all the peas are at the same temperature at the start of the experiment. Enclose the peas in three tubes, with fresh lime-water, as in the investigation with soil samples (Fig. 97).

This experiment is to test the hypothesis that the living cells of the pea produce carbon dioxide in their respiration and excrete this gas into the air. Evidence for this hypothesis comes from the observation that the lime-water in tubes A and B turns cloudy but that in tube C remains clear. The **controls** (tubes B and C) enable you to check that carbon dioxide is produced by the living cells of the peas, not by micro-organisms on the surface of the peas, and not by anything that is present even in freshly killed peas.

Air Spaces and Diffusion in a Flowering Plant

Parenchyma forms much of the bulk of the plant body and, because there are air spaces between the cells, oxygen and carbon dioxide diffuse rapidly through the plant from regions of higher to regions of lower concentration. Oxygen and carbon dioxide diffuse much faster through air than through water because the molecules in a gas are further apart than those in a liquid.

Water contains much less oxygen than does air, and there are larger air spaces in the underwater parts of aquatic flowering plants than in the aerial parts. These air passages allow the rapid movement of oxygen from the aerial parts to the submerged parts.

The Leaves of a Flowering Plant

Leaf Shape

Some plants have flat stems that look like leaves; but you can recognise a leaf by the presence of an **axillary bud** (Fig. 38). Leaves differ in shape. Most of them have a leaf stalk and a blade. Some are called **simple leaves** because the leaf blade is in one piece. Others, called **compound leaves**, have a number of leaflets.

A leaf has a very large upper surface and an equally large lower surface but, because it is very thin, it has a very large surface area in proportion to its very small volume. Also, because a leaf is so thin, light penetrates to all its cells. The shape and thinness of a leaf are appropriate for an organ in which **photosynthesis** takes place. This adaptive relationship between structure and function, which is a condition of life (see Chapter 4), is also evident if you study the microscopic anatomy of a leaf.

Tissues of the Leaf

The epidermal cells of a leaf form a protective skin and have a waxy cuticle which reduces water loss. But there are openings, called **stomata**, and most of these are in the lower **epidermis**. Indeed, some plants have no stomata in the upper epidermis.

The movement of molecules in the air spaces of a leaf (oxygen, carbon dioxide and water vapour) is by diffusion. The stomata may be wide open or, if the size of the openings is reduced, the diffusion of molecules into and out of the leaf is restricted.

Because the stomata are mostly on the lower surface, gaseous exchange between the air outside the leaf and the air spaces inside is mainly through the lower epidermis. Within the leaf the air spaces are largest near the lower epidermis and here the cells are larger and further apart than those near the upper epidermis. Because the leaf is so thin, the diffusion distances are very short and there is a rapid movement of oxygen and carbon dioxide within the leaf from regions of higher to regions of lower concentration.

The cells just below the upper epidermis look like parallel columns and are called **palisade parenchyma**. They are closely packed but have air spaces be-

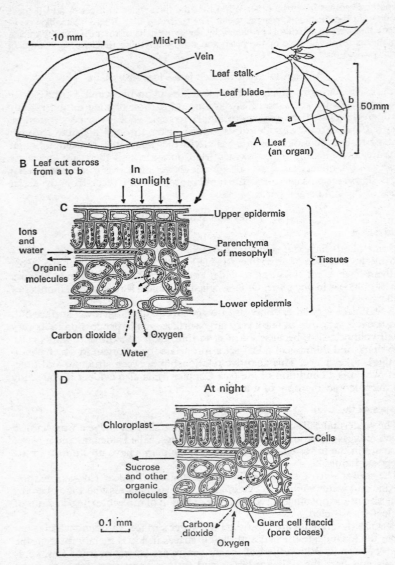

Fig. 98. Gaseous exchange between a leaf of a flowering plant and the air: C in sunlight; D at night.

tween them, continuous with the other air spaces of the leaf. Most of the light falling on the leaf passes through the transparent epidermis and enters the palisade cells. These contain many **chloroplasts**, which absorb light, but some light passes through into the larger parenchyma cells of the **spongy mesophyll** which also contain chloroplasts.

Respiration occurs in all cells at all times but in sunlight the rate of photosynthesis is usually greater than the rate of respiration. Some of the oxygen produced in photosynthesis is used in respiration but there is an excess of oxygen and this diffuses from the leaf. Similarly, the carbon dioxide produced in respiration is used in photosynthesis but additional carbon dioxide diffuses into the leaf from the air outside. The diffusion distances from the outside of the leaf to the inside are short and molecules diffuse rapidly in and out through the stomata. This gaseous exchange, in sunlight, is represented in Fig. 98C.

At night respiration continues but there is no photosynthesis. Oxygen is used in respiration and carbon dioxide is produced. Some oxygen diffuses into the leaf and some carbon dioxide is excreted (Fig. 98D) but gaseous exchange is restricted by the gradual closure of the stomata at night. At low light intensities, at dawn and dusk, there are times when the rate of respiration is the same as the rate of photosynthesis. This point, when there is no gaseous exchange, is called the **compensation point** (Fig. 44A).

The veins of a leaf contain **conducting tissues** (Fig. 98C). Water and mineral nutrients enter the leaf in the xylem and the chemical compounds manufactured in the leaf are exported through the phloem.

Respiratory Surfaces of Animals

As in plants, respiration occurs in all living cells and gaseous exchange takes place through any part of the body surface that is permeable to oxygen and carbon dioxide. In animals, any surface through which oxygen diffuses into the body and carbon dioxide diffuses out is called a **respiratory surface**.

In all unicellular animals (e.g. *Amoeba*, p. 60) and in many multicellular animals, including *Hydra* and the earthworm, the whole body surface is the respiratory surface. In *Hydra* all cells are near to this surface. Because oxygen is used in respiration there is always less in the cells than outside. Because carbon dioxide is produced in respiration there is always more in the cells than in the water. Therefore, oxygen diffuses into the cells and carbon dioxide diffuses out. See also Fig. 36.

The Tracheal System of an Insect

The cuticle of insects is impermeable but there are openings, called **spiracles**, at intervals along the sides of the body (Fig. 15). These lead into air-filled tubes called **tracheae** (Fig. 99). The finest branches, in the tissues, are called **tracheoles**. No body cell is far from a tracheole.

There are diffusion gradients from the cells at one end of this system of tubes, where oxygen is being used in respiration and carbon dioxide produced, to the air outside the insect at the other end. Because insects are so small, these diffusion distances are short and the oxygen and carbon dioxide diffuse rapidly through the air in the tracheal system. In some insects the larger tubes of the tracheal system are ventilated but the movement of molecules in the finer branches is by diffusion only. The spiracles have valves and they are open only when the carbon dioxide concentration in the tissues is above a certain level. They are closed, therefore, for much of the time when the insect is inactive (restricting water loss—see p. 198). Note that the blood of insects is not involved in oxygen transport.

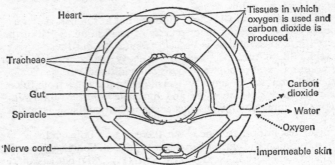

Fig. 99. Transverse section of an insect. Diagram not to scale.

The Skin of an Earthworm as a Respiratory Surface

Many of the cells of an earthworm are so far from the body surface that, in contrast to *Hydra*, oxygen does not penetrate to them by diffusion. However, the earthworm has a **blood circulatory system**: a system of tubes in which blood is pumped through all the tissues of the body. The blood contains a red

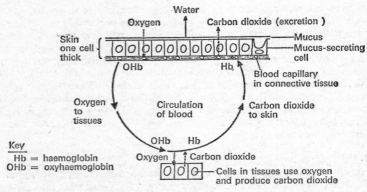

Fig. 100. Gaseous exchange between the blood of an earthworm and the air outside the skin.

pigment, **haemoglobin**, which combines with oxygen in regions of high oxygen concentration and forms **oxyhaemoglobin**. As a result the blood contains more oxygen than could be carried in solution. In regions of low oxygen concentration the oxyhaemoglobin gives up its oxygen. Blood, therefore, transports oxygen from the respiratory surface where there is a high oxygen concentration (the skin of the earthworm) to tissues where there is a low oxygen concentration (Fig. 100), including the muscles of the body wall and the tissues of the gut wall.

The skin of an earthworm is its respiratory surface. Study Fig. 100 and note the following:

1. There is a high oxygen concentration and a low carbon dioxide concentration outside the respiratory surface.

2. The respiratory surface is very thin and is permeable to oxygen and carbon dioxide.

3. Blood flowing through the numerous blood vessels, called **capillaries**, just below the respiratory surface, contains less oxygen but more carbon dioxide than the outside air.

4. Because of these diffusion gradients, oxygen diffuses into the blood and carbon dioxide diffuses out.

5. The blood is transported, in blood vessels, to other body tissues in which oxygen is being used and carbon dioxide produced in respiration.

6. The blood returning to the skin, therefore, contains less oxygen but more carbon dioxide; and so the diffusion gradients between the air and the blood are maintained at the respiratory surface.

7. The respiratory surface has a very large area in relation to the total volume of the living cells of the body (see Fig. 87).

Gaseous Exchange in Aquatic Vertebrates

In fishes gaseous exchange occurs across the surface of the **gills**. Each gill is small in relation to the size of the fish. However, because there are several gills and the surface of each gill is folded, the respiratory surface is very large.

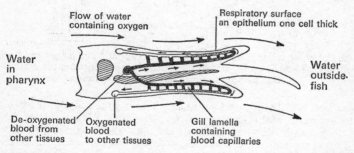

Fig. 101. Respiratory surface: section of one gill of a fish. Note the flow of water outside the gill and the flow of blood in capillaries immediately below the skin. Diagram not to scale.

Water passes in through the mouth and out over the gills (Fig. 101). This water supports the gills and holds apart the delicate gill lamellae (leaf-like folds). Each gill, therefore, has a very large surface in contact with the water—and the current of water **ventilates** the respiratory surface; that is to say, water containing oxygen flows over the gills. There is an exchange of oxygen and carbon dioxide between the water outside the gill and the blood inside the gill. Read the list above again but this time study Fig. 101 as you note the same things.

In amphibians (e.g. the frog, see Fig. 17) the skin is a respiratory surface but in the tadpole stage there are gills and the adult has lungs and breathes air. In reptiles, birds and mammals, even those that spend part or all of their lives in the water, the skin is not a respiratory surface and they all have lungs and breathe air.

The Respiratory System and Gaseous Exchange in Mammals

A mammal has two **lungs**, each of which lies in (and fills almost completely —see Fig. 102) a pulmonary cavity. The heart is between the lungs in the pericardial cavity. A tube, called the windpipe or trachea, opens at one end into the pharynx (see Fig. 50, p. 89). Within the thorax the other end of this tube divides into two bronchi, one of which enters each lung. In the lung this bronchus divides into smaller tubes called bronchioles. These branch many times and each of the finest branches ends blindly in a bunch of **air sacs** (the alveoli). The whole of this system of tubes and air sacs contains air.

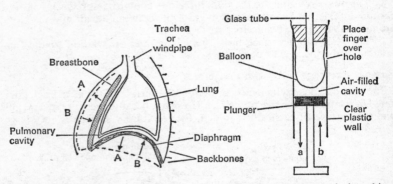

Fig. 102. Breathing in man. Movement of the rib cage and diaphragm in breathing (diagram not to scale); and a simple model used to demonstrate the action of a suction pump. A = inspiration, B = expiration.

When you breathe in you take more air into your lungs and when you breathe out much of this air rushes from your lungs. We can distinguish between deep breathing, when the lungs are filled almost completely with air (about 5.5 l) and emptied almost completely (leaving about 1.5 l residual air), and shallow breathing, when there is a much smaller volume of tidal air (about 0.5 l) at each inspiration and expiration. You breathe most rapidly and most deeply—that is, you take in the most air—when you are active and your body cells are using most oxygen and producing most carbon dioxide in respiration.

Breathing in results from muscle contraction, which raises the ribs and lowers the diaphragm (Fig. 102A); and breathing out results from the elasticity of the lungs and the return of the ribs and diaphragm to their resting position (Fig. 102B). These movements alternately (1) enlarge the thorax, reducing the pressure inside the lungs and acting as a suction pump, with the result that air is drawn into the lungs, and (2) reduce the size of the thorax and so pump air from the lungs. Breathing, therefore, results in the ventilation of the lungs.

In everyday language we sometimes say 'respiration' when we mean 'breathing'; and when someone stops breathing they may be given artificial respiration. To avoid confusion, in biology, the word **breathing** is used for the repeated filling and emptying of the lungs (of amphibians, reptiles, birds and mammals), **ventilation** for the flow of air in and out of the lungs (or for the flow of water over the gills of an aquatic animal); and **gaseous exchange** for the diffusion which occurs across all respiratory surfaces. The word **respiration** should then be restricted to the controlled release of energy from organic molecules, including sugars, which occurs all the time in all cells (see p. 180).

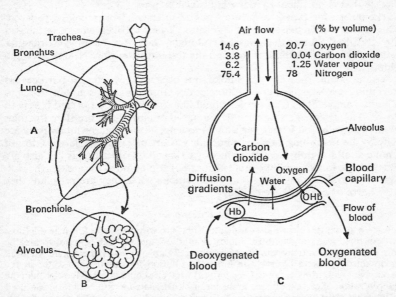

Fig. 103. Gaseous exchange in man: (A) part of the respiratory system; (B) alveoli at the end of a bronchiole; (C) gaseous exchange between blood in a capillary and the air in an alveolus (air sac). Hb = haemoglobin; OHb = oxyhaemoglobin.

Gaseous exchange takes place through the surface of the air sacs. Because they are so small and there are about 350 million in each lung, the air sacs form a very large respiratory surface (about 25 m² in each lung). As a result of breathing, the air in the lungs always contains oxygen. But because of gaseous exchange in the lungs the expired air always contains less oxygen and more carbon dioxide than the inspired air (see Fig. 103C). Breathing ventilates the lungs and maintains a high concentration of oxygen and a low concentration of carbon dioxide next to the respiratory surface. Read the list on p. 175 again but this time study Fig. 103 as you note the same points.

Air Pollution and Health

When you breathe in air polluted with fine dust particles, bacteria, fungal spores or gaseous chemicals, these contaminate the air passages of the nose, throat and lungs. The thin covering of mucus, secreted by cells in the lining of the air passages, acts like a filter and small amounts of dust settle and do no harm. On the other hand, the very fine particles produced in some industries, including coal and asbestos particles, irritate the lungs and may accumulate in the air sacs, making them less efficient.

Air containing sulphur dioxide is also harmful to health, because it irritates and damages the cells of the air passages of the lungs and exposes them to further damage by bacteria. This chemical is released when coal, oil and gas are burned as fuels, and it is probably the indirect cause of bronchitis—a disease that is prevalent in many industrial areas.

The most widespread form of air pollution results from smoking tobacco. This is a self-inflicted cause of ill-health. When tobacco smoke is inhaled directly into the lungs, the lungs are polluted by tar. Also, nicotine, a drug that is harmful to health, diffuses through the respiratory surface straight into the blood.

Young people may start to smoke, not because they enjoy it but because they think it makes them appear more adult. Unfortunately, smoking becomes a habit. Many adults who smoke would like to stop but do not find it easy to do so. The more cigarettes people smoke, the more likely are they to suffer from bronchitis and from gastric and duodenal ulcers, and the more likely are they to die from lung cancer or coronary heart disease. People who do not smoke at all not only have more money to spend on other things but also are likely to live longer; and the more cigarettes people smoke the greater the risk. Women should know, also, that if they smoke while they are pregnant they may harm or even kill their child.

Test Questions

1. When you use bicarbonate indicator solution, why must you (*a*) rinse the tubes with distilled water and with the indicator solution, and (*b*) take care not to breathe into the tubes, as you prepare the investigation? Explain: (*c*) what extra information is obtained by using bicarbonate indicator solution instead of lime-water in the experiment with fresh leaf discs (Fig. 96); (*d*) what else could affect pH, other than the concentration of carbon dioxide in the air, if bicarbonate indicator solution was used in an experiment on gaseous exchange in animals; and (*e*) what is the purpose of the wood and cotton wool in Fig. 95B.

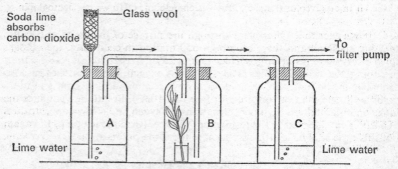

Fig. 104. Apparatus for studies of the effects of living organisms on the composition of air.

2. When air from which carbon dioxide had been removed was drawn slowly through a jar containing a green leafy shoot, in the dark, and then through lime-water (see Fig. 104), the lime-water turned milky.

(*a*) What do you conclude from this observation? (*b*) Would the lime-water in jar C turn milky if this investigation was repeated in bright sunlight? Would the lime-water in jar C turn milky if the plant in jar B was replaced by a living mouse and the investigation was repeated (*c*) in the dark and then (*d*) in sunlight? (*e*) In these investigations, what is the purpose of the lime-water in jar A?

3. Is oxygen a waste product of (A) respiration; (B) transpiration; (C) photosynthesis; (D) ventilation; or (E) excretion?

4. Does oxygen from the water move into the blood in the gills of a fish by: (A) conduction; (B) ventilation; (C) osmosis; (D) diffusion; or (E) excretion?

5. List four similarities between the gills of a fish and the lungs of a mammal.

THE USE OF MATERIALS AND ENERGY IN CELLS

Sources of Energy

Autotrophs: The Producers

Green plants use light energy from their environment. On land, they absorb water, nitrate and mineral ions from the soil and carbon dioxide from the air. Aquatic plants absorb these materials from the water in which they live. In photosynthesis plants use light energy, water and carbon dioxide in the production of carbohydrates (compounds of carbon, hydrogen and oxygen—see p. 55). Some of this carbohydrate is converted to lipids (waxes and oils) which are also compounds of carbon, hydrogen and oxygen. And with nitrogen, absorbed as nitrate ions, carbohydrates are raw materials in the synthesis of proteins (compounds that contain carbon, hydrogen, oxygen and nitrogen).

The mineral ions, essential for the normal growth of plants (see p. 17), are used: **calcium** is part of the middle lamella (see p. 142); **magnesium** is part of the chlorophyll molecule; **sulphur** and **phosphorus** are part of some protein molecules; and phosphorus is also part of the ATP molecule (see p. 184) and part of phospholipid molecules in cell membranes.

Heterotrophs: The Consumers and Decomposers

The different kinds of molecules synthesised by green plants (including sugars, fatty acids, glycerides, vitamins and amino acids) are the molecules absorbed by animals (after the materials that make up their diet have been digested) and by saprobionts (from faeces and decaying organisms in their environment). Once absorbed, by animals or by saprobionts, these organic molecules are used, as in green plants, in the synthesis of a variety of other organic molecules, including larger molecules of carbohydrates, lipids and proteins. In this way, the absorbed molecules become part of another organism. We then say that they have been assimilated (see p. 91).

Respiration

Some of the organic molecules manufactured by green plants and some of those absorbed by animals and saprobionts are used in respiration as a source of energy. Respiration goes on in all living cells at all times. The more active a cell is, the more energy it uses: the more it respires. A dormant seed respires so slowly that it is almost impossible to measure the low rate of gaseous exchange. During germination, when many cells are active, the rate of respiration increases. In animals, the rate of respiration is much greater when they are moving about than when they are still.

Aerobic and Anaerobic Respiration

Respiration may occur in the presence of oxygen, as it does in the cells of our bodies—most of the time. But when we are very active some cells do not get enough oxygen and then respiration continues in these cells (even in the absence of oxygen). Respiration in which oxygen is used is called **aerobic respiration**; and respiration without oxygen is called **anaerobic respiration**.

Some animals live in places where there is very little oxygen. Tapeworms in the intestine of their host, for example, obtain almost all their energy by anaerobic respiration. Some plants, including yeast (see p. 93), respire aerobically when oxygen is present but can respire anaerobically if there is no oxygen.

In both aerobic and anaerobic respiration carbon dioxide is produced and there is a loss of heat. In experiments, therefore, carbon dioxide production and the loss of heat are to be expected if respiration is taking place.

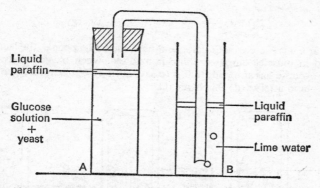

Fig. 105. Evolution of carbon dioxide by yeast in the absence of oxygen.

Investigation: *carbon dioxide production, in the absence of oxygen, in the anaerobic respiration of yeast.* Boil some glucose solution (5 per cent glucose by volume) to remove any dissolved oxygen. When this is cool use it to make a suspension of yeast (10 per cent yeast by volume). Pour some of this into a tube (Tube A in Fig. 105). Add a layer of liquid paraffin to exclude oxygen. Connect tube A to tube B (as indicated in Fig. 105). Add liquid paraffin to tube B to exclude air (which contains carbon dioxide). Keep the tubes at about 35 °C. The lime-water in tube B becomes cloudy as gas from tube A bubbles through it. Carbon dioxide must be produced in tube A, therefore, even in the absence of oxygen. What control experiment must you perform if you are to be sure that the carbon dioxide is produced by the yeast?

Investigation: *mass of germinating seeds.* Soak 100 seeds in water overnight. Kill 50 of these, by boiling, and place them in a dish with moist cotton wool. Place the other 50 seeds in a similar dish with moist cotton wool. On each of the next 5 days, remove 10 seeds from each dish and dry them in an oven overnight at 120 °C before you weigh them. The germinating seeds decrease in mass. The boiled seeds do not. How do you account for the loss of mass by the germinating seeds? What do you call the experiment with boiled seeds; and why is it necessary?

Investigation: *loss of heat from germinating seeds.* If three vacuum flasks are arranged as in Fig 106, the temperature rises most in flask A, less in flask B, and there is no increase in temperature in flask C. Flasks B and C are control experiments. Micro-organisms on the surface of the peas are killed by disinfectant and the peas are killed by boiling. The loss of heat from the seeds is an indication of chemical activity—as expected if respiration occurs in the living cells during the germination of the seeds.

A summary of the raw materials used and the products of aerobic and anaerobic respiration is as follows:

Aerobic respiration in plants and animals

$$C_6H_{12}O_6 + 6O_2 \longrightarrow 6CO_2 + 6H_2O + Energy$$
glucose   oxygen   carbon   water
dioxide

Anaerobic respiration (alcoholic fermentation) in plants

$$C_6H_{12}O_6 \longrightarrow 2C_2H_5OH + 2CO_2 + Energy$$
glucose   ethanol   carbon
dioxide

Anaerobic respiration in animals

$$C_6H_{12}O_6 \longrightarrow 2C_3H_6O_3 + Energy$$
glucose   lactic acid

Some animals excrete lactic acid. In others, including people, the lactic acid produced in muscles during exercise is oxidised, when oxygen is available, after the exercise has stopped: that is to say, during exercise an **oxygen debt** is incurred—and afterwards this is repaid.

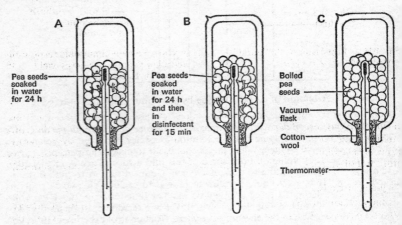

Fig. 106. Loss of heat from germinating seeds.

Much more energy is obtained in aerobic than in anaerobic respiration. The summary equations may cause you to think that respiration is just one chemical reaction. In fact there is a sequence of reactions and this makes possible the controlled release of energy, a little at a time. The first reactions are identical in aerobic and anaerobic respiration. Glucose, a 6-carbon sugar, is broken into two 3-carbon molecules and some energy is released. But in anaerobic respiration most of this energy is used in the production of either ethanol (in plants) or lactic acid (in animals). In contrast, in aerobic respiration, all the energy released in these first reactions is available for use in other activities. And even more energy is released in further reactions (which take place in the mitochondria) in which each of the 3-carbon molecules is completely oxidised to carbon dioxide and water (Fig. 107).

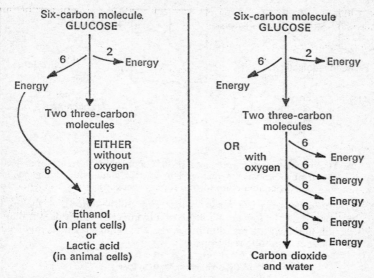

Fig. 107. Comparison of the amount of energy available from anaerobic respiration (energy yield = 2 ATP molecules) and from aerobic respiration (energy yield = 38 ATP molecules), from each molecule of glucose used.

Metabolism

In all cells there are two kinds of chemical reactions: (1) **anabolic** reactions in which large molecules such as starch (a polysaccharide) are made from smaller molecules (see p. 56); and (2) **catabolic** reactions in which larger molecules are split into smaller molecules (as in respiration). **Metabolism** is the sum total of all chemical reactions in the cell (anabolic + catabolic reactions).

Enzymes in Cells

Many chemical reactions take place only if there is an input of energy. When the reaction occurs in a test-tube energy may be provided by heating the reactants. In a cell the energy available from respiration provides the energy input and, in the presence of appropriate enzymes, reactions take place rapidly even at relatively low temperatures (as compared with the temperature in a heated test-tube).

In plants the sugars produced in photosynthesis are converted to starch (a reserve polysaccharide). The enzyme involved in this anabolic reaction is an amylase:

$$\text{maltose} \xrightarrow{\text{amylase}} \text{amylose}$$
$$\text{(a sugar)} \qquad \qquad \text{(starch)}$$

Starch, a reserve carbohydrate in many seeds (in the seed leaves or in the endosperm—see Fig. 4) and in roots, bulbs and tubers (see p. 30), is converted to sugars during germination and used in respiration as a source of energy:

$$\text{maltose} \xleftarrow{\text{amylase}} \text{amylose}$$

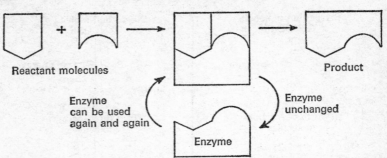

Fig. 108. The enzyme molecule provides a surface upon which the reactant molecules may become arranged close together and in correct alignment, aiding chemical combination (or the reverse reaction).

The enzyme speeds up the reaction (see Fig. 108)—indeed, it makes the reaction possible at the low temperature of a living cell—but it does not affect the direction in which the reaction proceeds. The same enzyme is involved in the anabolic and catabolic reactions:

$$\text{maltose} \xrightleftharpoons{\text{amylase}} \text{amylose}$$

Use of Materials and Energy in Cells

Starch, which can be broken down to maltose, is an energy store in plants. Glycogen, sometimes called animal starch, is a similar polysaccharide which is stored in the cells of many animals (for example, in the cells of the liver and in the muscles of mammals, see p. 187).

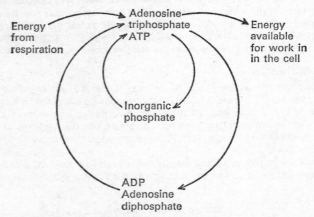

Fig. 109. Temporary storage of energy in cells by the formation of ATP.

Glucose is a more readily available source of energy which can be used in respiration (see p. 182). Another kind of molecule in the cell, called adenosine triphosphate or ATP, is an even more immediately available source of energy. The energy released in respiration is stored temporarily in cells by the formation of ATP from ADP (adenosine diphosphate) and inorganic phosphate (see Fig. 109). The ATP provides energy for work in the cell—for example, in the chemical reactions involved in the formation of food reserves, in cell maintenance and growth, in muscle contraction and the transport of nerve impulses in animal cells, and in the active absorption and secretion of materials by all cells.

Mineral salts dissociate in solution and exist as positively and negatively charged ions. Plants absorb these ions selectively from the soil (see p. 96). Many ions, therefore, are present in higher concentration in the cytoplasm and

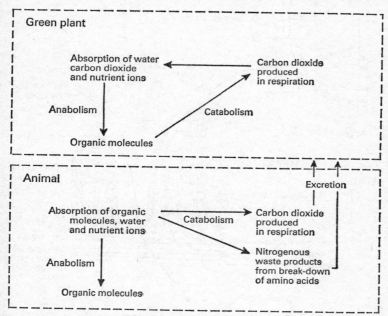

Fig. 110. Origin of some waste products of metabolism. Green plants in sunlight produce carbon dioxide in respiration but use it in photosynthesis. Animals excrete carbon dioxide and nitrogenous waste products.

vacuoles of plant cells than in the soil: that is to say, the intake of these ions occurs against a diffusion gradient, from regions of lower to regions of higher concentration. This is described as an **active intake** because energy must be used in the process. This means that the plant uses some of the energy stored in the formation of sugars in photosynthesis, in the absorption of elements that will be used in the formation of some other molecules (pp. 82 and 180).

Some Functions of the Liver of a Mammal

The liver differs from all other organs in the body of a mammal in that it has a double blood supply. It receives blood from the hepatic artery and from the hepatic portal vein. Note that the stomach and intestines receive blood from a number of arteries but all this blood, after flowing through blood capillaries

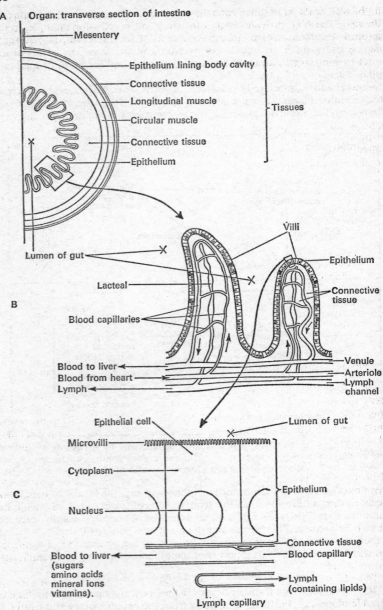

Fig. 111. Intestine of a mammal: (A) half of a transverse section; (B) two villi
(C) epithelial cell with microvilli. Diagram not to scale.

in the wall of the alimentary canal, flows into the hepatic portal vein and so to the liver. Most of the food molecules absorbed by the epithelial cells of the intestine pass into the blood and are transported directly to the liver (see p. 68, Fig. 37).

The liver plays a major part in **regulating** the amount of food passed on to other parts of the body. For example, after a meal most of the glucose absorbed from the intestine is converted into glycogen in the liver. This reduces the amount of glucose in the blood to about 0.1 g per 100 cm³ blood. Then, between meals glucose passes from the blood into the body cells, which use glucose in their respiration, and you might expect the concentration of glucose in the blood to fall. However, the concentration of glucose in the blood is kept fairly constant because glycogen in the liver is converted to glucose and this is returned to the blood.

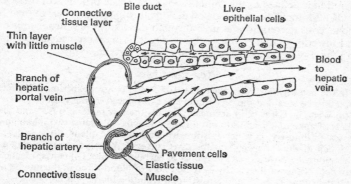

Fig. 112. Flow of blood and flow of bile in relation to liver epithelial cells.

Glucose is also converted to glycogen in muscles. The liver can store about 100 g glycogen and the muscles about 300 g. Any further glucose absorbed after a meal is converted to fat, which is stored especially in cells in the deeper parts of the dermis of the skin (see Fig. 89). Lipids absorbed after a meal may, like glucose, be used immediately in respiration or converted to storage materials (fats).

Some of the amino acids absorbed after a meal are used in the production of proteins in the tissues of the body—in cell maintenance and growth. But any amino acids that are in excess of immediate requirements cannot be stored. They are broken down in the liver, in a process called **de-amination**, and glucose and urea are formed. The blood always contains some urea and some is excreted all the time through the kidneys (see p. 206).

Iron, an essential element (see p. 190), and several vitamins (A, D and B₁₂) are stored in the liver. This is why liver is such a good source of several essential food materials (see Table 16).

The liver is a complex structure. It is concerned not only with the regulation of the composition of the blood but also with the **production of bile** (see p. 91). The diagram (Fig. 112) will help you to understand that the epithelial cells which carry out the regulatory functions are the gland cells which also produce bile. Blood from the hepatic artery and hepatic portal vein flows through spaces close to the liver epithelial cells. The narrow canals into which bile is secreted are between these cells. The flow of blood and the flow of bile are indicated by arrows in the diagram.

Large numbers of new red blood corpuscles are formed every day in the red bone marrow (see p. 214) and about the same number of older red blood corpuscles are destroyed in the liver. The red blood pigment, haemoglobin, contains iron which is stored in the liver. Other breakdown products of haemoglobin form the bile pigments.

Heat is released in many of the chemical reactions in the liver and this is why the liver plays a major part in **heat production**: helping to maintain a high and constant body temperature (see p. 235).

Excretion

Excretion is defined as the elimination of the waste products of metabolism (Fig. 110). Mammals excrete carbon dioxide through the surface of their lungs (carbonaceous excretion) and urea through their kidneys (nitrogenous excretion). Flowering plants excrete carbon dioxide at night but use carbon dioxide during the day in photosynthesis and excrete oxygen.

Test Questions

1. In the investigation with yeast (Fig. 105), what control experiment is necessary if you are to be sure that the carbon dioxide is produced by the yeast?

2. (*a*) Write in words or in chemical symbols the raw materials used and the end products of anaerobic respiration in a named fungus. (*b*) Name two manufacturing processes, in industry, in which this fungus is used, and explain why it is used.

3. Which of the following statements is correct? When you are running a long distance your leg muscles: (A) are short of carbon dioxide; (B) contain lactic acid; (C) are hot because of the greatly increased flow of blood through the muscle tissue; (D) use their food reserves and receive food from the blood plasma.

4. (*a*) What is metabolism? (*b*) Explain the difference between egestion and excretion. (*c*) Name two substances that are excreted by a mammal. (*d*) Where are these two substances produced in the body and (*e*) from which organs are they excreted? (*f*) Name two substances that are excreted by a flowering plant and state when they are excreted.

22

THE FOOD NEEDS OF PEOPLE

The study of the food needs of animals is of economic importance since correct feeding is the basis for good health and maximum productivity in animal husbandry. An adequate diet is also essential for the good health of people. However, it is not easy to decide what is an adequate diet. One problem is that even for people who are the same size, age and sex, an adequate diet for one might be insufficient for another and too much for another, even if they all live in the same place and do similar work.

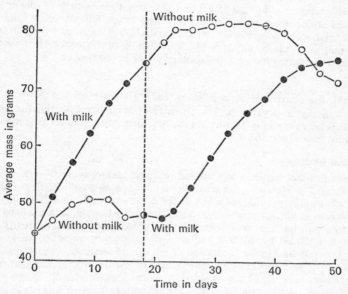

Fig. 113. Changes in the mass of rats on a diet of pure protein, fat, carbohydrate, mineral salts and water, but either with or without a milk supplement (data from Hopkins, F. G. (1912), *Journal of Physiology*, **44**).

The scientific study of nutrition began in the 19th century with the development of chemistry. Many foods were analysed and found to contain proteins, lipids and carbohydrates, in addition to mineral salts and water. But in 1912 a British scientist, Gowland Hopkins, fed laboratory rats on a mixture of pure protein, lipid, carbohydrate, mineral salts and water, and found that the rats did not grow properly (Fig. 113). Other rats fed on the same diet plus a little yeast or milk did grow normally. Hopkins concluded that the yeast and milk contained some essential that was not present in the purified diet. He called

189

this a vitamin (L. *vita* = life) because it was essential for a healthy life, but he did not know what this vitamin was.

Body-Building Foods

Proteins

Each kind of protein in your body contains some but not all of 18 different amino acids. Some amino acids can be formed in the body (for example, by converting one kind of amino acid into another). Others, because they must be present in your diet, are called the **essential amino acids**.

Because most plant proteins contain only small amounts of some essential amino acids they are called second-class proteins. First-class proteins, which are good sources of all the essential amino acids, are obtained from eggs, milk and cheese, lean meat and fish.

People who have enough to eat and yet do not get enough of one or more essential amino acids, suffer from **protein deficiency**. This disease is known by a Ghanaian word *Kwashiorkor*, which means 'the sickness of a child deprived of its mother's milk by a new baby'. The wasting of the muscles is masked by swellings caused by the accumulation of water in the tissues.

Lipids

Lipids are sources of energy (see p. 187). They are broken down to fatty acids and glycerides (see p. 91). Some fatty acids are essential for normal health. Fats, especially fish-liver oils, are also good sources of fat-soluble vitamins (see Table 16).

Mineral Elements

Some mineral elements are needed in much greater quantities than others (see Table 15). However, a varied diet which contains sufficient calcium and iron will usually provide sufficient of the other essential mineral elements.

Calcium, as calcium phosphate and calcium carbonate, is in the hard parts of bones and teeth. It is obtained from cheese, milk, eggs and bread. More calcium is needed by children and adolescents than by an adult, because calcium is being used in the formation of bones and teeth. And more calcium is needed by a woman during pregnancy and breast feeding, because calcium is being passed on to her baby. A shortage of calcium (or vitamin D, see p. 191) in childhood, results in a deficiency disease called **rickets** which is marked by poor growth and the deformation of the long bones of the legs.

Iron is part of the haemoglobin molecule, the red pigment of blood, and iron deficiency in the diet is one cause of **anaemia**, a disease in which there are too few red corpuscles in the blood. A woman needs extra iron in her diet to make good the iron lost in bleeding in her monthly periods (see p. 247). She needs still more iron in pregnancy, for the blood of her baby. Good sources of iron are liver, lean meat, wholemeal bread, eggs, green vegetables and groundnuts.

Iodine deficiency causes goitre (see p. 228) and in children prevents normal mental and physical development.

Fluorine contributes to enamel production in the teeth. In some regions enough is present in the drinking water. In other regions where there is little naturally occurring fluorine, more is added to water supplies. Also, some

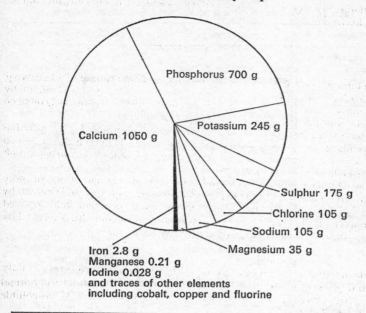

Fig. 114. Mineral elements in the body of man (based on Barrass, R., *Biology: Food and People*, Hodder & Stoughton, London).

toothpastes contain fluorine but this is not necessary if you live where there is already enough in the water.

Iodine, fluorine and other elements which are required only in very small amounts are called **trace elements**.

Vitamins

Like the trace elements, vitamins are present in foods in only very small amounts but they are organic molecules and are therefore distinct from the trace elements. They are not all stored in the body, and for good health you need small amounts in your diet every day.

The vitamins were known first by the letters A, B, C, D, E and K, before they were chemically identified. Now they also have an internationally agreed chemical name (see Table 14). Many vitamins are linked to proteins as part of enzyme molecules.

Rickets may be caused by vitamin D (calciferol) deficiency, as well as by a shortage of calcium. Vitamin D is formed in the body when the skin is exposed to the sun. Children, especially, should play out of doors.

Beri-beri, due to a deficiency of vitamin B_1 (thiamine), is a disease which affects the nerves and leads to paralysis. It was common in places where people eat mostly polished rice; and in 1896 Christiaan Eijkman, a Dutch doctor working in Java, found that a similar condition could be caused

Table 14. Vitamins, food sources and vitamin deficiency diseases.

Vitamin	Food sources	Deficiency diseases
Fat-soluble vitamins		
A Retinol	Carrots, butter, milk, eggs, liver, sardines and fish-liver oils.	Slow growth in children. Night blindness. Infertility.
D Calciferol	Formed in the skin in sunlight. Present in herrings, fish-liver oils, eggs and butter.	Rickets in children; bones not properly formed. Bone deformities in adults; especially in old people.
E Tocopherol	Fresh green vegetables and eggs.	Disorders of nerves and muscles.
K Phylloquinone	Made by bacteria in the intestine but needed in the diet of young babies. Present in fresh green vegetables.	Blood does not clot properly.
Water-soluble vitamins		
B complex		
B_1 Thiamine	Whole-grain rice, wholemeal bread, milk, meat, yeast and potatoes.	Check in growth of children. Mental depression. Beri-beri: swelling of legs, loss of appetite and paralysis.
B_2 Riboflavine	Milk, cheese and liver.	Check in growth of children. Cracks in corners of mouth.
Nicotinic acid (niacin)	Yeast, liver, beef, bread, fruit and vegetables.	Check in growth of children. Pellagra: skin rough red when exposed to light.
B_{12} Cobalmin	Very lightly cooked liver. Also in meat, milk, eggs and fish.	Pernicious anaemia. Degeneration of nerve cells.
C Ascorbic acid	Citrus fruits, blackcurrants and fresh green vegetables.	Check in growth of children. Wounds do not heal. Scurvy.

in chickens by feeding them only polished rice. We now know that the outer part of the rice, which is removed in milling and polishing, contains thiamine.

Scurvy, vitamin C (ascorbic acid) deficiency, used to result in the deaths of many sailors on long sea voyages. It was prevented in the 17th century by the daily consumption of citrus fruit juices, long before the cause of the disease was known.

Proteins, lipids, mineral elements and vitamins are essential structural materials. Foods which contain these essentials are therefore called **body-building foods.** Because the essential mineral elements and vitamins are required in small amounts, and because a shortage of any one of them results in a corresponding deficiency disease, foods containing these essentials are also called **protective foods.**

Energy-Giving Foods

Foods that contain lipids (butter, margarine and oils) or carbohydrates (sweet foods, bread, potatoes, cassava, yams) are called energy-giving foods (see p. 187), but energy is also obtained from proteins (also p. 187). Energy is used in many activities in the body (see p. 185). Also, every time energy is used some is lost as heat. In man (and in other mammals and birds) this heat may be conserved as part of temperature control (see p. 235).

Carbohydrates absorbed from the intestine, in excess of the body's immediate needs, are converted to glycogen (stored in the liver and muscles) or to fat (stored in the skin). Lipids in the diet may also be converted into body fat. Amino acids, absorbed from the intestine, cannot be stored; those that are in excess of the body's immediate requirements are converted to carbohydrates in the liver and stored as glycogen (see p. 187). In times of food shortage, first the food reserves are used and then the structural proteins of the body may be used as a source of energy. The person becomes thin and then emaciated.

A Balanced Diet

People obtain from their food: (1) proteins; (2) carbohydrates; (3) lipids (fats and oils); (4) mineral salts; (5) vitamins; and (6) water. These are used in maintenance and growth; in respiration as a source of energy; and in the formation of food reserves. The diet must also contain (7) sufficient roughage: indigestible fibres, especially cellulose (see p. 141), which give the diet bulk and help to prevent constipation.

It is not easy to say how much food a person should eat in one day. In general, a varied diet which provides enough energy will include other essentials. The daily requirement is usually expressed, therefore, as the amount of energy required.

A relatively inactive man who weighs about 86 kg requires about 12.7 MJ of energy each day. Of this, about 5.5 MJ will be used for physical work and 7.2 MJ will be used whether or not he is active. This **basal requirement** is due to the use of energy by all the cells of the body even when a person is resting (for example, in cell maintenance, cell division, cell growth, selective absorption and secretion, contraction of muscle, conduction of nerve impulses and the formation of food reserves). However, different people use different amounts of energy each day and the same person has different needs at different times (Table 15).

The more physical work we do, the more energy we require. A manual worker may use twice as much energy in a day as a moderately active person. Also, people who live in cold climates are likely to use more energy in producing body heat than do people who live in the tropics. The amount of energy-giving food you need, therefore, depends upon your **size** and therefore upon your **age**; but also upon your **occupation**, the **climate** where you live and your **sex**. Furthermore, there are individual differences that nobody understands.

The energy content of food is measured in joules (symbol J). The amount of heat energy required to raise the temperature of 1 g water by 1 °C is 4.2 J. The energy content of foods is measured as the amount of heat energy released in their complete combustion in air:

$$C_6H_{12}O_6 + 6O_2 \longrightarrow 6CO_2 + 6H_2O + \text{Energy}$$

glucose · · · oxygen · · · · · · · · carbon dioxide · · · water · · · 2·83 MJ mole^{-1}

Different foods contain different amounts of stored energy (see Table 16).

Table 15.   Food needed each day by people living in temperate climates.

Sex	Age	Body mass (kg)	Energy (MJ)	Protein (g)	Calcium (mg)	Iron (mg)	Vitamins					
							A (µg)	C (mg)	D (µg)	B_1 (mg)	B_2 (mg)	Niacin (mg)
Child	4	16.5	6.7	40	500	8	300	20	10	0.6	0.8	9
Boy	13	45.5	11.7	70	700	14	725	25	2.5	1.1	1.4	16
Girl	13	48.6	9.6	58	700	14	725	25	2.5	0.9	1.4	16
Boy	16	61.0	12.6	75	600	15	750	30	2.5	1.2	1.7	19
Girl	16	56.1	9.6	58	600	15	750	30	2.5	0.9	1.4	16
Man	25	65	12.6(a)	75	500	10	750	30	2.5	1.2	1.7	18
Woman	25	55	9.2(a)	55	500	12	750	30	2.5	0.9	1.3	15
Woman in pregnancy		(b)	10.0	60	1 200	15	1 200	60	10	1.0	1.6	18
While breast-feeding			11.3	68	1 200	15	1 200	60	10	1.1	1.8	21
Man	65	63	9.8	59	500	10	750	30	2.5	0.9	1.7	18
Woman	65	53	8.6	51	500	10	750	30	2.5	0.8	1.3	15

Notes
(a) Figures for moderately active people.
(b) Figures for last six months of pregnancy except that more vitamin D is needed throughout pregnancy, and the figure for calcium is for the last three months.
All figures for food needs, from the *Manual of Nutrition*, are published with the permission of the Controller of Her Majesty's Stationery Office.

Table 16. The composition of some of man's foods (per 100 g of food).

	Protein (g)	Fat (g)	Carbo-hydrate (g)	Energy content (kcal)	Energy content (kJ)	Calcium (mg)	Iron (mg)	Vitamins A (µg)	Vitamins B_1 (mg)	Vitamins C (mg)	Vitamins D (µg)
White bread	7.8	1.7	49.7	233	991	100	1.7	0	0.18	0	0
Wholemeal bread	8.8	2.7	41.8	216	918	23	2.5	0	0.26	0	0
Boiled polished rice	2.2	0.3	29.6	123	522	1	0.2	0	0.01	0	0
Fresh milk	3.3	3.8	4.7	65	272	120	0.05	30	0.04	1.5	0.02
Fresh butter	0.4	82.0	trace	740	3 041	15	0.16	750	trace	trace	0.76
Cheddar cheese	26.0	33.5	trace	406	1 682	800	0.4	310	0.04	0	0.26
Fresh eggs	12.3	10.9	trace	147	612	52	2.0	140	0.09	0	1.75
Cod-liver oil	trace	99.9	0	899	3 696	trace	trace	18 000	0	0	210
Fried bacon	24.9	40.6	0	465	1 926	13	1.3	trace	0.41	0	trace
Lean roast beef	27.6	9.1	0	192	806	10	2.1	trace	0.07	0	trace
Fried calf liver	26.9	13.2	7.3	254	1 063	15	7.5	17 400	0.27	13	0.25
Steamed cod	18.6	0.9	0	83	350	15	0.5	trace	0.09	trace	trace
Raw herring	16.8	18.5	0	234	970	33	0.8	45	trace	trace	22.5
Raw carrot	0.7	trace	5.4	23	98	48	0.6	0(a)	0.06	6	0
Boiled potatoes	1.4	0.1	19.7	80	343	4	0.3	0(a)	0.08	14(b)	0
Bramley apple	0.3	trace	11.9	46	196	4	0.3	0(a)	0.04	20	0
Lemon juice	0.3	trace	1.6	7	31	8	0.1	0	0.02	50	0

Notes
(a) Apples, carrots and potatoes contain carotene, a precursor of vitamin A.
(b) The vitamin C content for potatoes is for freshly dug main crop.
Figures from Paul and Southgate, *The Composition of Foods*, with permission of the Controller of Her Majesty's Stationery Office.

Note that the same amount of energy can be obtained by eating a lot of lean meat (mainly protein), less bread or potatoes (mainly carbohydrate), or even less butter or fat (mainly lipid). Active people can add energy to their diet without a corresponding increase in bulk if they eat more fat. Anyone who wishes to lose weight should eat less food. However, a balanced diet is an essential basis for a healthy life and there are dangers in slimming unless this is done with a doctor's advice.

Different people, in different parts of the world, eat different kinds of foods. People require a varied diet and this may be obtained by eating many combinations of different foods. The essential constituents of a **balanced diet** are provided each day by a mixed diet of, for example, milk, eggs, lean meat or fish, fresh vegetables and fruit, whole grain cereals, bread and butter, and citrus fruit juices. Each of these foods provides some essentials but may be a poor source of others. This varied diet, containing vegetable matter, will also provide enough roughage.

For young babies, if their mother is healthy and has a good diet, mother's milk provides a complete and balanced diet. It is the best and cheapest food that they could possibly have. Older babies require iron which they obtain when they start eating solid foods (see p. 190 and Table 16).

Malnourishment and Undernourishment

People of any age who eat even a little too much, day after day, are overfed. Many babies are overfed by mothers who think that they are being kind. Many children and adolescents are overfed; and many adults not only overeat but also overfeed their children. Many people are handicapped because they must carry their excess fat. They may suffer ill health and may die prematurely. Overfeeding is the commonest form of malnourishment in many countries.

People who do not get enough to eat are undernourished. Underfeeding, day after day, results in the use of food reserves and structural materials. Deaths due to underfeeding are common in times of famine, when there are more people than can be supported on the reduced food supply.

Many people get enough to eat but have a diet which lacks one or more of the essential constituents. Such people suffer from deficiency diseases (see pp. 190–2). They are malnourished even though they are not underfed. In many countries undernourishment and malnourishment are common due to food shortages, but even in countries where there is no shortage of food some people are malnourished because they either do not know how to plan a balanced diet or they do not trouble to do so.

Investigation: *food reserves in plants*. Grind a small piece of potato and examine the paste in a drop of water on a microscope slide. Note the characteristic layered appearance of starch grains. Mount some of the paste in a drop of iodine solution and examine this preparation. Look for starch in other organs of perennation and in seeds and grains. Do they all contain starch?

Some plant products (e.g. olives, peanuts and maize grains) contain oils which can be detected by grinding the material and smearing it on paper. Fats and oils make paper translucent.

There are other tests for different food materials but for some of these tests poisonous chemicals are required. They should be undertaken only when a qualified teacher of biology or chemistry is present.

Investigation: *energy content of foods*

1. Pour 20 cm³ water into a boiling tube.
2. Clamp the tube so that it does not point towards anyone.
3. Record the temperature of the water.
4. Fix a peanut to a mounted needle.
5. Set fire to the peanut and, as soon as it is alight, hold it so that it heats the water in the tube.
6. Record the temperature of the water as soon as the peanut has burned away. The energy content of the peanut, in joules, is calculated:

Mass of water at start × rise in temperature × 4.2

Test Questions

1. The food needed each day by people who live in temperate climates can be calculated from Table 15.

(*a*) Does a woman require more food in the later months of pregnancy than she did previously? (*b*) Why does she require more calcium during pregnancy? (*c*) When does a moderately active woman require most food? (*d*) Do older people need more food than younger people? (*e*) Do you think people who live in the tropics will require more or less food than the amounts recommended in the table? Apart from the requirements summarised in the table, people also require a certain amount of roughage in their diet. (*f*) What chemical substance, present in roughage, are we unable to digest? (*g*) Why is this indigestible material necessary in the diet?

2. In 100 g of the foods (A to F), which contains the most of each of the dietary requirements *a* to *f*?

A	fresh fish	*a*	vitamin C
B	fried liver	*b*	protein
C	fresh butter	*c*	energy
D	fresh orange juice	*d*	iron
E	fresh milk	*e*	vitamin A
F	boiled rice	*f*	calcium

3. The vitamin C content of potatoes decreases during their storage. Vitamin C is also destroyed by cooking. (*a*) Name two kinds of foods that are good sources of vitamin C. (*b*) How should these foods be prepared for the table? (*c*) Why are many convenience foods deficient in vitamin C? (*d*) What deficiency disease results if people do not have enough vitamin C in their diet, day after day?

4. Name the structures that: (*a*) contain large amounts of stored food in a seed; (*b*) can be observed in a squash of cells from a potato tuber; (*c*) are present in axils; (*d*) facilitate the dispersal of *Rhizopus*; (*e*) are present in other kinds of plants but absent from fungi.

23

WATER BALANCE

In plants the intake of nitrate and mineral ions from the environment takes place through permeable surfaces—from the water of the environment to the water inside the organism. In animals the absorption of food materials, after digestion, takes place through a permeable surface. In all organisms, gaseous exchange can take place only through a surface which is permeable to oxygen and carbon dioxide. However, the permeability that makes possible the intake of essential materials and the excretion of waste products of metabolism also favours the movement of water. Whether water moves in or out depends upon the conditions inside and outside the organism.

Water Intake and Water Loss in Flowering Plants

Terrestrial flowering plants absorb water through the surface of their roots, from the soil, and they lose water from their aerial parts, to the air.

Water Intake

The growth of root hairs between the soil particles greatly increases the surface area of the epidermal cells in contact with the soil. The cellulose cell walls of the epidermal cells of the root are permeable to water: they do not

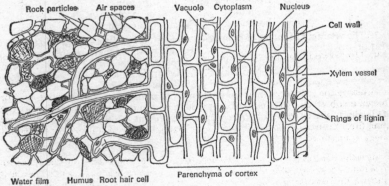

Fig. 115. Soil water, root hair cells and some other cells of a root of a flowering plant (longitudinal section). Diagram not to scale.

have a waxy cuticle. These cell walls are largely composed of long threads of cellulose which act like a sponge, taking up water from the soil and holding this water next to the plasmalemma.

In moist soil, water intake occurs not only through the root hair cells near the root tip, but also through all other epidermal cells of the root. Note also (see Fig. 115) that the cell wall of each epidermal cell has a large surface of contact with the cell walls of neighbouring root cells. Just as a fluid rises in a wick by capillarity, so water moves through the cell walls, from one cell wall to the next, and so there is water, continuous with the soil water, bathing all the cells of the root cortex.

The cells of the root absorb water by osmosis (see p. 157).

Water Loss

The evaporation of water from the aerial parts of a plant, to an unsaturated atmosphere, is called **transpiration**.

Investigation: *water loss from the shoot.* Tie a plastic bag over the shoot of a potted plant or cover a cut leafy shoot with a bell jar (Fig. 116A). Water condenses on the inside of the plastic or glass cover. Water makes white (anhydrous) copper sulphate turn blue and you can use this test to confirm that the fluid collected in this investigation is water.

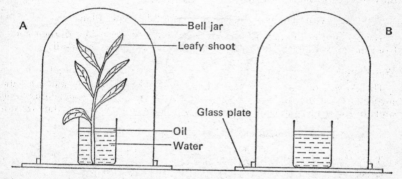

Fig. 116. Evaporation of water from a cut leafy shoot: (A) water condenses on the inner surface of the bell jar; (B) the control.

Investigation: *water loss and the distribution of stomata.* Fix cobalt chloride paper, between two sheets of glass or plastic, against the upper and lower surfaces of a leaf. This paper is blue when dry but turns pink as it absorbs water. Which paper turns pink first: the one in contact with the upper epidermis or the one in contact with the lower epidermis?

Investigation: *the distribution of stomata.* Strip the epidermis from the upper and lower surfaces of the leaf studied in the previous investigation. Examine these strips under a microscope. If water loss is mainly through the stomata you will expect to find the most stomata in the surface through which water loss is most rapid.

Investigation: *the rate of water loss by transpiration.* Water a potted plant and then tie a plastic bag around the pot and soil only (see Fig. 117) so that water cannot evaporate from the soil. Place the pot on a balance and record the mass of the potted plant at the start of your investigation. Record the mass again, at intervals, and determine the rate of water loss. Is this an accurate method for measuring the rate of water loss? (See Fig. 40 and p. 77.)

You could extend this investigation (see Fig. 118). For example, does a plant lose water most rapidly (*a*) in the day or at night; (*b*) near a closed or an open window; or (*c*) in sunlight or in the shade?

The parenchyma cells of the leaf and their cell walls contain water. As a result of the evaporation of this water, the air spaces in the leaf are saturated with water vapour. When the stomata are open—that is, whenever gaseous exchange is taking place (Figs. 98C and D)—water vapour passes out of the leaf unless the air outside the leaf is also saturated with water vapour.

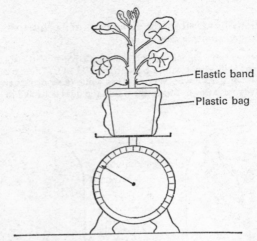

Fig. 117. Measuring the loss of mass by a potted plant.

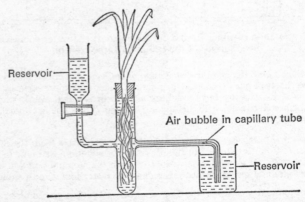

Fig. 118. Potometer used for measuring the rate of absorption of water by a small plant (or by a cut leafy shoot).

Most of the water absorbed by the roots is lost through the stomata. In terrestrial plants, **transpiration** is an inevitable consequence of the presence of permeable surfaces through which gaseous exchange takes place. This evaporation of water cools the plant on a hot day (just as sweating cools your body—

see p. 235). Transpiration probably also pulls the stream of water and nutrient ions through the plant (see p. 209).

The two cells on either side of a stoma are called **guard cells**. The guard cell wall next to the opening is thicker than the rest of the cell wall (see Fig. 119). It bends but does not stretch as the cell becomes turgid. Changes in turgidity result in stomatal opening and closing. When the guard cells are turgid the stomata are open. In some plants the guard cells are the only epidermal cells that contain chloroplasts. In the sunlight sugars are manufactured and this may increase the osmotic potential of the guard cells, resulting in an intake of

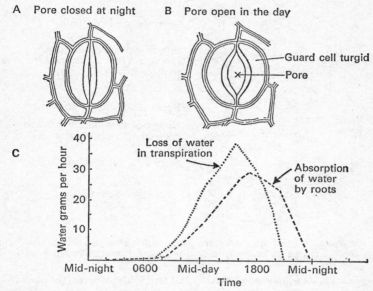

Fig. 119. Rate of transpiration and rate of water absorption throughout the night and day.

water that causes stomatal opening. However, this hypothesis could not apply to those plants in which the guard cells do not contain chloroplasts.

Water loss from the aerial parts of a plant is most rapid on those hot dry windy days when washed clothes, hung outside, dry most rapidly. On a hot dry day the humidity of the atmosphere is low and the air next to the leaf will hold more water than on a cold day. The wind moves water vapour away from the surface of the leaf and so maintains a maximum difference between the saturated air in the leaf and the unsaturated air outside. If the air outside the leaf, next to the stomata, is saturated with water vapour there is no water loss through the stomata.

The stomata are usually open during the day but if the plant wilts (see p. 155) the cells of the leaf are no longer turgid. When the guard cells are not turgid the stomata close and this reduces the rate of water loss. In some plants the stomata are at the bottom of pits in the epidermis, or they are surrounded by hair-like projections of other epidermal cells, or the leaf may curl. All these features restrict air movement next to the stomata and so reduce the rate of water loss. Plants with these features are able to survive in drier places than plants that lack these adaptations. They are called **xerophytes**.

Some desert plants have numerous widespread roots, near to the surface, which absorb the water that condenses in the surface of the soil at night. Others have very deep roots which absorb water, after rainfall, as it percolates through the soil. Many desert plants, called **succulents**, have water-storage tissues. These plants absorb water when it is available and can then survive for a long time without further water intake (see Fig. 120).

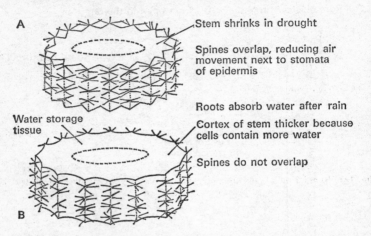

Fig. 120. Water is stored in a cactus: the stem expands after rain and shrinks during a drought (based on Leopold, A. S., *The Desert*, Time-Life International).

In some plants wilting is followed by leaf fall. Without leaves the plant loses less water and it may survive a dry period and then produce new leaves. There are therefore many anatomical and physiological features which contribute to the survival of flowering plants on land even though there may be an irregular water supply.

Water Intake and Water Loss in Animals with Backbones

Different vertebrates live in different environments. For example, some fishes live in the sea and some in fresh water; and others live part of their life in the sea and part in fresh water. Most amphibians, as their name indicates, live part of their lives in fresh water and part on the land. And most reptiles, birds and mammals live on land.

Many fresh-water animals take up water by osmosis and regulate the water content of their body by pumping out any excess water. But most animals that live in the sea have body fluids which have an osmotic concentration equal to that of sea water, and they neither take in nor lose water by osmosis: compare Figs. 121A and B.

The frog, an amphibian, takes in water through its skin, by osmosis, when

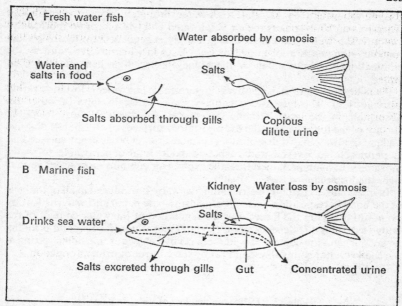

Fig. 121. Regulation of the salt and water content of the body of fresh-water and marine bony fish.

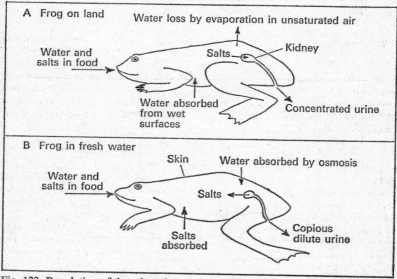

Fig. 122. Regulation of the salt and water content of the body of a frog: (A) on land (B) in fresh water.

it is in fresh water (Fig. 122B). It loses water through its skin, by evaporation, when it is on land—unless the air is saturated and will accept no more water vapour. The water content of a frog's body is regulated by the frog's behaviour—the selection of humid or wet places in which to live—and by the elimination of excess water by the kidney (especially when the frog is in water).

The skin of a mammal is relatively impermeable but water is lost in sweating (perspiration). The faeces also contain some water, in spite of water reabsorption in the large intestine (see p. 89). And water is lost from the surface of the lungs which, like the respiratory surfaces of all animals that live on land, is always moist. Respiratory surfaces are wet because any surface that is permeable to oxygen and carbon dioxide is also permeable to water molecules. In mammals, therefore, the expired air contains more water vapour than the inspired air (see Fig. 103C).

In mammals, as in all terrestrial animals, water is produced in all of the cells of the body in respiration (as in all organisms—see p. 60) and water is lost by evaporation and in the faeces. But the regulation of the water content of the body (see Table 17) depends upon the intake of water (feeding and drinking behaviour) and the control of water loss (1) by behaviour, including resting in the shade on hot sunny days, and (2) by the control of urine production.

Table 17. Daily gain and loss of water in man.

Sources of water (cm³)		Loss of water (cm³)	
Drink	1450	Urine	1500
Food	800	Evaporation of sweat	600
Oxidation of food in		Evaporation from lungs	400
respiration	350	Faeces	100
Total	2600	Total	2600

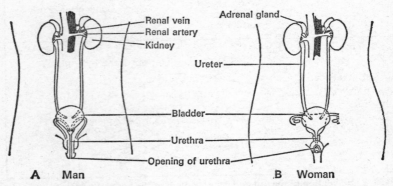

Fig. 123. Urinary system: (A) of a man; (B) of a woman.

Control of Water Loss from the Kidneys in Man

There are two kidneys. They are part of the urinary system (Fig. 123). A renal artery carries blood into each kidney and a renal vein carries blood from the kidney. Within each kidney the blood capillaries are closely associated with the renal tubules. There are about a million renal tubules in each kidney but only one is represented in the diagram (Fig. 124).

The parts of a **renal tubule** are the capsule, the first convoluted tubule, the U-shaped loop and the second convoluted tubule which opens into a collecting

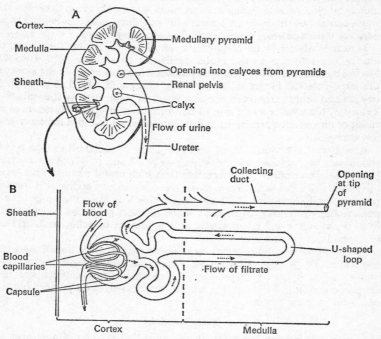

Fig. 124. Structure of a kidney: (A) kidney cut in half; (B) the parts of one renal tubule.

duct. Note (in Fig. 124A) that the capsule and the two convoluted tubules are in the cortex (the outer part of the kidney) and that the U-shaped loop and the collecting ducts are in the medulla (the inner part of the kidney).

Loops of blood capillaries (the **glomerular capillaries**) are closely associated with the cup-shaped end of each renal tubule. The blood in the capillary loops is under high arterial pressure and blood plasma (without plasma proteins which are too large to pass through) is pumped from the blood capillary loops into the renal tubule (see Fig. 124B). This fluid within the renal capsule is called **glomerular filtrate**.

As more is formed, from the blood plasma, the filtrate is forced along the renal tubule. Its composition changes as it passes along because the cells of the tubule absorb some materials (for example, most of the water and all the glucose) but not others (for example, urea—see p. 187); and mineral salts are selectively reabsorbed. As a result, the **urine** that eventually flows from each kidney, in the ureter, is very different in composition from the blood plasma. This urine accumulates in the bladder and is forced out through the urethra when the muscles of the bladder wall contract.

The volume of water lost in the urine each day varies, depending upon the amount of water absorbed from food and drink and the amount of water lost in other ways (see Table 17). By eliminating water when the body contains too much and by conserving water at other times, the kidneys help to maintain the water content of the body cells and fluids at a fairly constant level. The kidneys are **osmoregulatory organs** as well as **excretory organs**.

Materials absorbed by cells of the renal tubules, from the glomerular filtrate, are returned to the blood capillaries near these cells. The blood leaving the kidneys in the renal veins differs from that entering the kidneys in the renal arteries, in the following ways. It contains: (1) less glucose, less oxygen and more carbon dioxide as a result of respiration in the cells of the kidney; (2) less water as a result of the formation of urine; (3) less urea as a result of nitrogenous excretion; and (4) less salts as a result of the excretion of any excess salts.

Excretion, the elimination of waste-products of metabolism (see p. 188), should not be confused with egestion (see p. 59 and p. 89). Also, excretion should not be confused with **secretion** (in which useful materials are passed out of the cell). But note that in sweat there is a loss of sodium chloride (0.3 per cent) and some urea (0.03 per cent). This loss from the body is called **uncontrolled excretion** because the volume of sweat produced varies so much from time to time and is not related to the amount of water, salts and urea in the body.

People who lose a lot of water by sweating must replace the salt as well as the water. To prevent dehydration, which can cause death, water lost in vomit, and in diarrhoea (especially as a result of gastro-enteritis and other diseases), and in sweating during a fever, must be replaced by drinking large quantities of clean water.

Test Questions

1. How does stomatol closure in sunlight affect: (*a*) the rate of photosynthesis; (*b*) the rate of water loss; and (*c*) the leaf temperature?

2. (*a*) In what process is oxygen produced in a green leaf. (*b*) When does this process occur? (*c*) In what process is carbon dioxide produced in the leaf? (*d*) When does this process occur? (*e*) List the words needed to complete the following: Water loss from the leaf is called ——, and is a result of the presence of ——, through which —— —— occurs. (*f*) In the investigation (Fig. 116) why is the oil needed, and what would be the effect of smearing the under surface of every leaf with petroleum jelly?

3. (*a*) Name three different ways in which materials enter living cells. Give an example of each. (*b*) In which of these is energy from respiration used? (*c*) What is the function of the contractile vacuole in *Amoeba*?

4. (*a*) Name two materials lost from the body of a mammal through the surface of the lungs; and (*b*) two materials lost through the kidneys.

5. (*a*) When a kidney is cut in half, what parts can you see? Answer this question by preparing a labelled drawing. (*b*) State three different functions of the kidneys.

24

TRANSPORT SYSTEMS

Some cells grow and then divide. Others grow and then develop into a particular kind of cell. Most cells are very small and they therefore have a large surface area in proportion to their volume. In a small more or less spherical cell no part of the cell is far from the cell surface—that is to say, no part is far from the surface through which materials enter and leave the cell. This is one factor that must limit the size of cells.

The largest living cells include the parenchyma cells of plants and some nerve cells of animals. In parenchyma, because much of the cell is occupied by a central vacuole, the active cytoplasm and the nucleus have a small volume and they are near to the surface. The large vacuole increases the cell size and so increases its surface area without increasing the volume of active cytoplasm. Nerve cells have a very large surface area in proportion to their volume because they are not spheres: they are long but thread-like and therefore have a large surface area but a small volume.

Some unicellular organisms are quite large. An *Amoeba* is so large that you can just see it without a microscope. But because this is such a flat cell (Fig. 32) no part is far from the body surface, through which gaseous exchange takes place. Note also that food vacuoles are formed at one end of the body and egestion takes place at the other end. As digestion proceeds and as food is absorbed, the food vacuoles are not fixed in one place. They move in the cytoplasm. As a result, food molecules are absorbed in all parts of the cytoplasm.

In fungi a large vacuole occupies most of the central part of a hypha. The active cytoplasm has a much smaller volume and is spread as a thin layer next to the surface. It therefore has a very large surface in proportion to its volume. Also, the streaming of the cytoplasm carries materials absorbed by one part of the hypha to other parts.

In *Hydra* no cells are far from the body surface (the respiratory surface). Similarly, no cells are far from the cells of the endoderm which are concerned in the digestion and absorption of food molecules. *Hydra* is much larger than a unicellular organism but it has a very large surface area in proportion to the volume of its living cells. All the cells are near to both the inner and outer surfaces.

In a large multicellular animal such as an earthworm or a man some cells are a long way from the respiratory surface; and other cells are a long way from the epithelium of the alimentary canal. In large plants such as flowering plants some cells, which absorb materials from the soil, are remote from other cells—for example, from those in which photosynthesis takes place. As a result of specialisation and division of labour, different cells in a tissue, different tissues in an organ, and all the organs in the body, are **interdependent**. The life of these organisms depends upon the **movement of materials** from one part of the body to all others.

207

The Transpiration Stream through a Flowering Plant

Investigation: *movement of water in xylem.* Cut the stem of a young plant under water and place the cut end in a dilute solution of a dye (for example, a 1 per cent solution of methylene blue in water). The dye rises in the xylem vessels. By cutting sections of different plants at different times after immersion in the dye, find out how quickly the dye rises in the xylem.

Xylem vessels are formed from long cells, placed end to end, which lose their end walls and their living contents. They are, therefore, narrow channels that extend from near the root tips (Fig. 81), through all parts of the shoot (Fig. 84), to the shoot tip and leaves. In the leaves the xylem vessels are in the veins (Fig. 98B).

The xylem vessels are very narrow tubes and **capillary forces** (see p. 123) are sufficient to account for the movement of water up the shoots of most plants. However, capillarity alone could not account for the movement of water to the top of the tallest trees. Other forces must be involved.

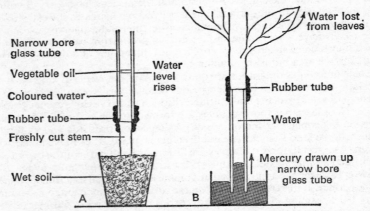

Fig. 125. Demonstrations of (A) root pressure and (B) leaf suction.

Investigation: *root pressure.* In his book *Vegetable Staticks*, published in 1727, Stephen Hales tells how he wished to discover the force of the sap in plants but he did not know how to begin the investigation. He writes: 'by mere accident I hit upon it, while I was endeavouring by several ways to stop the bleeding of an old stem of a vine. . . . Having, after other means proved ineffectual, tyed a piece of bladder over the transverse cut of the stem, I found the force of the sap did greatly extend the bladder; whence I concluded that if a long glass tube were fixed there . . . I should thereby obtain the real ascending force of the sap in the stem.'

The apparatus illustrated in Fig. 125A can be used, in the growing season, to demonstrate the existence of a force, called root pressure, which raises a column of water in the glass tube.

Investigation: *leaf suction.* The apparatus illustrated in Fig. 125B can be used to demonstrate that a cut leafy shoot exerts a pull on a column of water. The shoot should be cut under water and fitted to the glass tube. Then the tube full of water can be dipped in the mercury. Note that mercury vapour is toxic and this demonstration should be set up in a fume cupboard.

The Transpiration–Cohesion–Tension Theory

If you place two very smooth flat surfaces together they hold together. They are said to cohere. You may have difficulty in pulling them apart. This holding together which results from the attraction between molecules when they are very close to one another is called **cohesion**. In water the molecules are packed closely together. They also hold together. This property of water is also important in the rise of water in the xylem.

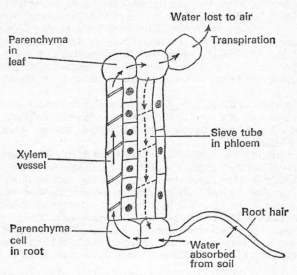

Fig. 126. Transport of materials in a flowering plant. The complete arrows represent the transpiration stream. The broken arrows represent the flow of solvent and dissolved organic molecules. Diagram not to scale.

Another force involved is the evaporation of water from the leaves (see *Transpiration*, p. 200). When water molecules pass out of the stomata the air spaces inside the leaf remain fully saturated because water **evaporates** from the cells of the leaf. This would make the cells of the leaf less turgid if it were not for the fact that it also increases their osmotic potential and they absorb more water from the xylem.

The removal of water from the xylem vessels of the leaf exerts a pull (leaf suction, Fig. 125B) on the column of water in the vessels. Because of cohesion the water column holds together and water is sucked into the xylem vessels in the root, from nearby root cells. This loss of water increases the osmotic potential of the root cells and they take in water from nearby root cells or from their cell walls. Other root cells may take in water from the soil.

This is believed to be the way that (1) all the cells of the plant remain turgid, in spite of water loss in transpiration from the aerial parts of the plant, and (2) water rises in the xylem vessels. The movement of water through the plant is called the **transpiration stream** (Fig. 126).

Transport of Organic Solutes in a Flowering Plant

Most of the sugar produced in photosynthesis is converted to starch and stored in the leaves during the day, but this starch is converted to sucrose (a disaccharide) at night and transported from the leaves to other parts of the plant (including growing regions and storage tissues). The leaves of a plant are destarched (see p. 76) by placing the plant in the dark overnight.

In a tree, the woody tissues (xylem) are inside a layer of dividing cells (the *Cambium*, see Fig. 84, p. 156) and the other tissues, including the phloem, are on the outside (see Fig. 84). When a ring of bark is removed from a woody shoot all other tissues are removed with the bark, leaving only the xylem. Ringing does not interrupt the transpiration stream. Nor does it stop the upward movement of ions. However, the plant soon dies as a result of ringing. A possible explanation for these observations is that water with ions in solution is transported in the xylem and organic molecules in the phloem (Fig. 126).

Each **sieve tube** in the phloem, like each vessel in the xylem, is formed from long cells arranged in a row. In the sieve tubes the end walls are perforated sieve plates. These tubes, therefore, look like pipes through which materials could be transported.

Aphids (greenfly) are insects that feed on plant fluids. When they feed, their mouthparts pierce the tissues of a plant and are inserted, like a hypodermic needle, directly into the sieve tubes. Aphids feed by sucking fluids from these tubes. If the aphid is killed while it is feeding, the stylets can be cut. This is like breaking a hypodermic needle. Fluid exudes from the cut end, directly from a sieve tube, and this fluid contains sugars and amino acids. If, in an experiment, a leaf is enclosed in an atmosphere containing $^{13}CO_2$ (radioactive carbon dioxide), sugars containing radioactive carbon can later be extracted from the sieve tubes. Thus, sugars produced in the leaf are transported to other parts of the plant in the phloem.

Soluble organic molecules (such as sucrose), which are transported in the phloem to all parts of the plant, are used: (1) in all living cells as a source of energy in respiration; (2) in the formation of new cell materials in the growth of cells, prior to cell division—for example, in the formation of fruits and seeds; (3) in the formation of insoluble storage materials such as starch in all cells but especially in seeds and in roots, bulbs and tubers (see p. 30); (4) in the formation of new cell materials in the repair and maintenance of all living tissues.

Because the xylem and phloem are concerned in the transport of materials, they are called **vascular tissues**. The strands of xylem and phloem in all parts of the plant (see Fig. 84) are called vascular bundles. The strands of xylem also provide support (see p. 155).

Open and Closed Circulatory Systems in Animals

The blood of an insect bathes the tissues of the body (see Fig. 127). All arthropods and molluscs have an open circulatory system. In contrast, many animals, including ourselves and all other animals with backbones, have a closed circulatory system—the blood is pumped around the body in tubes.

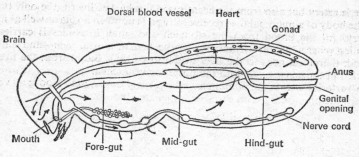

Fig. 127. Open circulatory system of an insect. Diagram not to scale.

The Blood Circulatory System of a Mammal

The circulatory system comprises the heart and a system of tubes (arteries, capillaries and veins) in which blood flows from the heart, into all tissues of the body, and from these tissues back to the heart (see Fig. 129).

The **heart** is a four-chambered muscular pump.

Arteries carry blood from the heart to all organs of the body. They have thick elastic and muscular walls. There is one artery to each of the organs of the body. The arteries branch in the organs and the branches, called **arterioles**, carry blood into the capillaries.

Capillaries are numerous thin-walled tubes which branch within the tissues. They carry blood close to all living cells and rejoin to form small veins, called **venules**, which are the tributaries of larger veins. Through the capillary network, therefore, the blood flows from the arterial end to the venous end.

Veins carry blood from the tissues back to the heart. They have a thinner wall than do arteries and there are valves at intervals which allow blood to flow only in one direction, from other organs towards the heart.

The heart, arteries, capillaries and veins are called the **circulatory system** because, as a result of the repeated contractions of the heart, blood circulates through this system of tubes throughout life. This fact was first established by a British physician, William Harvey, whose book *On the Anatomy and Motion of the Heart and Blood in Animals* was published in 1628.

In all mammals there is a **double circulation**: (1) blood from the right side of the heart is pumped to the lungs, from which it is returned to the left side of the heart, and (2) blood from the left side of the heart is pumped to all the other organs of the body, from which it is returned to the right side of the heart. In a diagram this double circulation can be represented as a figure of eight (Fig. 129A).

Some of the largest vessels in the circulatory system of a mammal are included in Fig. 37 (p. 68). Most vessels are named according to the organ they are associated with. For example, blood from the heart flows along a main artery (the **dorsal aorta**) and some of this blood flows into the kidney in the **renal artery**. Blood leaves the kidney in the **renal vein** and flows into a larger vein called the **posterior vena-cava** (see also Fig. 123, p. 204).

Note that the liver (see Figs. 37 and 129B) receives blood not only from the

hepatic artery but also from the **hepatic portal vein**. The liver is the only organ in the body of a mammal that receives a blood supply in a vein as well as in an artery. All the blood from the stomach and small intestines is carried in smaller veins which are tributaries of the hepatic portal vein—and all this blood, therefore, goes to the liver (see also p. 185). Blood from the liver is carried in the **hepatic vein** into the posterior vena-cava.

All arteries, except the pulmonary artery, carry oxygenated blood; all veins, except the pulmonary vein, carry deoxygenated blood.

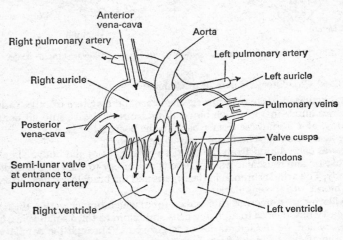

Fig. 128. The heart of a mammal. Diagram not to scale.

The Heart

Blood from the posterior part of the body (in the posterior vena-cava) and from the anterior part of the body (in two anterior vena-cavae) pours into the right auricle.

The **right auricle** has a thin muscular wall and when this contracts, it pumps blood into the **right ventricle**. The **tricuspid valve** (a valve with three flaps) between the auricle and the ventricle prevents any backflow of blood.

The right ventricle has a thicker and more muscular wall and when these muscles contract blood is pumped along the pulmonary arteries to the lungs. **Semi-lunar valves** at the entrance to the pulmonary artery prevent any backflow of blood. The blood pressure in the pulmonary artery is sufficient to force the blood through the capillaries of the lungs, along the pulmonary veins, and into the left auricle.

The **left auricle** has a thin muscular wall and, when this contracts, it pumps blood into the **left ventricle**. The **bicuspid valve** between the auricle and the ventricle prevents any backflow of blood.

The left ventricle has a very thick muscular wall and when it contracts blood is forced into the aorta and so to all organs of the body (except the lungs). **Semi-lunar valves** at the entrance to the aorta prevent any backflow of blood.

The heart, like all other organs, has a blood supply. The coronary arteries which branch from the aorta next to the heart, carry blood to the muscles of the heart. The flow of blood through these muscles is the **coronary circulation**. Heart muscle differs from all other muscles in that it does not fatigue. The heart beats repeatedly throughout life.

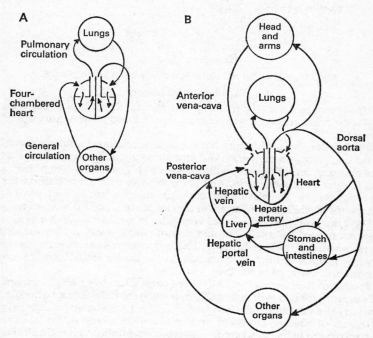

Fig. 129. Circulatory system of a mammal: (A) pulmonary and general circulation; (B) position of liver in general circulation.

The more active you are the faster your heart beats (about 70 times per minute when you are resting and faster when you are active or excited). This means that the flow of blood into the arteries from the heart is very variable. Blood is pumped into the arteries and after a short pause more blood is pumped in, yet the arteries are always full of blood. This is because they are elastic. As blood is forced into them their diameter increases but as the blood flows along their diameter decreases. The elasticity of the arteries allows them to accept different amounts of blood and yet remain full, and this also evens out the flow of blood to the tissues. If you are inactive your tissues receive blood at a fairly constant rate. If you are active your tissues receive more blood and it is pumped through more rapidly, but a steady flow is maintained.

The muscle in the walls of arteries is also important. When the muscles of a particular artery are contracted the lumen is smaller and less blood can flow through. In this way the blood supply to different organs is controlled (see p. 229 and p. 235).

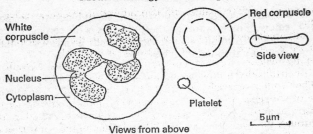

Fig. 130. White and red blood corpuscles and a blood platelet.

The Blood of Mammals

Blood comprises a fluid part, the blood plasma (55 per cent of the volume of blood), in which red and white corpuscles and blood platelets are suspended (Fig. 130).

Blood plasma is mostly water but it contains sodium chloride, sodium bicarbonate, glucose, amino acids and other food molecules in solution. Excretory products, including carbon dioxide (see p. 177) and urea (see p. 187), are also in solution in the plasma. And hormones (see p. 228) are transported in the blood plasma. The plasma also contains larger molecules, the plasma proteins, some of which are important in the clotting of blood in damaged tissues.

There are nearly five million **red corpuscles** in a cubic millimetre of blood. They are formed from cells but they do not have a nucleus. They are about 7·5 μm diameter. They live for about 120 days: about as many are formed each day in a tissue called red bone marrow, in the vertebrae and sternum especially, as are destroyed in the liver.

Because of their shape (Fig. 130) the red corpuscles have a very large surface area in proportion to their volume. They contain the red pigment haemoglobin (see p. 174), a protein which contains iron (see p. 190), and they accept oxygen in regions of high oxygen concentration (from the alveoli of the lungs) and give up oxygen in places where the oxygen concentration is low (in all tissues except those next to the alveoli).

There are about 5000 **white corpuscles** in a cubic millimetre of blood. They are cells, about 14 μm diameter, with a nucleus and cytoplasm. They are formed in the red bone marrow, and in swellings in the lymph vessels (see p. 216), and may live for many months. Like an *Amoeba*, they have pseudopodia and some white corpuscles pass through very small pores in the walls of venules and into the tissues where they move between the cells. In the blood, in the tissue fluids and in the lymphatic system, they ingest bacteria and viruses and help to prevent diseases. The ingestion of material is called phagocytosis and these white corpuscles are therefore called **phagocytes**.

White corpuscles also produce antibodies in response to the presence of antigens in the body. **Antigens** are foreign proteins or polysaccharides (see p. 56). Many antigens are produced by bacteria and some are toxic (see p. 108). There are different kinds of **antibodies**, including: (1) agglutinins which neutralise bacteria—causing them to stick together; (2) lysins, which destroy bacteria by dissolving their cell wall; and (3) antitoxins, which neutralise toxins. For example, the bacteria that cause diphtheria produce diphtheria toxins and in response the white corpuscles produce diphtheria antitoxins.

That is to say, a different antitoxin is produced in response to each kind of infection.

Immunity to disease may be either **innate**, due to the bactericidal properties of tears, saliva, sebum and other secretions, or **acquired**.

Immunity may be **acquired actively** either naturally as a result of an infection, or artificially following immunisation with dead or weakened bacteria. The white corpuscles then produce antibodies in response to the presence of antigens. Immunity may also be **acquired passively**, as a result of the transfer of antibodies produced by the mother to her child: some before birth (through the placenta—see p. 249) and some in the colostrum (the milk secreted in the first days of suckling—see p. 196). Passive immunity is also acquired artificially when part of the blood plasma, containing antibodies produced by another animal, is used in the treatment of a disease.

The Clotting of Blood

There are about 300 000 **platelets** in a cubic millimetre of blood. They are fragments of cytoplasm, 2 to 4 μm diameter (Fig. 130), formed from cells in the red bone marrow. In damaged tissues they disintegrate and release an enzyme which catalyses the first of a sequence of reactions involved in the clotting of blood. In the last reaction, fibrinogen, a blood protein, is converted to threads of fibrin and these form a mesh that plugs the wound.

The Formation of Tissue Fluid and Lymph

The blood capillaries are close to all the cells of the body. Only one cell is represented in Fig. 131. As blood in an artery enters any organ it is under high

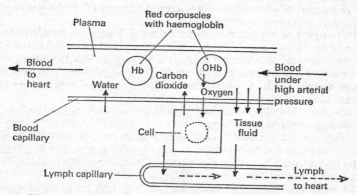

Fig. 131. Relationship between blood, tissue fluid and lymph.

pressure, resulting from the pumping of the heart. Some of the blood plasma (water with ions and food molecules in solution) but not the large plasma protein molecules or the blood corpuscles, passes through the walls of the capillaries and bathes all the cells nearby. These cells extract food molecules from this **tissue fluid** and absorb oxygen, and they excrete carbon dioxide and other waste products of their metabolism into the tissue fluid. The composition of this fluid might be expected to change, therefore, as it bathes the body cells.

The blood entering the tissues (except for that entering the tissues of the lungs) has a high concentration of oxygen and a low concentration of carbon dioxide. But the tissue cells use oxygen and produce carbon dioxide in their respiration. As a result there are diffusion gradients between the blood and the tissue cells and oxygen diffuses from the blood and carbon dioxide diffuses into the blood.

As a result of losing water to the tissues, the concentration of the blood plasma proteins in the capillaries quickly increases. And because the hydrostatic pressure is reduced as blood flows from the narrow capillaries into wider veins, some water is drawn back into the capillaries (by osmosis) nearer the venous end of the capillary network.

Also, some tissue fluid (which now contains fewer food molecules) passes into lymph capillaries. These capillaries end blindly in the tissues (e.g. *lacteal*, Fig. 111B) but they carry their fluid contents (called **lymph**) towards larger lymph vessels which have valves that prevent backflow. The largest lymph vessels drain into the large veins near to the heart. This system of lymph capillaries and vessels is called the **lymphatic system**. As a result of the drainage of lymph away from the tissues, the tissue fluid does not normally accumulate. The small amount of tissue fluid that permeates the tissues provides a watery environment, a mixture of almost constant composition, in which all cells of the body live.

Functions of the Blood

1. Transport of food materials from the small intestine to the liver and from the liver to all other body cells.

2. Transport of white blood corpuscles to all parts of the body where they play a part in combating disease.

3. Transport of hormones from the cells which produce them to all parts of the body.

4. In mammals and in most animals that have a circulatory system, but not in insects, the transport of oxygen from the respiratory surface to other tissues; and the transport of carbon dioxide from these tissues to the respiratory surface.

5. Contains blood platelets and plasma proteins which are necessary for the clotting of blood in damaged tissues.

6. Transport of the waste products of protein breakdown (urea in mammals) from the body cells in which they are produced (the liver in mammals) to the organ from which they are excreted (the kidneys of mammals).

7. Distribution of heat (see p. 235).

The double circulation of mammals (see Fig. 129) keeps the oxygenated blood in the left side of the heart separate from the deoxygenated blood in the right side of the heart, and results in the rapid flow of blood to the lungs and to other organs.

Test Questions

1. In which tissues are (a) water and (b) sugar transported to a developing fruit and (c) where are they transported from?

2. Name the blood vessels and the chambers of the heart, in their correct order, that a blood corpuscle must pass through as it is carried from the liver to a lung.

3. What are (*a*) lignin; (*b*) blood platelets; (*c*) cohesion; (*d*) haemoglobin; and (*e*) antigens?

4. There is more muscle and more elastic tissue in the wall of an artery than in the wall of a vein. Explain how these two tissues affect the flow of blood through the circulatory system of a mammal.

SENSITIVITY AND SURVIVAL

The movement of a *Chlamydomonas* towards light (see p. 62) keeps it in the surface waters when the sun is shining. Water absorbs light and there is, therefore, most light near the surface. The nearer *Chlamydomonas* is to the surface, the more rapidly will photosynthesis proceed in its chloroplast. The response to light contributes to the nutrition of the organism and therefore has survival value. Similarly, the feeding responses of an *Amoeba* are essential to its survival.

The movement of parts of an organism, as distinct from the movement of the organism as a whole, may also contribute to survival. For example, the tendril of the leaf of a pea plant (Fig. 132) curls round anything it touches. Without support the shoot falls over. This response of the tendril helps to keep the leaves and flowers in the air, and so contributes to photosynthesis in the leaves and to fruit formation and seed dispersal.

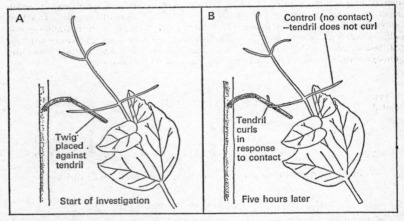

Fig. 132. A tendril of a leaf of a pea plant *Pisum sativum*: (A) twig placed in contact with tendril; (B) response of tendril to contact.

Investigation: *plant growth responses.* Most plants live fixed in one place. They are unable to maintain themselves in a favourable environment by moving about. Most plant responses are growth responses. Illuminate a green plant from one side and note that the shoot grows towards the light. The light is a stimulus. The plant's response to light is called a **phototropism** (Gk. *phōtos* = light; *tropos* = a turn) and because the growth is towards the light it is called a positive phototropism. There is no need to plant seeds the right way up. The shoot will grow up (through the soil and into the air) and the root will grow down (deeper into the soil). These responses to gravity are geotropisms (Gk. *geō* = the earth). Place a bean seedling on one side and

Start

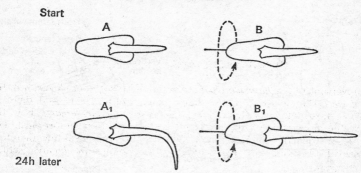

24h later

Fig. 133. Broad bean seedlings: (A) response to gravity in a seed placed on its side; (B) control in which the seed is rotated (by attaching it to a clinostat).

see how it grows (Fig. 133). The shoot is negatively geotropic and the root is positively geotropic.

Investigation: *woodlice in a choice chamber*. Place a woodlouse (or any other small animal) in a choice chamber (see Fig. 134). Record movements on a sheet of graph paper, by making a cross every 30 seconds to record the animal's position. One half of the chamber may be illuminated and the other half shaded; or the humidity in one half may be high (above water) and in the other half low (over anhydrous calcium chloride or silica gel). What can you conclude from your observations about the animal's sensitivity to light and to the humidity of the atmosphere?

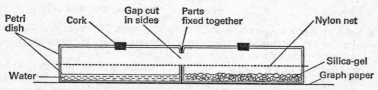

Fig. 134. A choice chamber constructed from plastic Petri dishes.

Sense Organs of Animals

The antennae and compound eyes of insects are **sense organs**. The antennae are extended in front of the head. Some of the hair-like processes on the antennae are sensitive to touch and others to chemicals: the antennae are both mechanoreceptors and chemoreceptors.

Each compound eye is composed of many essentially similar units (Fig. 135). Each unit has a lens which focuses light on light **receptor cells**. Because each lens points in a different direction from every other lens, some insects must be able to see where they have been as well as where they are going. This is one reason why it is not easy to catch a fly. However, you may be able to catch a fly by placing your hand over it very slowly. This is because the eyes of insects are particularly sensitive to movement. A movement will be detected first by some parts of the eye and then by others.

There is some overlap in what is seen through neighbouring lenses. Some

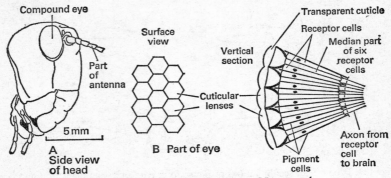

Fig. 135. Compound eye of an insect. Not to scale.

things will be seen through many lenses. The eye, therefore, contrary to what scientists once thought, probably does not form a mosaic image—similar to a newspaper photograph that is made up of separate dots.

Mammals obtain information about their external environment by way of their eyes, ears, nose, tongue and skin:

Senses	Sense organs	Stimuli
Sight	Eyes	Light
Hearing and position	Ears	Sound, movement and gravity
Smell	Nose	Chemicals in the air
Taste	Tongue	Chemicals in solution
Contact	Skin	Pressure, heat and cold

We taste with our tongue and smell with our nose. However, the tongue is sensitive only to the qualities sweet, sour, salt and bitter. We appreciate other flavours, as we chew food, by our sense of smell.

The sensitivity of the skin to touch and pressure, to heat and cold, and the sensation of pain are due to sensory nerve endings associated with the hair follicles and other living cells of the epidermis and to the presence of other kinds of receptors in the dermis (see Fig. 89).

Hearing, Balance and Posture in Man

The Parts of an Ear (see Fig. 136)

1. The outer ear includes the part that you see on the outside (the **pinna**), which is included in Fig. 37, and the passage (Fig. 136) that admits sound waves to the eardrum (tympanic membrane).

2. The middle ear is connected to the pharynx by the **Eustachian tube**. As a result, the middle ear contains air at the same pressure as the outside air. Three small bones transmit vibrations from the eardrum to the membrane of the **oval window**.

3. The fluid-filled inner ear comprises (*a*) the **cochlea** which, with the outer and middle parts of the ear, is an organ of hearing; and (*b*) the **semicircular canals** with their **ampullae** which, with the **utriculus** and **sacculus**, contribute to balance and posture.

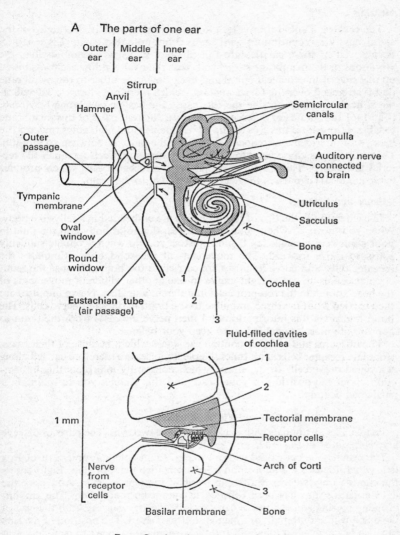

A The parts of one ear

Outer ear | Middle ear | Inner ear

Stirrup
Anvil
Hammer

Semicircular canals

Outer passage

Ampulla

Auditory nerve connected to brain

Tympanic membrane

Utriculus

Oval window

Sacculus

Round window

Bone

Eustachian tube (air passage)

Cochlea

1
2
3

Fluid-filled cavities of cochlea

1

2

Tectorial membrane

1 mm

Receptor cells

Arch of Corti

Nerve from receptor cells

3

Basilar membrane

Bone

B Section through part of cochlea

Fig. 136. Ear of man. Not to scale.

Hearing

The **cochlea**, a spiral tube (Fig. 136), is divided internally. At the tip of th
spiral, cavity 1 is continuous with cavity 3 but note that cavity 2 is separate
Because all of these cavities are full of fluid, which is incompressible, th
vibrations of the membrane stretched across the oval window are transmitte
up one side of the cochlear spiral and back down the other to the membran
that is stretched over the **round window**—which therefore vibrates. The vibra
tions, due to sounds outside the ear, cause the **basilar membrane** to vibrat
(Fig. 136) and sounds of different pitch cause different parts of this membran
to vibrate (low notes towards the tip of the cochlea and high notes towards th
base, with intermediate frequencies causing the parts in between to vibrate)
These vibrations cause receptor cells in the **organ of Corti** to touch the tec
torial membrane. This, in turn, stimulates the **receptor cells** which produc
nerve impulses (signals) in the nerve from the ear to the brain.

Balance and Posture

In each ampulla the tips of receptor cells are embedded in a jelly-like body
When you move, or when your head moves, this solid body and the fluid i
your **semicircular canals** lag behind; just as you do when a vehicle suddenl
starts to move forward. The movement of the solid body stimulates th
receptor cells, and nerve impulses are carried to the brain. Because the semi
circular canals are set at right-angles to one another, different movements o
the head stimulate the receptor cells in different **ampullae**. Nerve impulses ar
then carried from the three ampullae to the brain in different nerve cells. Th
brain interprets this information and then nerve impulses from the brain t
appropriate muscles enable you to keep your balance.

The utriculus and sacculus contain **ear stones** which, because of their mass
stimulate **receptor cells** at all times. Nerve impulses are therefore carried alon
associated nerve cells to the brain, which constantly interprets this inform
ation about the position of your head, and this enables you to maintain
particular posture.

Vision in Man

People, like all animals with backbones, have two eyes. The parts of one ey
are represented in Fig. 137.

The eye may be compared with a camera. Light enters a camera through
lens which focuses the light upon a light-sensitive plate or film. Light enter
the camera only when a shutter in front of the lens is open. And once th
light sensitive film has been exposed it cannot be used again. The amoun
of light entering some cameras can be controlled by varying both the size o
the opening and the length of time the shutter is open. The position of the len
can also be changed so that light from a particular distance can be focused o
the film.

Each eye is protected by the bones of the skull, by the eyelids and by tears
(secretions of the tear glands) which always bathe the outer surface. Light
enters the eye through the transparent skin (the **conjunctiva**) and through the
transparent part of the outer fibrous coat (the **cornea**) and is focused on the
light **receptor cells** of the **retina**. Focusing involves not a change in the position
of the lens, as is essential in a rigid camera, but a change in the shape of the

lens. The **lens** is elastic and is flattest when distant objects are in focus (Fig. 138A). Contraction of the **ciliary muscle** reduces the tension on the **suspensory ligament** and, as a result of its elasticity, the lens becomes more nearly spherical when nearby objects are in focus (Fig. 138B). There is less eye-strain, therefore, if you do not hold the page too near your eyes when reading.

You see most clearly the objects which are immediately in front of your eyes. The contraction of muscles attached to the outside of your eyes (not included in the diagram) enables you to keep your eyes on a moving object

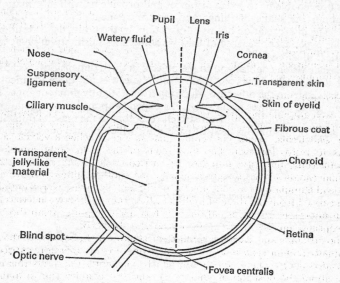

Fig. 137. Horizontal section through the right eye of a man. Not to scale.

when your head is still or upon an object that is still when your head is moving. Control over the amount of light entering each eye depends partly upon behaviour, as when you turn away from a bright light or shade your eyes, but also upon changes in the size of an opening, the **pupil**, as a result of the contraction of the **iris** muscles. As with a camera the sharpest image is formed, in bright light, with a small aperture.

There are two kinds of light-receptor cells in your retina: **rods** which are not colour sensitive—but do function at low light intensities; and **cones** which are colour sensitive but do not function at low light intensities. This is why you do not see colours at night. The cones are most abundant in the centre of the retina, on or near the optical axis (dotted line in Fig. 137), and this is why you see images and colours most clearly in bright light when they are sharply focused on the fovea.

The **choroid**, immediately below the retina, contains pigmented cells which absorb the light that passes through the light-sensitive cells and, like the black inside of a camera, prevents the scattering of light that would blur the image. The choroid also contains the blood vessels of the eye.

Nerve cells in the retina and optic nerve connect the light-receptor cells of the retina to the brain. Where nerve cells converge on the **optic nerve** there are no receptor cells and this is therefore a blind spot. Close your left eye and look at the cross below. Move the book towards you and note that the black dot disappears and then reappears. The image of the black spot is not visible when this is formed on the **blind spot.**

+   ●

Our eyes enable us to judge distances and provide us with information not only about the shape of things and their movement, but also about their colour. The interpretation of this information, by the brain, depends upon our previous experience. Because of this, we sometimes misinterpret what we see (in optical illusions).

Binocular vision enables you to see objects in three dimensions, because the information received by your brain from one eye is not quite identical with that received from the other eye—looking from a slightly different angle. Also, you can judge distances accurately: this depends upon the interpretation, by your brain, of information from stretch receptors in the muscles (attached to the outside of the fibrous coat of each eye), which point your eyes towards things.

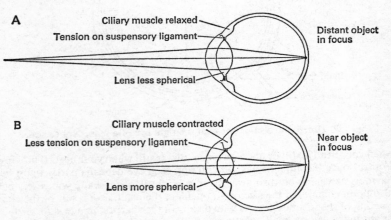

Fig. 138. The eye of a mammal: (A) focused on a distant object; (B) focused on a nearby object.

Defects of Vision

People who cannot see distant objects clearly, because the light from them is focused in front of the retina, are said to be **short-sighted.** This defect can be corrected by wearing spectacles with appropriate biconcave lenses. On the other hand, people who cannot see nearby objects clearly, because light from them is focused behind the retina, are said to be **long-sighted.** This defect of vision can be corrected by wearing spectacles with appropriate biconvex lenses. As people grow older the lens becomes less elastic. As a result, they are unable to focus on nearby objects. This form of long-sightedness can also be corrected by wearing appropriate biconvex lenses.

Test Questions

1. There is no wax layer in the skin of a woodlouse. Woodlice walk faster in dry air than in humid air, and faster in the light than in the dark. Explain how these responses help to maintain woodlice in a favourable habitat.

2. Which part of the ear (see Fig. 136): (*a*) carries coded messages to the brain; (*b*) helps you to balance; (*c*) helps you to stand still; (*d*) helps to maintain the pressure in the middle ear the same as in the outside air; (*e*) contains the receptor cells involved in hearing?

3. Explain, in about 200 words, how the structure of either (*a*) a leaf or (*b*) an eye is related to its functions.

26

COORDINATION AND CONTROL

In biology, the word coordination refers to the working together of the parts of a cell, tissue, organ or organism (see also social behaviour—p. 117). Their working together—that is, their coordinated activity—is an indication that the life of the organism and its parts is regulated (controlled). This control depends not only upon the movement of materials from one part of the body to all others (Chapter 24) but also upon the different parts working together in harmony.

Chemical Control in Flowering Plants

In the 1870s Charles Darwin observed that a grass seedling, illuminated from one side, bends just below its tip (Fig. 139A) and then grows directly towards the light. Darwin thought that it might be the tip that was sensitive to light, even though the bend appeared first just below the tip. To test this hypothesis, he covered the tip with a little cap of blackened tinfoil (Fig. 139B) and illuminated the seedlings from one side. He observed that the seedling grew straight up, even though the region just below the tip was still illuminated. Darwin concluded (1) that the tip is sensitive to light (a **stimulus**) and (2) that some influence which causes bending is transmitted from the tip (the **receptor region**) to the region just below the tip (the **effector region**) which bends (makes a **response**). This simple investigation was the first experimental study of the control of plant growth. It is also a good illustration of the way scientists work. Observation is followed by interpretation, and then further observations are made in an attempt to obtain more evidence.

We now know that the increase in length of a root or shoot results from the production of cells near the tip and the elongation of newly formed cells a few millimetres away from the tip (see p. 151). Growth towards the light, therefore, is due to the greater elongation of cells which are on the side away from the light.

In the early years of the 20th century scientists found that if the tip is removed elongation behind the tip ceases, and that if the tip is replaced the elongation continues. These observations were further evidence related to Darwin's conclusions and indicated that something produced at the tip can pass through the cut surfaces. In 1928 an American scientist, called Frits Went, showed that a substance (or substances) produced in the tip could be collected in a block of agar jelly and then the jelly containing the substance could be used instead of the tip to promote elongation (Fig. 139C). Such growth-promoting chemicals are now called **auxins**.

Auxins are plant hormones. A **hormone** (Gk. *hormao* = to excite) is a chemical which (1) is produced by cells in one part of the body, (2) is transported and (3) affects only those cells which are particularly sensitive to it. Auxins, for example, (1) are produced by cells in the tip, (2) are transported away from the tip and (3) they promote the elongation of the cells a few millimetres away from the tip.

When the apical bud is removed from a plant each axillary bud starts to grow into a branch. So long as the apical bud is intact the growth of the axillary buds is inhibited. This phenomenon is called apical dominance. If the apical bud is removed and replaced by a block of agar jelly containing auxin, this has the same effect as an apical bud. Auxin (1) produced in the tip, (2) is transported away from the tip and (3) it inhibits the growth of the axillary buds.

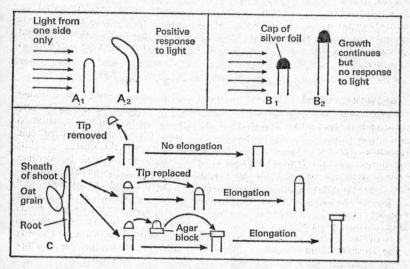

Fig. 139. (A) Darwin's observation; (B) Darwin's experiment; (C) experiments by later workers.

Auxin stimulates growth near the shoot tip but inhibits the growth of axillary buds. This is another feature of hormone action. The action of a hormone depends upon the production of the hormone by cells in one part of the plant but also upon the response of other cells (the target tissue) in other parts of the plant. The same chemical may have growth-promoting effects on one tissue and growth-inhibiting effects on another.

Indole acetic acid (IAA) is a naturally occurring auxin. Synthetic substances which have auxin properties are sold commercially and used, for example, as rooting powders (for the rooting of cuttings—see p. 242). However, you may be surprised to learn that the widest commercial use of these plant growth substances is as weed-killers in which auxin is present in high concentrations that cause abnormal growth and the death of the plant.

Chemical Control in Mammals

The control of digestion in mammals depends upon differences in the structure of successive parts of the alimentary canal and to a physiological division of labour, just as the control of a process in a factory depends upon the use of different kinds of machines for different kinds of work. In the body, the activity of the muscles and glands of the gut is controlled partly by nerves (see p. 231) but also by hormones. For example: (1) after a meal some epithelial cells of the stomach and duodenum secrete a hormone, called **secretin**, which (2) is carried to all parts of the body in the bloodstream, and (3) affects only those cells of the pancreas which are sensitive to it (the target tissue). Compare this example, noting points (1) to (3), with the definition of a hormone given on p. 226. The effect of this hormone, secretin, is that pancreatic juices are secreted when food is present in the stomach and duodenum.

Secretin is secreted by cells in an epithelium. However, many hormones are produced in glands which, because they secrete into the bloodstream, are called **endocrine glands** (or ductless glands) to distinguish them from the **exocrine glands** (such as sweat glands and sebaceous glands) which secrete into a duct (see Fig. 89). The endocrine glands of a mammal, and some other parts of the body which produce hormones, are listed in Fig. 140.

The Pituitary Gland

The pituitary, which is just below the brain, produces a hormone called growth hormone that is essential for normal growth. A person may grow into a giant if too much of this hormone is secreted during childhood and adolescence; or into a dwarf if too little is secreted. Other pituitary hormones affect the activity of particular parts of the body. This is why the pituitary is sometimes called a **master gland**. It secretes a hormone that stimulates the thyroid gland, and another that affects the kidney, reducing water loss when the water content of the body falls to a certain level. Other pituitary hormones, the gonadotrophic hormones, stimulate the gonads (the testes of the male and the ovaries of the female).

The Thyroid Gland

The thyroid gland, between the larynx (voice box) and the skin of the neck produces a hormone called thyroxin which stimulates respiration in all cells of the body—that is to say, it increases the basal metabolic rate, and anyone who has an over-active thyroid is thin, restless and highly strung, whereas someone with an underactive thyroid is likely to be overweight and sluggish.

Thyroxin contains iodine and if there is a shortage of iodine in the diet the thyroid cannot produce enough thyroxin. Because thyroxin stimulates the secretion of growth hormone by the pituitary, children who do not have enough iodine in their diet do not grow properly. Iodine deficiency, therefore is the cause of one kind of dwarfism and mental retardation (called cretinism).

Iodine deficiency also results in the disease called **goitre** which is marked by the enlargement of the thyroid gland. The pituitary secretes thyroid-stimulating hormone and the thyroid grows but the enlarged thyroid still cannot produce more thyroxin if there is not enough iodine in the body. When there is no shortage of iodine enough thyroxin is produced and one of its effects is to inhibit the production of thyroid-stimulating hormone by the pituitary. In the absence of this **negative feedback control**, which is part of the normal balance between the activities of the thyroid and pituitary glands, the pituitary continues to secrete thyroid-stimulating hormone and the thyroid enlarges further, producing a goitre.

Iodine deficiency diseases used to be common in mountainous regions, because iodine is washed from the soil and there may be little iodine in the drink

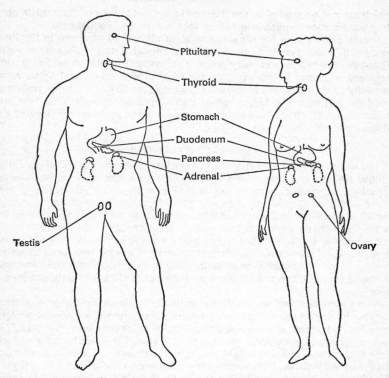

Fig. 140. Some parts of the body that secrete hormones. Diagram not to scale.

ing water or in locally grown vegetables. However, now that the cause of these diseases is known, people who live in regions where there is a possibility of iodine deficiency can buy iodised table salt.

The Adrenal Glands

There are two adrenal glands: one next to each kidney. One of the hormones secreted by the adrenals, **adrenalin**, helps you to punch someone or to jump a high fence. It helps you to fight or to run away. For example, when adrenalin is secreted into your blood your heart beats faster and you breathe faster. Also, the arterioles of your skeletal muscles dilate and those of the alimentary canal are constricted. The result of these changes is to increase the supply of oxygenated blood to the muscles of your arms and legs that you use in punching, running and jumping.

The Pancreas

The pancreas produces two kinds of secretions: (1) pancreatic juices are secreted into the pancreatic duct and they pass into the duodenum (see Fig. 50, p. 50); and (2) there are small groups of cells (called islets of Langerhans) which are not connected to the pancreatic duct—the cells of these islets produce the hormone **insulin** which they secrete into the bloodstream.

Insulin is necessary for the conversion of glucose to glycogen in the liver (see p. 187), and people who do not have enough insulin suffer from **sugar diabetes**—in which any excess glucose is removed from the blood in the kidneys and is present in the urine. People who suffer from sugar diabetes must carefully control their sugar intake. They may also be given insulin, prepared from the pancreas of cattle, either by injection or by taking tablets. Without this extra insulin their blood sugar is not maintained at the normal level (0.1 glucose per 100 cm³ blood).

Nerves and Nerve Impulses

The nervous system of a mammal comprises the brain and spinal cord (the central nervous system) and the nerves which are a link between the brain or spinal cord and other parts of the body (Fig. 90B). As in *Hydra* (see p. 66) nerve cells carry nerve impulses and provide a **link** between **receptor** cells (which are sensitive to stimuli and which produce nerve impulses) and **effector** cells (which are either muscle cells that contract or gland cells that secrete). A nerve impulse is a signal that passes along a nerve cell but we do not know how this signal is transmitted. The transmission of a nerve impulse is an active process in which energy is used, and which is associated with electrical and chemical changes. It is not the same as a current of electricity passing along a wire.

Some activities are **automatically controlled**. We make many responses without having to think about what we are doing. Indeed, we cannot prevent ourselves from making these responses—called **reflex responses**. If you look at one of your eyes in a mirror you can see the size of the pupil through which light enters the eye. Shine a light into the mirror and your pupils almost immediately get smaller. This appropriate response to the stimulus of a higher light intensity is made possible by nerve cells that link the eyes with the brain and the brain with the eyes. It is called a **cranial reflex** response.

Some activities are controlled by nerve cells in the spinal cord. The brain is not directly involved. The knee-jerk reflex is an example of such a **spinal reflex**. If you cross your legs and then strike the tendon immediately below your kneecap your foot will jerk forward. This is called the knee-jerk response. The arrangement of the two types of nerve cells involved in the knee-jerk reflex is represented in Fig. 141. Also, there are **stretch receptors** in the muscle. These are sensitive to the slight pulling on the tendon (a stimulus). The nerve cell that carries **nerve impulses** from a receptor cell into the spinal cord is called a **sensory neurone**. This is a very long nerve cell and its cell body is in the dorsal root ganglion, a swelling in the nerve just outside the spinal cord. The nerve cell that carries nerve impulses away from the spinal cord to a muscle in the upper part of the leg is called a **motor neurone**. The muscle that contracts (makes a **response**) is an example of an **effector**.

The sensory and motor neurones are a link between the receptor and the effector cells. Together, they form what is called a **reflex arc** with the sensory neurone carrying nerve impulses into, and the motor neurone carrying nerve impulses out of, the central nervous system. By way of such reflex arcs, stretch receptors provide information about the state of muscle contraction that makes possible both the maintenance of posture and the control of movement.

The gaps between the receptor cell and the sensory neurone, between the sensory neurone and the motor neurone, and between the motor neurone and the effector, are all called **synapses**. The knee-jerk is an example of a response to stimuli in which information is transported in the body not by the distribution of hormones in the blood but by the passage of nerve impulses in neurones. It is an example of neural as distinct from hormonal control. Some idea of the complexity of neural control is obtained if you consider, for example, the input of information (into the nervous system) about the position of the body (about posture) from: pressure receptors in the skin (p. 162); touch receptor cells in the ear (p. 222); light receptor cells in the eye (p. 223); and stretch receptor cells in the muscles and tendons.

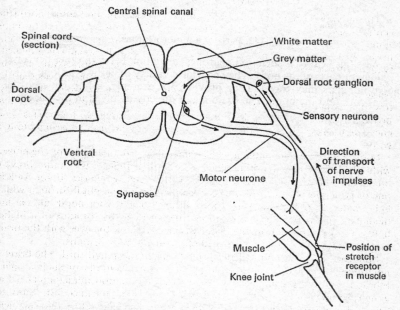

Fig. 141. Spinal reflex arc. Diagram not to scale.

We are born with many reflexes but we acquire others as a result of experience. The secretion of saliva by the salivary glands (see p. 88) is an inborn reflex response to the presence of food in the buccal cavity, but we also produce saliva at the sight of food—especially when we see foods that we particularly like. In other words, the reflex is affected by experience: it is no longer just a response to the presence of food in the buccal cavity. Pavlov, a Russian scientist, showed at the beginning of this century that if a bell was rung each time a dog was fed the dog soon started to produce saliva when the bell rang even if no food was provided. This is called a **conditioned reflex**—the dog has learned (has been trained or conditioned) to respond to a stimulus that, previously, it did not associate with food.

The parts of a motor neurone (Fig. 142) are the **cell body**, which includes the nucleus, short processes (called **dendrites**) which carry nerve impulses into the cell body, and one long process (the **axon**) which carries nerve impulses away from the cell body. In most reflex responses more than two neurones are directly involved. Additional neurones, similar to motor neurones, are placed between the sensory neurone and the motor neurone. These **connector**

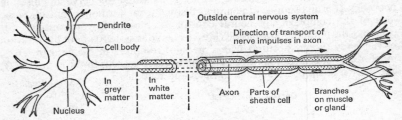

Fig. 142. Parts of a motor neurone.

neurones (also called association neurones) are a link between other neurones in different parts of the body. They provide a variety of pathways along which nerve impulses may travel. They provide, for example, a link between the spinal cord and the brain. The brain is not directly involved in the knee-jerk

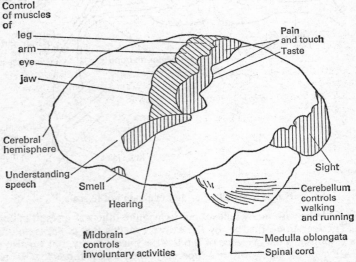

Fig. 143. Left side of the brain of man. The areas of the cerebral cortex that receive nerve impulses from sense organs are labelled, as are those concerned in the control of muscles in different parts of the body. Other areas are concerned with thinking, understanding and remembering.

reflex but connector neurones convey information to the brain and we know that the reflex response has happened. Similarly, when you prick yourself you quickly take your finger away from the pin. But, in addition to this rapid reflex response, you learn not to do the same thing again.

Many actions are not automatic. The brain is involved in all voluntary activities—those in which we benefit from previous experience that helps us to decide what to do. The brain is also involved in many involuntary activities—in many reflex responses and in all conditioned reflexes. We know, for example, from studies of the behaviour of people suffering from brain damage, which parts of the brain are concerned with different kinds of activity (see Fig. 143). Usually, as a result of the analysis of information by the brain, in any situation we behave in an appropriate way.

Differences between Hormonal and Neural Control

Hormonal (chemical control) differs from neural control (by the transmission of nerve impulses) in many ways:

1. Hormones are carried in the blood and they are therefore present in the tissue fluids that bathe every cell in the body. Their action depends upon certain cells being affected by them (target cells) while most cells are not affected. Nerve impulses are carried directly, as in a reflex arc, from the receptor to an appropriate effector.

2. The reaction to most hormones is automatic, like the reflex responses controlled by nerves, but hormones are not involved in the conscious control of our actions. This conscious control, mainly the control of our skeletal muscles, is made possible by the nerve cells.

3. Hormonal control is quite rapid since a hormone is transported in the blood, from the secretory cell to all parts of the body, in the time it takes for the blood to circulate around the body (less than 30 s in people). But neural control is much faster. A nerve impulse travels at about 100 m/s. Hormones also control long-term changes (such as the 28-day menstrual cycle in a woman—see p. 247) and changes that take several years (such as the development of the body to sexual maturity during adolescence).

Constancy Based on Change: Homeostasis

Apart from the engineering problems involved in sending men into space, there are also problems in keeping them alive. Their survival depends upon the proper functioning of the apparatus that keeps the air pressure and the composition of the atmosphere in their space suits or space vehicles the same as on Earth. Arrangements have to be made for a food supply and for the storage of faeces. Also, sufficient water must be carried for the whole journey or arrangements must be made for the purification of water from the urine so that water can be used and then re-used. All these problems should cause you to think of many things that are involved in maintaining your body, even on Earth.

If a non-living thing such as this book is essentially the same this week as it was last week, then this is because it has not changed much during the week. But, in contrast, if you are much the same this week as you were last week then this is because you have been changing all the time. You have been taking energy and materials from your environment and losing energy and materials to your environment. Many cells in your body have been destroyed and many new cells have been formed by cell division. The circulation of your blood, linking all parts of your body, and the activity of the separate parts, have maintained the constant composition of your tissue fluids (see p. 216). The flow of lymph in your lymphatic system has prevented the swelling of your tissues with tissue fluid. This *condition of constancy* (in any cell, in the body fluids and in the body as a whole) that results from continuous change is called **homeostasis** (Gk. *homoios* = similar; *stasis* = standing).

The working together of different parts of the body, made possible by hormonal and neural control, results in the maintenance of homeostasis. The life of a mammal goes on in a changing external environment.

Reactions to Danger in Mammals

A mammal's reactions to danger may include any of the behavioural responses involved in keeping still, fighting and running away. Any or all of these may be responses to odours, to sounds or to things the mammal sees, which it has learnt to associate with danger.

The behavioural responses involve neurones from one or more sense organs to the brain, connector neurones from the brain to the spinal cord, and motor neurones to the effectors involved in the responses to danger. These effectors include the skeletal muscles used in moving or in keeping still and the adrenal glands. The presence of adrenalin in the blood results in an increase in the supply of oxygenated blood to the muscles used in fighting and running (see p. 229).

These changes involve both hormonal and neural control. By avoiding danger, by fighting, or by running away, the mammal may regain a favourable environment, and this contributes to the maintenance of a constant internal environment and so to survival.

Alcohol and some other drugs interfere with the functioning of the nervous system. Alcohol, for example, slows down responses to danger and makes people less able to control their behaviour. Because their reflexes are slower than normal, they are more likely to be involved in accidents and are quite likely to behave irresponsibly. Under the influence of alcohol people say things that they may afterwards regret and, for example, a girl who does not wish to have a baby may be made pregnant by a man whom she would not otherwise have chosen to be the father of her child.

Control of Blood Sugar Level in Mammals

The behaviour that leads to feeding, and also the feeding behaviour, which are mainly under neural control, are essential for the maintenance of the constant composition of the blood. The input of sugars into the body is by absorption from the small intestine, after the digestion of carbohydrates (see p. 90). The sugars absorbed are carried to the liver (see p. 187). The cells of the liver absorb sugars, and glucose is converted to glycogen in these cells.

The amount of glucose in the blood leaving your liver, unless you have sugar diabetes (see p. 230), is usually about 0.1 g glucose per 100 cm^3 blood (but may be higher for a short time after a meal).

Control of the blood sugar level in mammals depends upon: (1) feeding and the absorption of glucose after a meal; (2) the conversion of glucose to glycogen in the liver after a meal; (3) the conversion of glycogen to glucose in the liver between meals; (4) the use of glucose by all body cells at all times in respiration; and (5) the reabsorption of glucose from the glomerular filtrate in the kidney with the result that there is no glucose in the urine. The hormones involved in this control of blood sugar include: insulin secreted by the pancreas, which causes the conversion of glucose to glycogen in the liver (see p. 230); and thyroxine secreted by the thyroid gland, which stimulates respiration in all cells (see p. 228).

Control of Body Temperature in a Mammal

It will help you to remember some aspects of the control of body temperature if you consider five things that are needed to maintain a constant temperature throughout a house in hot and cold weather: (1) a source of heat; (2) a means of distributing the heat throughout the house; (3) thermostatic control; (4) insulation to reduce heat loss in cold weather; and (5) a means of increasing heat loss in hot weather.

The maintenance of a high and constant temperature throughout the body of a mammal depends upon six things:

1. Heat is produced in all cells in their respiration, but especially in the liver (see p. 188) and in skeletal muscles during movement and shivering.

2. Heat is distributed throughout the body. This results from the presence of blood capillaries near to all cells and the rapid circulation of the blood.

3. There are temperature receptors in the skin. Also, certain cells in the brain are sensitive to the temperature of the blood. Nerves from the brain carry impulses to the parts of the body which make appropriate responses leading to heat production, heat conservation or more rapid heat loss.

4. Heat is lost in breathing and through the skin, especially in cold weather. However, in cold weather the erector muscles of the hairs contract and, in mammals with more hair than we have, more air is trapped between the hairs. This air acts like a blanket and reduces heat loss. Also in cold weather, the arterioles in the skin are constricted and less blood flows through the blood capillaries near the surface (see Fig. 89). The layer of fat, deeper in the dermis, is then effective in reducing heat loss from the internal organs.

5. In hot weather the hairs are not erected and so less air is trapped near the body surface. Also, more heat is carried to the skin because the arterioles in the skin are now dilated and more blood flows through the capillaries of the dermis. The fat layer in the skin does not therefore act as an insulation layer in hot weather. These things facilitate heat loss but there is also a cooling mechanism: sweating. If the body temperature rises (even 0.2 to 0.5 °C) above the normal temperature (36.9 °C in man) sweat pours from the sweat glands, and spreads over the surface of the skin. The evaporation of this sweat removes heat from the body.

6. Mammals avoid extreme temperatures. Most mammals rest in the shade on hot sunny days. Some burrow in the ground where the temperature is less variable than at the surface. Some build nests. Some rest close together when it is cold and so reduce the area of their exposed surface. Some migrate and others hibernate before the cold weather starts. These are some of the behavioural responses that contribute to temperature control. Without such behaviour temperature control would be impossible.

Birds and mammals are called **homeotherms**. All other animals are called **poikilotherms**: their temperature is the same, or very nearly the same, as the temperature of their environment.

Birds and mammals are the only animals that maintain a high and constant body temperature. They are sometimes described as warm-blooded and the poikilotherms as cold-blooded. However, the expression cold-blooded is misleading because poikilotherms are not cold-blooded: their body temperature varies with the temperature of their environment and on a hot day their body temperature may be higher than that of a homeotherm.

There are advantages in homeothermy. For example, a homeotherm is always ready for action and nerve impulses travel faster at higher temperatures. Also, the high temperature of the brain is considered to be necessary for the development of your memory. However, there are also disadvantages in homeothermy. The smaller a bird or mammal is, the larger is its surface area in proportion to its volume (see p. 58). Small animals lose heat rapidly when the air is cooler than their body. In such conditions, small homeotherms survive only by resting in warm places and by eating more food in proportion to their volume than would be necessary for a larger homeotherm: much of the small homeotherms' food is used in heat production.

Some small mammals **hibernate**. These are exceptional in that their body temperature falls in hibernation, almost to the temperature of their environment. Hibernating mammals, therefore, like poikilotherms and like all plants, use less and less of their food reserves as the air temperature and their body temperatures fall, because as the temperature decreases so do all processes in the body including the rate of respiration in every cell: as a result they are able to survive unfavourable periods when little food is available.

Most homeotherms soon die, of heat or cold, if they cannot maintain their temperature at the normal level. Old people are likely to die from hypothermia, especially if they are underfed, if they sleep in inadequately heated rooms.

This chapter has been mainly about coordination and control in mammals, with particular reference to man, and in flowering plants, but remember that coordination and control are features of the life of every organism. The maintenance of the constant composition of each cell, of the body fluids, and of the organism as a whole—the maintenance of homeostasis—is a condition of life for each cell and for every organism. All the activities of the body contribute to the maintenance of homeostasis, which makes possible survival, growth and reproduction.

Good Health

There is more to good health than being free of disease. Good health is that state of mental, physical and social well-being which enables you to enjoy work and relaxation, and to lead an active and satisfying life.

Many illnesses are self-inflicted: due to over-eating, smoking, idleness or stress. You can help to keep your body in good condition.

1. Do not eat too much.
2. Do not drink alcohol as a habit.
3. Do not smoke.
4. Recognise your abilities and limitations. Attempt things that you know you can complete to your own satisfaction. If necessary, establish an order of priority and complete first any tasks that are causing you anxiety.
5. Develop recreational interests and satisfying personal relationships.
6. Take regular exercise.

Test Questions

1. Which of the words numbered 1 to 18 is the most appropriate match for each of the words A to M? Any number may be used only once.

1	penicillin	A	mitosis
2	ribonucleic acid	B	insulin
3	lymph	C	antibiotic
4	water	D	homeostasis
5	receptor	E	ribosome
6	constancy	F	glycogen
7	chromatids	G	effector
8	lipid	H	tissue fluid
9	digestion	J	osmosis
10	muscle	K	calcium deficiency
11	hormone	L	tendon
12	carbohydrate	M	adrenalin
13	respiration		
14	pancreas		
15	root		
16	rickets		
17	epithelium		
18	gland		

2. In an experiment a scientist removed the terminal buds of two plants A and B. He covered the cut surface of A with a paste containing indole acetic acid (IAA). B was left untreated. (*a*) After five weeks he observed that the axillary buds just below the cut surface of plant B were developing into shoots. What do you conclude from this observation? (*b*) Even after ten weeks the axillary buds of plant A had not developed into shoots. What do you conclude from this observation? (*c*) How would you have treated plant B, at the start of the investigation, to make it a better control experiment? (*d*) What other changes would you have made so that you could be more confident that any differences recorded later were due to the difference between the two treatments?

3. Prepare a large diagram of the arrangement of the nerve cells involved in a spinal reflex response. Label on your diagram: (*a*) the parts of the spinal cord; (*b*) the names of two kinds of nerve cells; (*c*) a receptor and an effector. Indicate by arrows on your diagram the direction in which nerve impulses pass along the two nerve cells.

4. Explain how hormonal control differs from neural control.

5. What is involved in the maintenance of a high and constant body temperature in a mammal?

6. (*a*) Make a list of the words needed to complete the following passage:

The control of breathing. The amount of carbon dioxide in the blood rises during exercise. —— **cells** in the hind-brain, which are **sensitive** to small changes in the carbon dioxide concentration of the blood, are associated with **neurones** which carry —— —— from the brain to the muscles of the rib cage and ——. The more frequent and more complete contraction of these muscles makes you breathe more —— and fill and empty your lungs more ——. This —— response increases the supply of —— to the **tissues** of the body and increases the rate at which —— —— is lost from the **respiratory surface**.

(*b*) Explain the meaning of the terms printed in bold letters.

PART 4: LIFE GOES ON

27

REPRODUCTION

Because each individual has a limited life span, the continuance of the species depends upon reproduction: the production of new individuals of the same kind.

Reproduction without Gametes: Asexual Reproduction

In favourable weather, when food is abundant, an *Amoeba* grows. Then its nucleus divides into two, by mitosis (see p. 147), and the cytoplasm also divides. This process, called **binary fission** (division into two), results in the production of two individuals from one.

The interstitial cells of *Hydra* (see Fig. 36C, p. 66) have the ability to divide and to develop into different cell types. In favourable weather, when food is abundant, bulges form on the side of the body (see Fig. 144) and when these are fully developed—with tentacles, a mouth and a basal disc—they break away and live as new individuals. This method of asexual reproduction is called **budding**. Other examples of asexual reproduction are the budding of yeast (see Fig. 51B and C, p. 93) and the production of spores by the bread mould *Rhizopus* (see Fig. 52, p. 94).

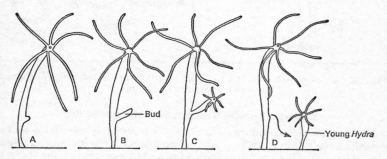

Fig. 144. Budding of *Hydra*.

Many flowering plants reproduce asexually. Here are a few examples: (1) The shoots of many plants take root where they touch the soil. (2) The lateral buds formed in the axils of the leaves of a bulb during one growing season develop into new bulbs in the next growing season (see Fig. 18A). In this way several bulbs are formed. (3) Potato tubers are swollen underground shoots that are produced in one growing season. When the rest of the plant dies back the potatoes remain in the ground and develop into new plants in the following year (Fig. 18B). Note that all roots that develop from a shoot (as from a runner, bulb or tuber in these examples of asexual reproduction) are called **adventitious roots.**

In horticulture new plants are produced by the rooting of cuttings. If cuttings from a shoot are kept warm and well watered, adventitious roots will develop at the base of the stem. That is to say, the plant will **regenerate** the missing parts. The advantages of producing new individuals in this way, by **artificial propagation**, are that the grower can obtain many plants quickly, in the same growing season, and they will all grow into plants that are essentially similar to the plant from which the cuttings were taken (see p. 263).

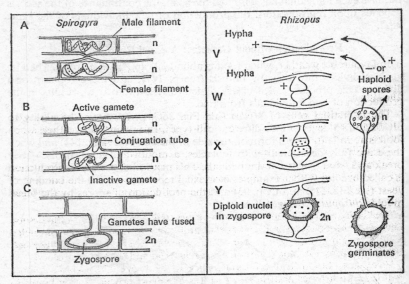

Fig. 145. Sexual reproduction: (A to C) *Spirogyra*; (V to Y) *Rhizopus*; (Z) germination of a zygospore of *Rhizopus*.

Reproduction with Gametes: Sexual Reproduction

Many organisms reproduce asexually but it is probably true to say that all organisms reproduce sexually. Sexual reproduction is the production of new individuals following the formation and fusion of **gametes** (see Fig. 145A to C). In many organisms there are two kinds of gametes: (1) small active cells called **sperms**, and (2) larger immobile cells called **eggs**. Some individuals produce only sperms and are called **males**. Other individuals produce only eggs and are called **females**. However, in many species (including *Hydra*, the earthworm, and many flowering plants) both sperms and eggs are produced in the same individual, and such organisms are called **hermaphrodites**.

In *Hydra* (see Fig. 146) eggs and sperms are produced, in late summer, in bulges in the ectoderm. The **ovaries**, in each of which one egg is produced from an interstitial cell, are just above the basal disc. The **testes**, in each of which many sperms are produced, are nearer the tentacles. In each testis the interstitial cells divide and grow and divide again; and by repeated growth and division thousands of sperms are produced. There is a **division of labour** between the egg and the sperm. Both are single cells with a nucleus, but they differ in their cytoplasm. The egg is large because its cytoplasm contains a lot of yolk (a food reserve). The sperm is much smaller and has very little cytoplasm. The sperm has a tail and when the testis breaks open the sperms swim in the pond water. If one sperm touches an egg the sperm nucleus moves through the cytoplasm of the egg and fuses with the egg nucleus. The chances of a sperm encountering an egg are increased by (1) the large number of sperm released from each testis, (2) the activity of the sperm and (3) the large size of the egg which presents a good target. However. each *Hydra* produces sperms before eggs and this makes impossible the fusion of a sperm with an egg from the same individual.

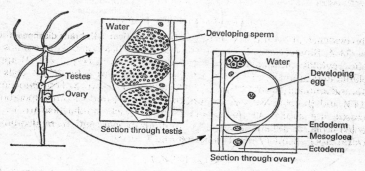

Fig. 146. Sexual reproduction of *Hydra*.

The fusion of the sperm and egg is called **fertilisation**. After fertilisation and the fusion of the egg and sperm nuclei, the new cell is called a **zygote** (Gk. *zygosis* = a joining). This cell divides. Then the two cells so formed divide again, producing four cells; and by repeated mitotic division a multicellular **embryo** is formed. This secretes a hard case and drops from the ovary to the bottom of the pond. Adult *Hydra* are killed by cold or desiccation but the embryo is resistant to cold and drought and it may survive a cold or dry season. It may also be carried in mud on the feet of wading birds, and this contributes to the dispersal of the species. At the end of the unfavourable period the protective wall breaks open and the embryo develops a mouth and tentacles. The yolk, stored in the cytoplasm during egg formation, nourishes the embryo and the developing *Hydra* until it starts to feed.

The Meiotic Division of a Diploid Cell

The chromosomes are in pairs in the nucleus of a diploid cell (see p. 149) and in meiotic cell division the chromosomes are shared equally between two new cells in such a way that each new cell receives only one member of each pair. These new cells, with only half the chromosome number of a diploid cell, are called **haploid** cells. The word **diploid**, based on the Greek word *diplous* which means double, refers to the fact that there are twice as many chromosomes in a diploid cell as in a haploid cell.

In meiosis (Gk. *meiosis* = a lessening) there are two divisions: (1) a reduction division in which two haploid cells are formed from a diploid cell;

followed by (2) a division similar to mitosis in which two more haploid cells are formed from each of the first two haploid cells.

In the reduction division of meiosis the chromosomes of a diploid cell can be stained and pairs of chromosomes can be recognised (Fig. 147A). The nuclear membrane and the nucleolus disappear and a spindle of fibres forms between the centrioles. The chromosomes move to the equator of the spindle

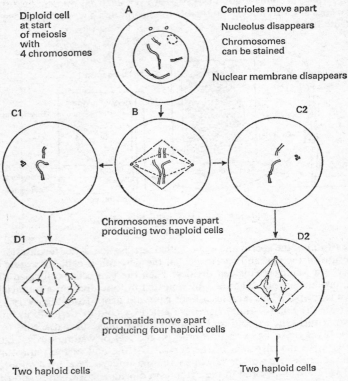

Diploid cell at start of meiosis with 4 chromosomes

A

Centrioles move apart

Nucleolus disappears

Chromosomes can be stained

Nuclear membrane disappears

C1   B   C2

Chromosomes move apart producing two haploid cells

D1   D2

Chromatids move apart producing four haploid cells

Two haploid cells   Two haploid cells

Fig. 147. Meiosis: the formation of four haploid cells from one diploid cell.

where they are arranged, at random, in **homologous** pairs (Fig. 147B). (The word 'homologous' means essentially similar.) The chromosomes move apart towards the opposite poles of the spindle. The spindle disappears (Fig. 147 C1 and C2) and *either* a nuclear membrane may form around each group of chromosomes *or* the second division of meiosis may follow immediately after the cytoplasm has divided.

The second division of meiosis is essentially similar to mitosis. A spindle forms and the chromosomes move to the equator. The chromosomes split into two and the chromatids move apart (Fig. 147 D1 and D2). A nuclear membrane forms around each group of chromatids and the cytoplasm is shared between the new cells. In this way, in meiosis, four haploid cells are formed from each diploid cell.

Fertilisation

Meiosis occurs, for example, in the formation of gametes. Haploid gametes (sperms or eggs) are formed by meiotic division from one diploid cell. The gametes do not usually develop further until they have fused in pairs: a sperm with an egg. This fusion of two haploid cells is called **conjugation** (see Fig. 145) or **fertilisation**. Fertilisation doubles the chromosome number (the egg and sperm contribute the same number of chromosomes) as one diploid cell is formed from two haploid cells.

In some organisms this diploid cell, the zygote, is a resting stage which survives a cold or dry season (see Fig. 145); but in other organisms the fertilised egg immediately starts to divide by mitosis. In sexual reproduction each new individual develops from one diploid cell (the fertilised egg). By mitotic division more cells are formed, all with the same number of chromosomes. However, if the gametes were also diploid their fusion would result in the formation of a cell with twice the diploid number of chromosomes. Because meiosis halves the chromosome number, the conjugation of two haploid cells restores the diploid number—and the chromosome number remains the same in all generations.

Reproduction of People

Reproductive Systems of a Man and a Woman

A man has two testes. These develop in the abdominal cavity but they move, usually before birth, into the scrotal sac which is between the legs (Fig. 148). Very many sperms are produced, in both testes, and a sperm duct carries sperms from each testis to the urethra. The urethra, which leads through the penis to the outside, is both a urine duct and a sperm duct.

A woman has two ovaries, one on either side of her body in the abdominal cavity. One egg is released each month, by one of these ovaries, into the funnel of the nearby oviduct (Fig. 148). The egg moves along the oviduct, wafted by the cilia of the epithelial lining, and it may be fertilised, if sperms are present, in the oviduct or uterus. The uterus is a hollow pear-shaped sac which projects into the vagina, the passage from the uterus to the outside. The part of the uterus which projects into the vagina is called the cervix. The opening of the vagina, and the inner and outer lips over the opening of the vagina, are between the legs.

The time when a boy is growing into a man, and a girl into a woman, between childhood and adolescence, is called the age of **puberty**. The pituitary gland secretes a hormone called follicle-stimulating hormone (FSH). In a boy FSH stimulates the testes, which start (*a*) to produce sperms and (*b*) to secrete a sex hormone called **testosterone**. In a girl FSH stimulates the ovaries which start (*a*) to produce eggs and (*b*) to secrete a sex hormone called **oestrogen**.

The sex hormones are secreted into the blood and carried to all tissues of the body. They are necessary for the normal development of the reproductive system and during adolescence a boy's penis and a girl's vagina, for example, increase in size. These are their primary sexual characteristics.

The sex hormones are also necessary for the development of the **secondary**

sexual characteristics, which make a boy look more like a man and a girl more like a woman. The secondary sexual characteristics of a boy are the further development of his limb and chest muscles, the breaking of his voice, the growth of hair on his face and chest, in his arm pits, near his genitals, and in a triangle up to his navel. The secondary sexual characteristics of a girl are the deposition of fat in her breasts and hips, and the growth of hair in her arm pits and around her genitals. The sex hormones also affect behaviour: boys take more interest in girls; and girls take more interest in boys.

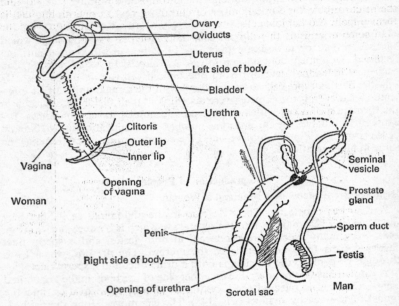

Fig. 148. Reproductive systems of a woman and of a man.

The primary and secondary sexual characteristics develop in adolescence. Childhood does not end suddenly at puberty, and **adolescence** is a time of change. The end of childhood in a girl is marked by the release of an egg (every 28 days) and the monthly menstruation (see p. 247). There is no equivalent event in the life of a boy; but the start of sperm production may be marked by a thick cream-coloured fluid (containing sperms) passing from his penis at night. These nocturnal emissions happen from time to time, and usually when he is dreaming of girls.

Puberty, the start of adolescence, is earlier in most girls than in most boys, and is at different ages in different races. Some girls of eleven, twelve and thirteen may be much more mature in looks and personality than boys of the same age. The changes which follow puberty are almost complete in some boys and girls when they have hardly started in other boys and girls of the same age. Growth continues throughout childhood, and in adolescence there is a spurt in growth. Because of variations in the age of puberty some adolescents are almost fully grown when others have not yet started this growth spurt.

Gamete Production

Sperms are produced in the seminiferous tubules of the testes. Some diploid cells divide, by mitosis, and produce more diploid cells. Following this phase of multiplication many cells divide by meiosis, in which four haploid cells are produced from each diploid cell. Each of these haploid cells changes in form, developing a tail and losing much of its cytoplasm. The parts of a sperm are the head (mostly the nucleus, which contains the chromosomes), the middle piece (mostly the mitochondria, which release energy in respiration), and the tail (which moves and provides the propulsive force in swimming).

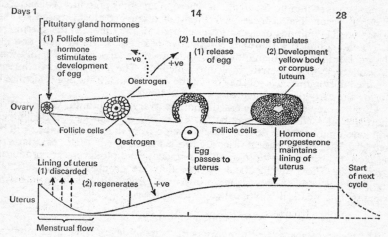

Fig. 149. The development of an egg and the menstrual cycle.

Eggs are produced in follicles, groups of diploid cells, just below the surface of the ovary (Fig. 149). The follicle cells pass on nutriment to the developing egg cell. One egg is released from the ovary, a process called **ovulation**, at about the middle of every 28-day cycle. Egg production starts at puberty and continues for about thirty years. The age at which egg production stops is called the **menopause**.

The cycle of activity in the ovary is controlled by hormones secreted by the pituitary gland, and hormones secreted by the ovary influence what is happening in both the pituitary and in the uterus. These changes in the pituitary, ovary and uterus and the mechanism of hormonal control are represented in Fig. 149. The lining of the uterus is discarded, with bleeding, after every 28-day cycle; that is to say, during the first few days of the next cycle. This flow of blood is called a period or **menstruation**, or the menstrual or monthly flow.

Reproduction

In people, as in all mammals, the egg is fertilised inside the reproductive passages of the female: **fertilisation is internal.** Spongy tissues in the penis and in the wall of the vagina swell with blood. This makes the penis longer and stiffer and it increases the length and diameter of the vagina. The vagina is lubricated with **mucus** secreted by glands in its wall; and the penis slides in—as a finger fits into the finger of a glove. This coupling or copulation is also called **mating** or sexual intercourse.

In mating, **seminal fluid** (a mixture of sperms with fluid secreted by the prostate gland and the seminal vesicles) spurts from the penis, deep in the vagina, next to the opening from the vagina into the uterus. The emission of seminal fluid is called ejaculation and the quantity of fluid ejaculated is an ejaculate.

The seminal fluid, with other fluids present in the reproductive passages of the woman, provides a watery medium and many sperms swim into the uterus. Some sperms swim into the oviducts where, if an egg is present, fertilisation is likely to occur. The **chances** of fertilisation occurring are increased by the facts that: (1) millions of sperms are released at one time; (2) the sperm are active and confined within the reproductive passages of the woman; and (3) the egg is much larger than most cells and presents a large target. Fertilisation takes place, as in all animals, in a watery medium. The food reserves in the egg are used during the egg's journey down the oviduct and, if the egg is fertilised, during the early development of the new individual.

Usually, only one egg is released from the ovary each month. When two or more are released they all may be fertilised. Two separate eggs, for example, will develop into twins. Because these develop from different eggs they will be **non-identical twins. Identical twins** are formed when one fertilised egg starts to develop. From the new diploid cell, many identical diploid cells are produced by mitosis. These are identical because they are produced from the same fertilised egg, and if they separate into two groups they develop into two separate but identical babies called **identical twins.**

Contraception

The fusion of a sperm with an egg is the start of development, the moment when a child is conceived, and it is therefore called **conception.** People have sexual intercourse not only when they wish to have children but also as an expression of their love for each other; and normally as part of the lasting relationship that is essential if parents are to care for their children. Contraception (L. *contra* = against) is the prevention of conception. The following methods of **contraception** are used by many people:

1. Covering the penis with a thin rubber sheath which the man unrolls on to his erect penis before sexual intercourse.

2. The use of contraceptive pills (birth-prevention pills) which are taken every day (except during menstruation—see Fig. 149) by the woman, to prevent the release of an egg from her ovary.

3. The use of a rubber cap or diaphragm which the woman inserts into her vagina, to cover the entrance to her uterus, before sexual intercourse.

4. The use of a spermicidal cream or tablet which the woman inserts into her vagina before sexual intercourse, and which is best used in combination with a cap or diaphragm.

5. The insertion of a specially manufactured loop of plastic into the uterus (by a doctor) to prevent the fertilised egg from continuing its development.

6. The avoidance of sexual intercourse near the middle of a 28-day cycle when an egg is most likely to be present in the oviducts or uterus (see Fig. 149), but this **rhythm method** is not safe and is best combined with some other method.

Whichever method of contraception is used, the manufacturer's instructions (supplied with the contraceptive) or a doctor's advice must be followed exactly. In some countries contraceptives can be obtained, free of charge, from government-supported clinics. Many governments encourage the use of contraceptives in an attempt to avoid the personal and social problems that result from the birth of an unwanted child. Some governments encourage contraception as a contribution to population control (see p. 135).

Many young girls become pregnant because they have sexual intercourse without *either* taking contraceptive pills themselves *or* ensuring that their partner uses a sheath. Withdrawal of the penis from the vagina before the ejaculation of sperms, or *being careful* as it is sometimes called, is not a reliable method of avoiding pregnancy because sperms are present in the drops of clear fluid which pass from the penis just before and during sexual intercourse, and ejaculation may occur sooner than expected.

Many unwanted pregnancies end with the surgical removal of the developing child from the uterus so that it is unable to complete its development. This operation, which is called an **abortion**, should not be regarded as an alternative to contraception. An abortion may harm the mental and physical health of the mother.

All young people should consider, before they enter into any sexual encounter, their responsibilities to themselves, to their partner, to the child that might be conceived and to other people who might care about their future. Otherwise, irresponsible behaviour, lasting a few seconds, may be regretted by all the people involved (especially the boy, the girl and their child) for the rest of their lives (see also p. 110).

Development of an Embryo into a Baby

The fertilised egg divides by mitosis and the cells produced keep dividing until a ball of cells is formed. This becomes attached to the wall of the uterus: a process called implantation. The embryo develops from the ball of cells. So do the membranes which enclose the developing embryo, and the placenta, and the umbilical cord.

Because the membranes do not form part of the embryo they are described as extra-embryonic membranes (L. *extra* = outside). The developing embryo is enclosed in these membranes, in a sac of fluid, and like the embryos of other vertebrates (and all other animals), it develops in a watery medium. The embryo is therefore protected against water loss and against mechanical shocks by these membranes and by being within its mother.

The placenta is closely applied to the wall of the uterus. Here the blood capillaries of the mother are very close to those of the placenta, and the umbilical cord is like a life-line (see Fig. 150) through which an artery carries blood from the developing baby to the capillaries of the placenta and a vein carries blood back to the baby. Food materials, and also oxygen, pass to the baby through the placenta and umbilical cord (from the mother) and waste products pass from the baby through the umbilical cord and placenta (to the mother).

After about six weeks the embryo is fully developed (with a full set of organs) and it is called a **foetus**. All the changes which transform the fertilised egg into an embryo, and the embryo into a foetus, are called **development**. The development and growth of a baby in the uterus takes about nine months. This is called the **gestation period** (or pregnancy) and a woman who is carrying a baby in her uterus is described as pregnant. At the end of pregnancy the

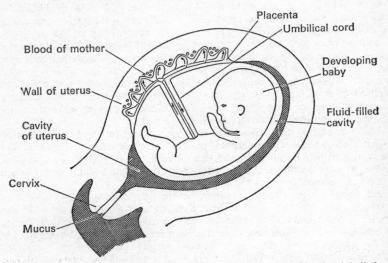

Fig. 150. A baby developing in the uterus of its mother. Parts of mother labelled on left of page.

muscles in the wall of the uterus contract, bursting the embryonic membranes. The fluid in which the baby has developed, and then the baby itself, are forced through the distended cervix and vagina (Fig. 151). This process, called **parturition** (or labour), is completed with the birth of the baby. The baby is still connected to the placenta by the umbilical cord; but immediately after birth the baby starts to breathe.

Parental Care

The mammary glands of the mother develop further during pregnancy and by the time the baby is born they have started to produce milk. The secretion of milk is called **lactation**. Breast-feeding should start within six hours of birth. Mother's milk is the best food for young babies and breast-feeding is satisfying for the mother; it helps to reinforce and maintain the bond between a mother and her child.

Parental care is a characteristic feature of the life of all mammals. Suckling their young, in a nest, not only provides the young animals with milk but also helps to keep them warm.

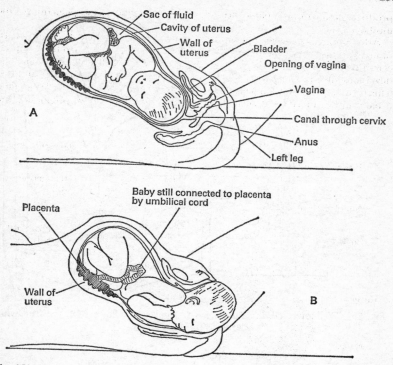

Fig. 151. Two stages in the birth of a baby: (A) at the beginning of labour; (B) baby emerging through the distended cervix and vagina.

Sexual Reproduction in Flowering Plants

The parts of a flower are at the end of a flower stalk upon a receptacle (Fig. 152). The sepals and petals enclose and therefore protect the developing stamens and one (or more) carpel(s). The cells of the flower, like those in other parts of the plant, are diploid. But **meiosis** occurs in the formation of **pollen grains**, in the anthers, and each pollen grain contains two haploid nuclei which share the same cytoplasm. Meiosis also occurs in the formation of an **embryo sac**, in the ovule, and one of the haploid nuclei so formed is called the egg nucleus (Fig. 153).

Pollination and Fertilisation

Pollen grains germinate only if they are transferred to a stigma to the same plant (self pollination) or to a stigma of another plant of the same species (cross pollination). The transfer of pollen is called **pollination**.

Pollen may be carried on the body of an insect or in the wind. Most **insect-pollinated** plants (Fig. 152, for example) have flowers with large petals which do not contain chlorophyll. The petals are conspicuous and/or scented—and are attractive to some insects (see p. 117, for example). The insects feed on a

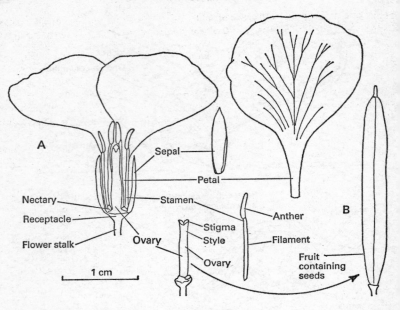

Fig. 152. Wallflower *Cheiranthus cheiri*: (A) parts of a flower; (B) the fruit which
develops from the ovary.

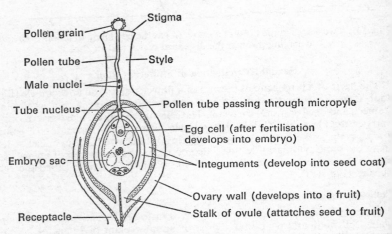

Fig. 153. An ovule inside an ovary; and a pollen grain with a pollen tube which ha
grown through the style and entered the ovule through the micropyle. Diagram nc
to scale.

sugar solution, called nectar, secreted by nectaries, and in so doing they carry pollen from one flower to another. Most **wind-pollinated** plants (Fig. 16C, for example) have small inconspicuous flowers with very small green sepals and petals. They are not scented and they do not produce nectar. Their anthers and stigmas are exposed to the wind.

The pollen grain germinates on the stigma. The pollen tube grows out from the pollen grain, through the style and ovary, to the embryo sac. One haploid nucleus divides in the pollen tube, producing two male nuclei which enter the embryo sac. One male nucleus fuses with the egg nucleus (Fig. 153). This fusion of nuclei is called **fertilisation**. Note that the nuclei fuse in the cytoplasm of the embryo sac. In all plants, as in all animals, fertilisation takes place in a watery medium. In flowering plants, as in mammals, fertilisation is internal.

Seed and Fruit Formation

A seed develops from the tissues of a fertilised ovule: the embryo from the embryo sac and the seed coat from the integuments. The seed coat protects the internal parts: the embryonic root and shoot, and one or two seed leaves (see p. 40). The ovary wall also develops further after fertilisation—into a **fruit**. In some flowers the receptacle enlarges, forming a **false fruit**, and the ovaries remain small.

Since fertilisation is essential for the development of seeds and fruits, and many crop plants are insect-pollinated, bee-keeping contributes to increased yields from many crop plants. This is why it is a good idea to keep bees in orchards. They not only produce honey but also increase the number of fruits harvested from the trees.

Seed Dispersal and Survival

Some seeds will fall below the plant upon which they were formed. However, the dispersal of seeds increases the chances that some of them will germinate in places where conditions are favourable to their growth—other than the places in which this kind of plant is already growing. The more widely the seeds are distributed, the more likely is it that some plants will survive unfavourable years and seasons. Seed dispersal also contributes to the continuance of the species in another way—by making possible the colonisation of new habitats.

The seeds of different plants are distributed in many different ways. For example, some fruits are winged (Fig. 16, p. 27), some are light-weight and small, some are light-weight and have parachute-like structures. All these are carried in the wind. Some fruits fling away their seeds. Some have processes which hook on to the fur of passing mammals. Some are eaten by birds and mammals and because the whole seeds are indigestible they are later egested. And between ingestion and egestion some birds fly over seas and mountain ranges.

Seeds contain very little water and they respire very slowly. With their tough seed coat and their food reserves they may survive in the soil from one growing season to the next, or for many years. Some seeds germinate as soon as environmental conditions are again favourable. Some remain dormant even if conditions are favourable for their growth. Their longer period of dormancy increases the chances of the survival of a species of plant in any habitat, especially if there is a poor growing season or a succession of unfavourable years.

Differences between Asexual and Sexual Reproduction

Asexual Reproduction

1. No gametes are formed.
2. More organisms of the same kind are formed by precise copying (see mitosis, p. 149).
3. One organism that is living in a place, to which it is therefore adapted, produces more organisms with the same qualities—which enable them to continue to exploit the same opportunities in the same place.
4. More organisms of the same kind are produced in the same favourable season, or organs of perennation may be formed.
5. Few offspring are produced.

Sexual Reproduction

1. Sexual reproduction involves the formation and fusion of gametes.
2. Because of meiosis and fertilisation the offspring are not exactly the same as their parents.
3. Because of differences between individuals, some are better adapted than others to life in a particular place.
4. New individuals start life as a single cell, the fertilised egg or a zygote. This may develop into a resistant stage which survives unfavourable periods and which may be carried to another place, contributing to the dispersal of the species.
5. Many offspring are produced but few of them survive for long enough to reproduce; except that in some species few offspring are produced but parental care increases their chances of survival.

Investigations

1. Examine prepared microscope slides of *Spirogyra* with conjugation tubes, gametes and zygospores.
2. Plan an investigation to help you to determine whether or not pollination is essential for fruit formation.
3. Study the flowers of a wind-pollinated plant (any cereal plant); of an insect-pollinated plant (compare with Fig. 152); and of a self-pollinated plant (see Fig. 154).
4. Study the fruits and seeds of different plants. Prepare a list of the fruits you have examined with notes on how the seeds of each one are dispersed.
5. Observe the courtship and mating of jewel wasps (see p. 114).
6. Examine demonstration dissections or museum specimens of the reproductive systems of male and female mammals.

Test Questions

1. Define the following terms: (*a*) fertilisation; (*b*) fruit; (*c*) zygote; (*d*) zygospore; and (*e*) hermaphrodite.
2. Starting with germination, write the following words in the sequence in which they occur in the life-cycle of a flowering plant: germination; pollination, seed formation, flowers, seedling, fertilisation; mature plant.
3. Draw a large labelled diagram of the parts of a **named** flower. State how pollination occurs in this plant. After pollination, what happens to each of the parts labelled in your diagram? How are the seeds of this plant dispersed?

4. (*a*) Draw a labelled diagram of the reproductive system of a woman. (*b*) Label the vagina, cervix, uterus, oviducts and ovaries. Put an X on your diagram to indicate where sperms are deposited, an O where eggs are produced; and F where fertilisation is most likely to occur, and an I where implantation occurs.

5. In the 28-day menstrual cycle, which starts with the beginning of menstruation, state: (*a*) on what day is an egg most likely to be released from the ovary; (*b*) on which days is sexual intercourse most likely to result in pregnancy. Name the hormones secreted by the ovary (*c*) at the beginning of the cycle and (*d*) in the second half of the cycle.

28

HEREDITY

All members of a species are so much alike that the sperm of any male can fertilise the eggs of any female and produce more organisms of their kind. Indeed, we may define a **species** by saying that it is made up of organisms which can interbreed and produce fertile offspring.

If we sow seeds from one plant, more plants of the same kind will grow. If we place the eggs of a house-fly on a suitable food, they will develop into house-flies. Like begets like. Yet within any species of plant or animal we can recognise individuals: no two are exactly alike.

Parents and Their Offspring

Although children resemble their parents and other people in most respects, they differ even from their parents and from their brothers and sisters. No two

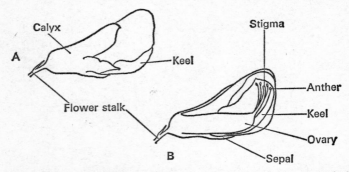

Fig. 154. Flower of the garden pea *Pisum sativum*: (A) whole flower bud; (B) the flower bud cut in half.

people (even identical twins) are exactly alike. Some children strongly resemble one of their parents, or one of their grandparents, and there may be particular features which are recognised as family characteristics.

The egg and the sperm of animals, and the pollen grain and ovule of flowering plants, are the only link between one generation and the next. Those characteristics of the parents which can be recognised in later generations must therefore be represented in some way in the gametes. The study of the way the characteristics of the parents are represented in the gametes—that is to say, the study of heredity or the mechanism of inheritance—is called **genetics** (Gk. *genesis* = descent or origin).

Mendel's Experiments with Pea Plants

Genetics as a modern science began with the work of Gregor Mendel (1822–84), a monk in the Augustinian monastery at Brün in Austria (now

256

Brno in Czechoslovakia). The results of his experiments with the garden pea *Pisum sativum* were published in 1866.

The petals of the flower of the garden pea enclose the anthers and the stigma (Fig. 154B). As a result, when pollen is released from the anthers it can

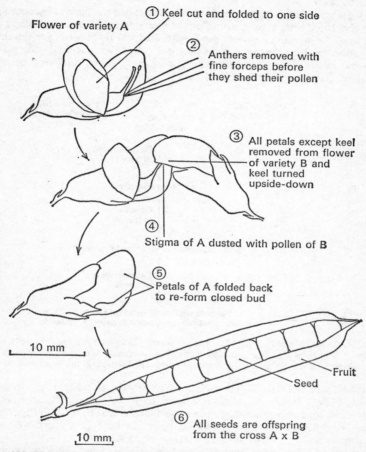

① Keel cut and folded to one side

Flower of variety A

② Anthers removed with fine forceps before they shed their pollen

③ All petals except keel removed from flower of variety B and keel turned upside-down

④ Stigma of A dusted with pollen of B

⑤ Petals of A folded back to re-form closed bud

10 mm

⑥ All seeds are offspring from the cross A x B

Fruit

Seed

10 mm

Fig. 155. The production of hybrid offspring by transferring pollen from the flower of one variety to the stigma of the flower of another variety.

be transferred only to the stigma of the same flower. Because they are self-pollinating, pure-breeding varieties of garden peas breed true and this makes them especially useful in breeding experiments. For example, seeds with a smooth seed coat from a variety of plants which breeds true for smooth seeds will grow into plants which produce only smooth seeds; and wrinkled seeds from a variety of plants which breeds true for wrinkled seeds will grow into plants which produce only wrinkled seeds.

Mendel carried out crosses which would never occur in nature (Fig. 155). For example, he crossed plants of a variety that bred true for smooth seeds with plants of a variety that bred true for wrinkled seeds. In all his experiments with peas Mendel crossed varieties with such pairs of contrasting characteristics.

The plants of the two pure-bred varieties are called the parental generation (P in Fig. 156). After cross-pollination the ovary ripened into a fruit (the pea pod) and this contained smooth seeds only. Because these seeds are the first generation resulting from the cross they are called the first filial generation (F_1 seeds in Fig. 156) (*L. filialis* = pertaining to a son or daughter, or offspring of the same two parents).

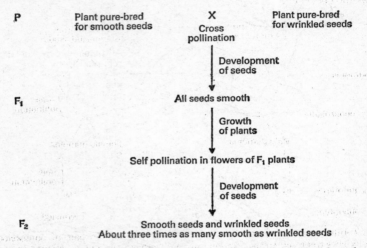

Fig. 156. Cross between a variety of pea plants that bred true for smooth seeds and a variety that bred true for wrinkled seeds (P = parents). After self-pollination in flowers of the F_1 plants, both smooth and wrinkled seeds are produced.

Mendel grew these smooth seeds into plants (F_1 plants in Fig. 156) and then allowed self-pollination to take place naturally in the flowers. The pods produced contained both smooth seeds and wrinkled seeds (F_2 seeds in Fig. 156). When he counted the seeds from all the pods Mendel found that there were about three times as many smooth seeds as wrinkled seeds.

The process of crossing two pure-bred varieties is called **hybridisation** and the offspring which result from the cross are called **hybrids**. A cross such as this, involving one pair of contrasted characteristics (smoothness and wrinkledness) is called a **monohybrid cross** (Gk. *monos* = single; L. *hybrida* = cross).

Interpretation of Mendel's Results

Since the gametes are the only link between one generation and the next, Mendel argued that the gametes (or germ cells) of the plant that is pure-bred for smooth seeds must all contain a factor (or germinal unit) for smoothness

(S in Fig. 157). Similarly, the gametes of the plant that is pure-bred for wrinkled seeds must contain a factor (or germinal unit) for wrinkledness (s in Fig. 157). The germinal units are now called **genes**.

Because the F₁ seeds are formed following a cross between these pure-bred parent plants, by the fusion of two gametes, one with a gene for smoothness (S) and one with a gene for wrinkledness (s), these F₁ plants must contain both genes (F₁ = Ss in Fig. 157).

A capital S is used as the symbol for the gene for smooth and a small s as the symbol for the gene for wrinkled because when S and s are present together (Ss in the F₁) the seeds are all smooth. The gene for smoothness (S) is said to be **dominant** to that for wrinkledness (s) which is said to be **recessive** because S masks the effect of s.

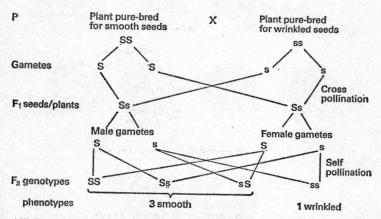

Fig. 157. Interpretation of Mendel's results. Note that of the pair of contrasted characteristics (represented by S and s) only one (either S or s) is represented in any gamete. As a result of the fusion of one male gamete with one female gamete, the fusion cell (zygote) and all the cells produced from this by cell division (mitosis) have both S and S, or S and s, or s and s.

If some of the male gametes of the F₁ plants contain a gene for smoothness (S) and some a gene for wrinkledness (s), and if the same applies to the female gametes, then there are four possible combinations of these male and female gametes: SS; Ss; sS; and ss.

If the male and female gametes fuse at random, then each of these combinations of genes is equally likely. This would explain why there are about three times as many smooth seeds as wrinkled seeds in the F₂ generation (a ratio of about 3:1).

In an attempt to find out whether or not this explanation is correct, Mendel collected the seeds from these F₂ plants, keeping the seeds from each plant separately. When he planted the wrinkled seeds they grew into plants which produced only wrinkled seeds—that is, they all bred true. But of the smooth seeds, those from about one third of the plants grew into plants which produced only smooth seeds (bred true) and those from the other two thirds grew into plants which produced both smooth and wrinkled seeds (like the F₂

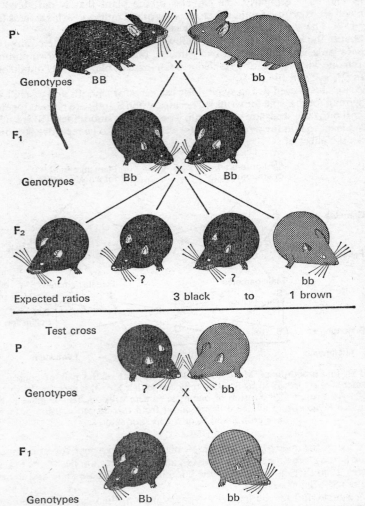

P

Genotypes BB ✕ bb

F₁

Genotypes Bb ✕ Bb

F₂

Expected ratios 3 black to 1 brown

? ? ? bb

Test cross

P

Genotypes ? ✕ bb

F₁

Genotypes Bb bb

Fig. 158. Monohybrid cross. All the F₁ animals are black and must be hybrids since they are the offspring of a cross between animals that are pure-bred for coat colour (black BB and brown bb). Some of the black animals in the F₂ will be homozygous (BB) and some will be heterozygous (Bb). In a test cross, sometimes called a back cross, the animal to be tested is crossed with a double recessive from the original parental cross. If some of the offspring are brown the genotype of the unknown animal must be Bb, since if both parents were homozygous for coat colour all the offspring would be black.

generation produced following the self-pollination of F_1 plants). This confirms that the explanation shown in Fig. 157 is correct: the F_2 comprised plants with the genetic constitutions SS, Ss and ss, in the approximate ratio of 1:2:1.

Note that the genes are present in pairs in the plants of each generation (SS or Ss or ss) but singly in the gametes (either S or s). The following law is based on Mendel's experiments in plant hybridisation: *of a pair of contrasted characteristics only one can be represented in any gamete by its gene*. This is known as *Mendel's first law* or the **law of segregation** of genes.

We may distinguish between the genetic constitution of an organism (the set of genes present in the zygote and in each body cell) and the outward appearance of the organism. For example, smooth seeds may have the genetic constitution SS or Ss. They differ in their genetic constitution even though they look alike—that is to say, organisms with different combinations of genes (different **genotypes**) may develop into similar **phenotypes** (Gk. *phainein* = to appear).

The two genes that make up a pair are called an allelomorphic pair (or simply **alleles**). The genotypes SS and ss are described as homozygous because, in each of these, the two genes are identical (Gk. *homos* = alike; *zygosis* = joining). When the two genes of a pair are different (for example, Ss) the genotype is described as heterozygous (Gk. *hetero* = different).

In the heterozygote the recessive gene s is masked by the dominant gene S. But note that the recessive gene must remain distinct in the heterozygote because its effects are apparent in later generations. In this cross, for example, s is masked in the F_1 but in the F_2 some seeds have wrinkled seed coats.

Experiments with Animals

Mendel's experiments with pea plants attracted little attention when they were published in 1867 and the few biologists who knew about his work did not appreciate its importance. However, Mendel's work was read again in 1900. Since then other people have carried out similar experiments, with pairs of contrasted characteristics in pea plants and in other organisms, and their results can be interpreted in a similar way.

For example, if a pure-bred black mouse is mated with a pure-bred brown mouse all the offspring are black. If two of these F_1 black mice are crossed, some of their offspring are black and some are brown (Fig. 158). Some black mice are likely to be homozygous (BB) and others heterozygous (Bb). The homozygous animals will breed true for coat colour but the heterozygous animals will not.

Mendel could distinguish homozygous and heterozygous pea plants by allowing each plant to self-pollinate and then examining the offspring. How could you find out if one of these F_2 blank mice is homozygous? (See Fig. 158: test cross.)

In some crosses between pure-bred varieties the hybrids can be recognised by their appearance; that is to say, they are phenotypically distinct. For example, the blue Andalusian fowl is a hybrid produced when pure-bred black and pure-bred splashed white fowl are crossed (Fig. 159). This phenomenon is called blending or **incomplete dominance** because both genes have an effect on the phenotype but neither of the genes (for black or for splashed white) dominates the other.

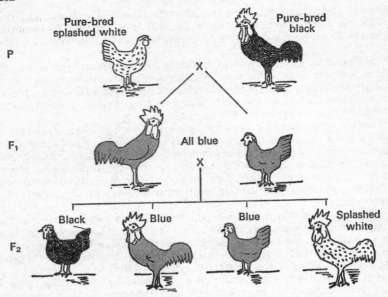

Fig. 159. Incomplete dominance or blending in a monohybrid cross. Phenotypes are black, splashed white and blue; and the corresponding genotypes are BB, bb and Bb. In the heterozygote one gene does not completely dominate the other.

A Dihybrid Cross

In his experiments with the garden pea Mendel also studied the inheritance of two pairs of contrasted characteristics. When he crossed plants which bred true for smooth yellow seeds with plants which bred true for wrinkled green seeds all the F_1 seeds were smooth and yellow. This indicated that smooth is dominant to wrinkled (as in Fig. 156) and that yellow is dominant to green.

After the F_1 plants had been allowed to self-pollinate, the F_2 comprised smooth yellow seeds, smooth green seeds, wrinkled yellow seeds and wrinkled green seeds (Fig. 160). The 9:3:3:1 ratio in the F_2 depends upon two things. The first, Mendel's second law, or the law of **independent assortment**, is that *in any gamete either of a pair of contrasted characteristics may be combined with either of another pair.* The second is that, because they fuse at random, any male gamete may combine with any female gamete and each of the possible combinations shown on the chequer board (Fig. 160) is equally likely.

The Role of the Nucleus in Heredity

There is a parallel between the behaviour of chromosomes in meiosis and the segregation of alleles in gamete formation. In meiosis, in the first division of a diploid cell (the reduction division) one of each pair of homologous chromosomes passes to one haploid cell, and the other passes to the other haploid cell (Fig. 147). And in the segregation of a pair of genes (such as S and s) only one of the pair may be present in a gamete.

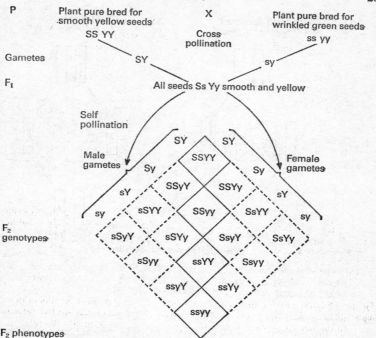

P
Plant pure bred for
smooth yellow seeds
SS YY
X
Cross
pollination
Plant pure bred for
wrinkled green seeds
ss yy

Gametes — SY — sy

F₁ — All seeds Ss Yy smooth and yellow

Self pollination

F₂ genotypes

Male gametes — SY SY — Female gametes

F₂ phenotypes
9 smooth yellow: 3 smooth green: 3 wrinkled yellow: 1 wrinkled green

Fig. 160. Dihybrid cross between two varieties of pea plants, one of which is pure-bred for a smooth coat/yellow seed and the other for wrinkled coat/green seed. Note that (*a*) only one of a pair of contrasted characteristics may be represented in any gamete (Mendel's first law); that (*b*) in the F₁ there are four kinds of gametes because either of one pair of genes may be combined with either of another pair (Mendel's second law); that (*c*) the four kinds of male gametes are identical with the four kinds of female gametes because both male and female gametes are formed in the same flower; and that (*d*) only four of the sixteen genotypes shown on the chequer board will breed true for these seed characteristics because only these four are homozygous.

Since meiosis occurs in the formation of gametes, and each gamete receives only one of each homologous pair of chromosomes (see Fig. 147), a logical explanation for the segregation of pairs of genes is part of one chromosome and the other is part of the other chromosome of a homologous pair (Fig. 161). This **chromosome theory of heredity** is now generally accepted. Each chromosome is made up of protein molecules and DNA molecules, closely associated, and the replication of DNA molecules (see p. 149) allows the copying of genetic information (genes).

The result of mitosis is that each cell produced receives an **identical** set of chromosomes. Therefore: (1) all the body cells of one individual are genetically alike; (2) the body cells of identical twins are genetically alike; (3) plants grown by vegetative propagation are genetically identical with the plant from

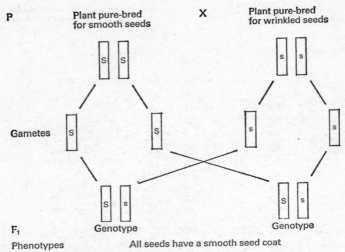

Fig. 161. The chromosome theory of heredity is that the genes are part of the chromosomes. Each symbol in this diagram represents one chromosome; and the letters represent the genes for smooth (S) and wrinkled (s) seed-coat.

which they were produced; and (4) when unicellular organisms divide in asexual reproduction (see Fig. 34, p. 63) the resulting cells are genetically alike.

The result of meiosis, in which each gamete receives only one of each pair of chromosomes, is that the gametes are not all alike. And when gametes fuse there is not only (1) a transfer of genes from one generation to the next (the new individual has characteristics of its parents and of other members of the species) but also (2) a new combination of genes (the new individual differs from other members of the species and even from its parents). The result of sexual reproduction, therefore, is that all members of each species are very much alike, and yet great **variation** exists within each species (see p. 17).

Sex Determination and Sex Linkage

The body cells of flowering plants, and those of multicellular animals, have twice as many chromosomes (2 sets = 2n = diploid) as the gametes (which have 1 set = n = haploid).

In each body cell of a man or a woman the 23 chromosomes received from one parent look very similar to the 23 from the other parent and a cytologist can recognise the two chromosomes that belong to each homologous pair. But in the cells of a man the chromosomes of one pair, the **sex chromosomes**, are not alike.

Sex Determination

In the body cells of a woman the two sex chromosomes are the same length, and are called X chromosomes. But in the body cells of a man there is one X chromosome and one Y chromosome; and the X chromosome is longer than

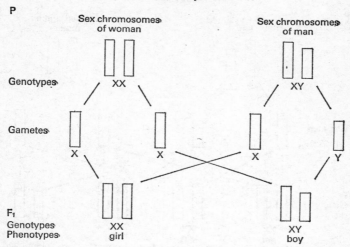

Fig. 162. Sex determination in man: XX = female; XY = male.

the Y chromosome. In the formation of gametes all egg cells must receive an X chromosome but the sperm may receive either an X or a Y chromosome (Fig. 162).

Whether a baby is to be a girl or a boy depends upon the chance of an egg being fertilised either by a sperm with an X chromosome (when the fertilised egg will develop into a girl) or by a sperm with a Y chromosome (when the fertilised egg will develop into a boy). We should therefore expect there to be a fifty-fifty chance that a baby will be a girl.

Sex Linkage

Because the X chromosome is longer than the Y chromosome (see Fig. 162), there is part of the X chromosome that is not matched by a corresponding part of the Y chromosome. Genes on this part of the X chromosome exist by themselves in the male, therefore, not as one of a pair (Fig. 163). For example, red–green colour blindness is caused by a gene c which is recessive to the gene C. A girl will be red–green colour blind, therefore, only if both X chromosomes have the recessive gene (cc = homozygous). In the hetero-zygote cC the recessive gene c is masked by the dominant gene C. However, whether or not a boy is red–green colour blind depends upon which of the genes is present. Note also (Fig. 163) that a woman who has only one gene for red–green colour blindness (who can be described as a carrier) will not suffer from this sight defect but if she marries a man who is not colour-blind there is a fifty-fifty chance that her son will be colour blind.

Heritable and Non-Heritable Variation

The variation which exists in any species is so great that no two individuals are exactly alike. They differ from one another because of differences in their genotype. But superimposed upon these genetic differences are the effects of non-genetic influences during development and growth. The growth of a plant

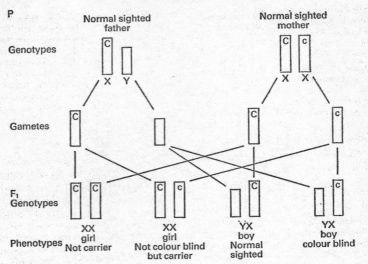

Fig. 163. Sex linkage in man. C and c represent genes, one of which is present on each X chromosome. But there is no corresponding gene on the Y chromosome. The possible genotypes, therefore, are CC, Cc or cc in the female and either C or c in the male.

is influenced by the structure and fertility of the soil and by climate. In animals, increased activity may promote muscle development; overfeeding may be followed by the deposition of fat; and malnutrition may retard growth.

The variation in structure and physiology between members of the same species is due in part to genetic differences (**heritable variation**) and in part to the interaction between the organism and its environment (**non-heritable variation**). But differences between the fully formed leaves of one plant must be due to differences in their position on the plant, to differences in climate at the time of their formation, and to other effects of their environment, since (as part of the one plant) they are genetically alike.

The term non-heritable variation is used for those characteristics of the parents which cannot be passed on to their offspring. If the growth of a plant is restricted because of poor soil fertility the plant may be stunted but if seeds from this plant are sown on fertile soil the seedlings will not be stunted. If a man develops his muscles by weight-lifting and then has children, the children will have to take a similar form of exercise if they too wish to have over-developed muscles.

The structure and physiology of each individual depends not only upon its genotype but also upon the interaction between the organism and its environment during development and growth (see Chapter 3). But note that these are not two separate things since the genotype of an organism affects its ability to respond to its environment.

Investigation: *probability—the operation of the laws of chance.* In a monohybrid cross a 3:1 ratio (see p. 260) or a 1:2:1 ratio (see p. 262) may be expected in the F₂ generation. Similarly, when you toss a coin repeatedly you expect that it will come down heads about as often as it comes down tails. This expectation is based on your knowledge of the operation of the laws of chance; upon what scientists call the laws of probability. Each time you toss a coin the chance that it will come down heads is the same as the chance that it will come down tails: there is an equal chance of a head or a tail. We say that both are equally probable or that we expect a head as often as a tail. If you toss a coin 10 times how often would you expect it to come down heads? If you toss a coin 100 times how often would you expect it to come down heads? Try this and see how close the result you obtain is to the result that you expected. Remember, when you carry out a genetic cross, that the ratios you obtain are unlikely to be precisely the same as the ratios you expected.

Choice of Organisms for Genetics

There are advantages in using small organisms for experimental work. The smaller an organism is, in general, the less food and the less space it requires. For example, many more animals can be reared in an animal room and less food will be required if mice are preferred to rabbits. Similarly, many fruit-flies *Drosophila* can be kept in one glass specimen tube. It is especially useful, in experiments in genetics, to use small organisms that complete their life cycle quickly and produce many offspring in a short time, because genetic ratios cannot be determined with small numbers of offspring. Another reason for using mice and fruit-flies in genetics is that many genetically pure strains are available from biological suppliers. A wild-type *Drosophila* has long wings, red eyes and a grey body, but pure-breeding cultures can be obtained of insects which have small wings, or white eyes, or black bodies (see p. 272). In genetic crosses the gene for long wings is dominant to that for short wings, the gene for red eyes is dominant to that for white eyes, and the gene for grey body is dominant to that for black body.

For further advice see: Haskell, G., *Practical Heredity with Drosophila*, Oliver & Boyd, Edinburgh; and Wallace, M. E., *Learning Genetics with Mice*, Heinemann, London.

Test Questions

1. (*a*) How are genes shared between the two cells produced in mitosis? (*b*) Why are identical twins so like one another? (*c*) Why are identical twins never exactly alike? (*d*) Why do pure-breeding varieties of the garden pea breed true?

2. What is the difference between: (*a*) mitosis and meiosis; (*b*) haploid and diploid; (*c*) chromosome and gene; (*d*) homozygous and heterozygous; (*e*) genotype and phenotype.

3. When pure-bred red-eyed fruit-flies were crossed with pure-bred white-eyed fruit-flies, all the offspring had red eyes. When two of these F_1 flies were mated some of the offspring had red eyes and some had white eyes. (*a*) With the aid of a diagram, explain these results. (*b*) What proportion of the F_2 flies would you expect to have white eyes? (*c*) How could you establish the genotype of one of the F_2 red-eyed flies?

4. (*a*) State Mendel's first law. (*b*) Name the nuclear process which results in segregation.

5. It is easier to carry out fundamental research in genetics with insects such as the fruit-fly *Drosophila* or the flour-beetle *Tribolium* than with mammals such as mice, rabbits or cattle. (*a*) Give three reasons why *Drosophila* has been used so much in genetics. (*b*) Why do some geneticists study cattle?

6. Plants of a variety that breeds true for red flowers were crossed with plants of a variety that breeds true for white flowers. The seeds produced were collected and sown. They all grew into plants which had pink flowers. Explain this result and

prepare a diagram to show what kinds of plants you would expect to be produced, and in what proportions, in the F_2 generation.

7. The most likely distribution of genotypes in 1000 offspring of a cross between male flies with the genotype Ww and female flies with the genotype ww is: (A) 256 Ww:744 ww; (B) 753 WW:247 ww; (C) 493 Ww:507 ww; (D) 246 WW:503 Ww:251 ww.

8. (*a*) What is the normal diploid chromosome number in man? (*b*) How is the sex of a human child determined? (*c*) Explain why a child may suffer from haemophilia, a disease in which the blood does not clot properly, even though neither of his parents suffers from the disease.

THE ORIGIN AND EVOLUTION OF LIFE

When this planet was formed, about 5000 million years ago, it was very hot and the atmosphere contained methane, ammonia, hydrogen and water vapour. Life was not possible. Gradually the surface cooled, water vapour condensed and formed lakes, rivers and seas, and the atmosphere changed (Fig. 1). We do not know how living things originated, probably about 4000 million years ago, but there were micro-organisms, thought to be similar to the bacteria of today, living on Earth about 3750 million years ago.

The Origin of Species

Fossil Evidence

The only traces of the life of past ages remaining today are the shells and bones and other hard parts preserved in sedimentary rocks, the casts of organisms, and even such things as footprints preserved as impressions or casts. All these remains in the rocks are called **fossils**; and fossils in rocks of different ages are a record of life on Earth.

A logical interpretation of the fossil record, which is in accordance with all the evidence available, is that the organisms which are present later in the record were the descendants of pre-existing organisms. For example, the first animals with backbones, known only as they are now **extinct**, were fishes preserved in rocks formed about 450 million years ago. The first amphibians found so far, and the first reptiles, birds and mammals, were preserved in rocks formed more and more recently (see Fig. 1).

The fishes that lived so long ago could be the ancestors of all present-day fishes, and also of the first amphibians. The first amphibians could be the ancestors not only of the amphibia of today but also of the reptiles; and the first reptiles could be the ancestors not only of the reptiles of today but also of the birds and mammals. This interpretation of the history of animals with backbones is in accordance with other evidence.

Evidence from Comparative Anatomy

The bones of the fore-limbs of all amphibians, reptiles, birds and mammals are arranged in a similar way (see Fig. 164), which is what you might expect if all of these animals are descended from the first amphibia—that is to say, such evidence from the study of the anatomy of different animals can be interpreted in the same way as the fossil evidence.

Evidence from Classification

Similarly, the natural system of classification, devised by Linnaeus (see p. 34), can be understood in terms of the history of any group of organisms. Since later organisms are descended from earlier organisms, a logical explanation for the fact that organisms can be placed in groups, according to the things they have in common which distinguish them from the members of other groups, is that all the members of any group had the same ancestors. The species in a genus are so much alike because they are descended from the same ancestral stock. The genera in a family are more distantly related; and the families in an order are even more distantly related; etc.

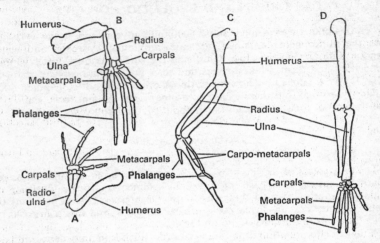

Fig. 164. Fore-limbs of different vertebrates: (A) fore-leg of a frog *Rana*; (B) flipper of a turtle *Chelone*; (C) wing of a bird *Columba*; (D) arm of a man *Homo*. (Drawings not to same scale.)

Evidence from Geographical Distribution

There are different species of the genus *Canis* in different parts of the world (see p. 35). Similarly, the different races of people originated in different parts of the world. A possible interpretation of these differences is that when members of a species are isolated into geographically separate groups, the members of each group may change in appearance and in physiology over many generations. If this is so, then the longer they are isolated the more different they could become.

The hypothesis that organisms are not the same as they have always been, and that there has been a gradual process of **organic evolution**, was proposed by Charles Darwin and Alfred Russell Wallace in 1858; and in 1859 Darwin published a book called *The Origin of Species*.

Selection

Artificial Selection

All our crop plants, farm animals and domestic animals are descended from wild species. They have been changed over thousands of years by a process of artificial selection; by people keeping the individuals which best served their purposes and using these to produce the next generation. In this century, with the application of our knowledge of genetics in plant and animal breeding, much higher yielding varieties of plants and animals are now available to the farmer (see also p. 131). Plant and animal breeding is a continuing process of organic change by artificial selection.

Eugenics

Some people consider that an attempt should be made to improve the human race by a process of selection. The science of eugenics is concerned with our knowledge of human heredity and the possibility of improvement. In some countries genetic counsellors will advise people who suffer from inherited diseases or deformities (or who are closely related to people with such conditions) of the chances that their children will be affected in the same way.

Natural Selection

Darwin and Wallace argued that if species can be changed by artificial selection, then it is possible that they also change in nature by a process of natural selection. They suggested that the mechanism of natural selection might be as follows:

1. Every species has a great potential for increase—that is to say, in birds, for example, each female may lay many eggs in its life.
2. The numbers of each species vary from year to year but there is not the constant increase in numbers that would be expected if all the offspring of each female survived to reproduce.
3. There is great variation in any natural population of organisms.
4. Most offspring do not survive to maturity and therefore they do not reproduce. Those that do reproduce are likely to include many that are best adapted or best fitted to survive.

In other words, Darwin suggested that there is a process of natural selection which results in the survival of the fittest or best adapted individuals in each generation.

In a changing biotic and physical environment, natural selection may result in the survival of organisms with particular characteristics and the elimination of others. This could account for (1) the phenomenon of adaptation to mode of life (Figs. 165 and 166); (2) organic evolution; and (3) the extinction of organisms that are no longer adapted.

Constancy and Change

The passing of genetic information from generation to generation in sexual reproduction results in new combinations of genes. Except for identical twins (see p. 248) no two people are genetically alike. The sharing of the available genes throughout the population, by precise copying (see p. 150) and sexual reproduction, results in all members of the population looking very much alike. Their genes, present in the population as a whole, can be thought of as a gene pool; and the genes of each individual are a sample from this gene pool. We recognise the members of a species by the things they have in common; by this condition of relative constancy that is based on the passage of genetic information from one generation to the next.

Changes in the chromosomes, called **mutations** (L. *mutare* = to change) may be changes in one gene (gene mutations) or in various ways chromosomes or parts of chromosomes may be gained or lost (chromosome mutations) in the formation of gametes. In a laboratory culture of wild-type

Drosophila the flies have red eyes, but very rarely a white-eyed fly is produced. This is a result of a change in one gene. The white-eyed fly is called a **mutant**. Such mutants have been used by geneticists to produce pure-breeding strains (see p. 267). Both gene and chromosome mutations occur in natural populations and they play a part in the origin of new species. However, the rate at which mutations occur can be increased by our actions. For example, people who are exposed to X-rays (in hospitals) or to atomic radiation (as a result of accidents in industry or atomic warfare) may suffer genetic damage due to harmful mutations.

In Britain, as a result of the use of coal in homes and factories, the trees and buildings in many industrial towns have been blackened by dirty smoke. Populations of certain species of moths in these towns were affected by this change in their environment. For example, nearly all the peppered moths *Biston betularia* living in the countryside are white-mottled with dark markings but from time to time a black (melanic) form is produced as a result of gene mutation. In the countryside, where the trees and buildings are not black, the black moths are conspicuous and are more likely to be eaten by birds than are the less conspicuous non-melanic forms. On the other hand, melanic forms are less conspicuous in the smoke-blackened towns and this is believed to be why they have replaced the non-melanic forms in many towns. The melanic form was first recorded in Manchester in 1848, but by 1895 about 95 per cent of the population were melanic. This is an example of how local populations of a species may change as a result of natural selection.

Living organisms are adapted to conditions as they are—now. If conditions

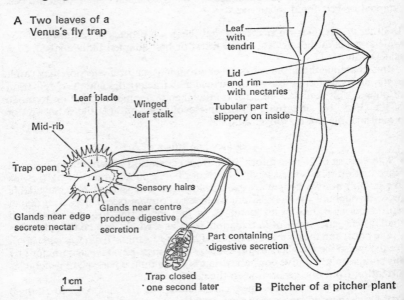

Fig. 165. Carnivorous plants: (A) two leaves of a Venus's fly-trap *Dionaea*; (B) part of one leaf of a pitcher plant *Nepenthes*.

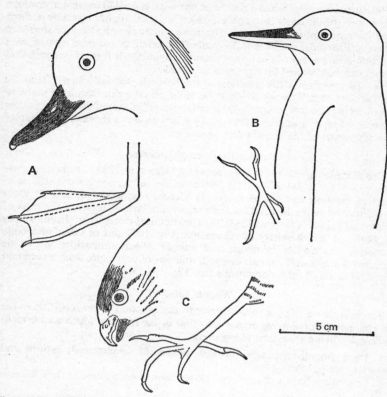

Fig. 166. Adaptation: feet and beaks of three birds which live in different ways and have different feeding habits. (A) A duck *Aythys*; (B) a woodpecker *Picus*; (C) a hawk *Acipiter*.

change some or all of the individuals in any species may still be able to survive and reproduce; that is to say, they may still be adapted even though the conditions change. If none of them is able to survive and reproduce in these changing conditions the species becomes extinct. This is why many organisms are known only from the fossil record.

Conditions on Earth have been changed in many ways by the activities of mankind. Many species have become extinct in the last few hundred years, and especially in the 20th century, as a result of man's activities. However, man cannot necessarily eliminate a species if he tries to do so. For example, a new pesticide is introduced following tests in which it has been proved to be effective in killing pests, and a new drug is introduced only after it has been established that it is effective in curing a disease. Yet, after a new pesticide or drug has been used for some time it may cease to be effective. This problem of resistance to a pesticide or to a drug is a major problem in pest and disease control operations.

Resistance develops when a new toxic chemical is used in control operations only if some of the organisms against which it is used are not killed by it. Such organisms are said to be resistant. The more a toxic chemical is used the more are we selecting for resistant individuals. The origin of resistant strains, as a result of killing many of the non-resistant individuals, is further evidence that species can be changed by a process of selection.

Natural selection is the selection of the best adapted individuals from the great variety of individuals living at the time, and the elimination of many of those that are less well adapted. Adaptation is a condition of life. No organism survives unless it is adapted. This is why adaptation is a characteristic feature of every aspect of the life of every organism.

Further Evidence of Evolution

The evidence of evolution considered by Darwin in 1859 is summarised on pages 33–4. Since Darwin's time further evidence has come from studies of **genetics, cytology** and **biochemistry**. (1) Mendel's laws (see pp. 261–2) apply to plants and animals. (2) There are many similarities between the cells of plants and animals (see pp. 142–3). (3) The chemical structure of chromosomes (p. 149) and the chemistry of respiration (Fig. 107) and of other metabolic processes, are similar in plants and animals. Such similarities are to be expected if plants and animals evolved, millions of years ago, from a common ancestral stock of micro-organisms (see Fig. 1, p. 5).

What is Life?

The nearest we can get to an answer to the question *What is life?* is to list the **characteristics of living organisms**—that is, the features which enable us to distinguish living from non-living things:

1. Each organism passes through phases of **development, growth and maturity** (see p. 15).

2. Organisms have a characteristic body **form** at each phase in their life (see p. 7).

3. Organisms are of different kinds called **species** (see pp. 17 and 34).

4. The form of an organism is influenced by the environment in which it lives and this is one reason for the **variation** which exists within a species (see p. 17).

5. The form and mode of life of an organism is appropriate to the place in which it lives; we say that the organism is **adapted** to its environment (see pp. 26 and 274).

6. Similar species can be arranged in groups, in a **natural classification** (see p. 35).

7. Organisms are composed of **organic molecules** (including proteins, lipids, sugars, vitamins and nucleic acids) as well as of inorganic molecules (see pp. 54 and 55).

8. Organisms are either single **cells** or are composed of many cells and extracellular materials (see p. 67).

9. The parts of a cell and the parts of an organism are **interdependent** and working together, they maintain the **constant composition** of the cell and the organism: see homeostasis, pp. 62, 234 and 236.

10. Organisms are **distinct** from their environment but there is a constan

exchange of energy and matter between each organism and its environment (see p. 61).

11. All organisms respire and make efficient use of the energy released in **respiration** (see p. 185).

12. Organisms are **sensitive** to changes in their external and internal environment, to which they make **appropriate responses** which contribute to survival (see p. 218).

13. Organisms do not live alone. They interact with members of their own species and with members of other species. They are part of a **community** (see p. 129).

14. Organisms affect and are affected by their physical environment. They are part of an **ecosystem** (see p. 120).

15. Each organism has a limited **life span**, but reproduction (see p. 241) and dispersal make possible the maintenance of the species.

16. Organisms are **produced** only from pre-existing organisms. The resemblance between members of a species, and many of the differences between them, are the result of the passage of information, coded in nucleic acid molecules, from one generation to the next (see p. 254).

17. **Adaptation** is a condition of life: a condition for **survival**. If any individual is not adapted it dies. If none of the individuals of a species is adapted the species becomes **extinct**. Species that continue to be adapted in a changing environment themselves change. This process is called **organic evolution** (see p. 270).

18. Life exists on Earth but, as far as we know, nowhere else in the Universe.

Investigations

1. Try to visit a museum so that you can (*a*) examine some fossils; (*b*) compare the skeletons of different kinds of animals; and (*c*) look at the displays of organisms classified in different groups.

2. Try to visit botanical and zoological gardens so that you can see plants and animals that do not live in the wild in your country.

3. Try to observe animals of one species closely to see if you can see differences between them. For example, find land snails in different habitats. Make notes on the colours of the shell. Handle the snails carefully and replace them where you find them. Are there differences in colour and colour pattern? Are there differences between snails from different habitats? Can you think of any way in which the appearance of its shell may affect a snail's chances of survival?

Test Questions

1. State two advantages of asexual reproduction and two advantages of sexual reproduction.

2. The pericarp of the fruit of the maple (Fig. 16) has large flat extensions. Do you think the seeds of the maple are dispersed by (A) birds; (B) becoming attached to the fur of mammals; (C) an explosion mechanism; (D) the wind; or (E) insects?

3. State briefly what evidence from the study of (*a*) cell structure, (*b*) the process of mitosis and meiosis, (*c*) the chemical processes in cells, and (*d*) the mechanism of inheritance, could be considered in support of the view that the plants and animals of today have evolved from ancestors which had many features in common.

4. Explain the meaning of the terms: (*a*) adaptation; (*b*) variation; (*c*) mutation; and (*d*) natural selection, in a natural community of living organisms.

5. Write an account of: (*a*) variation in a named plant or animal species that you have studied; or (*b*) the distribution of a species in an area you have studied; or (*c*) the concept of adaptation as illustrated by examples taken from your own study of an ecological succession; or (*d*) your own investigations on the culture of bacteria.

Appendix 1

EXAMINATION TECHNIQUE

If you are using this book for revision, in preparation for an examination, consider the following advice.

1. Study the syllabus for the examination that you are taking.

2. Obtain a copy of each of the question papers set in this same examination in the last two or three years. See how the papers are arranged and what kinds of questions are set.

3. If you cannot answer any question, revise this topic.

4. Some people like to prepare detailed notes and diagrams on each aspect of their work from their textbook, and then they learn from these notes when they wish to revise. Others find this a waste of time; and mistakes can be made in copying. You may remember your work better if you spend the time needed for note-taking (a) on reading and re-reading about each aspect of the subject from this book, and (b) on reading your practical notebook.

Before the Examination

5. Check that your pen is full of ink, that your pencils are sharp and that you have a bottle of ink, a clean rubber (eraser) and a ruler marked in centimetres and millimetres.

6. Arrive at the examination in good time but do not talk to others about the examination while you are waiting to enter the room.

During the Examination

7. Read the instructions at the top of the first page of the examination paper to make sure that you know how much time you are allowed and which questions you have to answer, and to see if you have any choice of questions.

8. If you have a choice in any paper or in part of the paper, read all the questions before you decide which ones you can answer best.

9. Before you answer any question make sure that you understand what the examiner wants to know.

10. Think about your answer.

11. If the question is set in parts, answer all parts and answer them in the order in which they appear in the question.

12. Follow the examiner's instructions for each question. Some questions are to be answered by writing one letter or one word, or perhaps by underlining the correct answer, or perhaps with one line of writing. If the examiner asks for one example or one reason do not give two. On some examination papers there is a space for each answer. This should tell you how many lines of writing are needed for an adequate answer to this question. The number of marks allocated may be indicated in the right-hand margin. This is another indication of the number of points to be included in your answer. For some answers a short essay may be required. In this, use concise headings to draw attention to the orderly arrangement of the paragraphs of your answer.

13. Answer any compulsory questions; but if you have difficulty with any questions, or any part of a question, do not spend too much time thinking about it. Press on with other questions and, if you have time at the end, complete all your answers.

14. Allocate your time so that you can answer the right number of questions. The instructions at the head of the paper may give you guidance about how much time you should spend on the parts of a paper. If the number of marks allocated to a

question (or to the parts of the question) is stated in the right-hand margin of the question paper or at the end of the question, this is another indication of how you should allocate your time.

15. Do not leave before the end of the examination. Try to leave yourself time to read through all your answers towards the end of the examination, to correct any slips of the pen and to add any details that you did not remember the first time through.

Appendix 2

ANSWERS TO TEST QUESTIONS

Following the number of the question *either* the answer is given *or* the page number on which the answer is to be found.

Chapter 1 (1 to 5) 3–5.

Chapter 2 (1) 146 and 151 (2) Fig. 4B. (3) Record your own observations; (4) (*a*) 28 mm, 44 mm and 60 mm approx.; (*b*) about 7 weeks; (*c*) no increase in length after 51 days (see Table 3).

Chapter 3 (1) (*a*) Control (see Index); (*b*) grow several plants in each culture solution; (2) (*a* and *b*) see Figs. 12 and 15; (*c*) 22: remember differences in anatomy, physiology and habitat.

Chapter 4 (1) (*a*) 26; (*b*) 29; (*c*) 21. (2) 26. (3) Record your own observations (see also p. 29). (4) (*a*) See dormant buds and seed (Fig. 16); (*b*) the seed contributes to survival in unfavourable periods and to dispersal.

Chapter 5 (1) (*a*) All algae, all bryophytes and all tracheophytes (39); (*b*) fungi (39). (2) Add to examples given in this book from your own observations.

Chapters 6 and 7 (1) (*a*) 55; (*b*) 56; (*c*) 180; (*d*) see Index. (2) Table 9. (3) A, B and C. (4) See Index. (5) (*a*) 58; (*b*) 61. (6) 59–61. (7) 52. (8) Figs. 27 and 28.

Chapter 8 (1) (*a*) 68 (see also Index); (*b*) 65–67. (2) 68–70.

Chapter 9 (1) 81. (2) 78. (3) Iron (see p. 17) and magnesium (pp. 17 and 180). (4) 82. (5) See Fig. 98. (6) 78. (7) (*a*) On a clear sunny day; (*b*) respiration takes place all the time but the rate of photosynthesis varies with variations in light intensity (see Fig. 80); (*c*) on a very dull day, if the light intensity is very low the rate of respiration could exceed the rate of photosynthesis; (*d*) the gap allows diffusion between the water above and below the funnel, with the result that on a fine day there is always carbon dioxide in the water next to the plant.

Chapter 10 (1) (*a*) plants; (*b*) kinds of teeth labelled in Fig. 48; (*c*) see Fig. 48 and examine skulls if you can; (*d*) omnivore. (2) (*a*) Fig. 50; (*b*) A = liver; B = small intestine (especially duodenum); (*c*) small intestine (especially ileum); D = stomach; (E) salivary gland or pancreas. (3) 94 (and Fig. 165).

Chapter 11 (1) (*a*) They both live in one place and absorb nutrients through their body surface; (*b*) fungi differ from green plants in that they do not have chlorophyll and they require organic molecules from their environment. (2) (*a*) budding; (*b*) spores; (*c*) oxygen; (*d*) carbon dioxide; anaerobic. (3) Fig. 53 or Fig. 55, for example. (4) Table 11. (5) See investigation on micro-organisms in milk (p. 101).

Chapter 12 (1) leguminous; root nodules; symbiotic; *Rhizobium*; nitrogen; nitrogen fixation. (2) (*a*) 103; 104–105. (3) The drones, workers and queen are all members of the same species; the sperm of the drones (males) are essential for the production of workers and queens (females). (4) See Index. (5) (*a*) See Fig. 55; (*b*) 107; (*c*) 93. (6) (*a*) C; (*b*) B; (*c*) A; (*d*) F; (*e*) E; (*f*) D. (7) Animals are kept in quarantine to give time for the symptoms of any disease to develop; and isolation reduces the chances of a disease being passed on to others.

Chapter 13 (1) 114. (2) 115–117. (3) 118.

Chapter 14 (1) Record your own observations. (2) (*a*) green plants; (*b*) rabbits; (*c*) saprobiotic bacteria; (*d*) people; (*e*) rabbit fleas. (3) 120. (4) B. (5) Record your own observations.

Chapter 15 (1) (*b*) Recycling means recovering waste (such as scrap metal) so that we can use materials again (and again). (2) Base your answer on the examples discussed in this book and on your experience based on such things as reading newspapers and your own observations.

Chapter 16 (1) Fig. 75A. (2) B and D (see Fig. 75B).

Chapter 17 (1) nucleus; protein; cytoplasm; ribosomes; amino acids; enzymes (2) (*a*) B; (*b*) C; (*c*) A; (*d*) B; (*e*) C. (3) Diagram similar to Fig. 79, except that a plant cell has a cell wall (see notes on pp. 147 and 149).

Chapters 18 and 19 (1) A. (2) See Fig. 84; (*a*) A, B and C; (*b*) E; (*c*) C. (3)(*a*) See Fig. 89; (*b*) All of them. (4) (*a*) 163; (*b*) all of them; (*c*) the epidermis supports the plant body and protects the internal tissues. (5) (*a* to *d*) see p. 164; (*e*) A and C.

Chapter 20 (1) (*a*) Rinse to ensure that the tube is clean; (*b*) carbon dioxide in your breath would affect the pH of the indicator solution; (*c*) you record any decrease in carbon dioxide concentration in the air due to photosynthesis as well as any increase due to respiration; (*d*) materials egested or nitrogenous excretions could contaminate the indicator solution; (*e*) B is a control experiment which should be similar to A in all respects except that it does not contain a locust. (2) (*a*) The respiration of living cells increased the carbon dioxide concentration of the air in B (*b*) no; (*c* and *d*) yes; (*e*) to confirm that all the carbon dioxide has been removed from the air stream entering B. (3) C. (4) D. (5) 175 and 177.

Chapter 21 (1) The control should contain no yeast but should be similar in all other respects. (2) (*a*) 182; (*b*) 94. (3) B and D. (4) (*a*) 183; (*b*) 59 and 60; (*c* to *e*) carbon dioxide produced in all living cells is excreted through the lungs; and urea produced in the liver is excreted through the kidneys; (*f*) see Fig. 98 C and D.

Chapter 22 (1) (*a*) Yes; (*b*) 190; (*c*) while she is breast-feeding her baby; (*d*) in general bigger people need more food than smaller people, but note the figures in this table for people aged 65; (*e*) less if they are healthy; (*f*) cellulose (see also p. 102); (*g*) 193. (2) (*a*) D; (*b*) B; (*c*) C; (*d*) B; (*e*) B; (*f*) E. (3) (*a* and *b*) Citrus fruits should be eaten fresh; fresh vegetables should be eaten fresh and should be eaten raw or cooked as quickly as possible; (*c*) the vitamin C content of food is reduced by heat during some manufacturing processes; (*d*) scurvy. (4) (*a*) Seed leaves (Fig. 4B) or endosperm (Fig. 4W); (*b*) starch grains (196); (*c*) axillary buds (Fig. 69); (*d*) spores (Fig. 52); (*e*) chloroplasts (see p. 39).

Chapter 23 (1) (*a* and *b*) The rate will be reduced; (*c*) the temperature will rise (2) (*a*) Photosynthesis; (*b*) in sunlight; (*c*) respiration; (*d*) all the time; (*e*) for example, as a solvent; as a transport medium, in providing support; and as a raw material in photosynthesis; (*f*) transpiration; stomata; gaseous exchange; (*g*) oil prevents the evaporation of water directly from the beaker; and the jelly would block the stomata on the under surface and so reduce the rate of transpiration considerably. (3) (*a*) for example, oxygen by diffusion (60); mineral ions by active intake (185); and food by the formation of food vacuoles (59); (*b*) in active intake and in the formation of food vacuoles; (*c*) elimination of excess water. (4) (*a*) carbon dioxide and water; (*b*) water and urea. (5) (*a*) Fig. 124A; (*b*) excretion of urea; and regulating the salt and water content of the body.

Chapter 24 (1) (*a*) xylem; (*b*) phloem; (*c*) water from root and sugar from leaves. (2) Hepatic vein, posterior vena-cava; right auricle; right ventricle; pulmonary artery. (3) (*a*) A rigid material added inside the cellulose cell walls of xylem vessels; (*b*) 215; (*c*) 209; (*d*) 214; (*e*) 214. (4) 213.

Chapter 25 (1) Base your answer on your own observations. (2) (*a*) auditory nerve; (*b*) ampullae of semi-circular canals; (*c*) utriculus and sacculus; (*d*) Eustachian tube; (*e*) cochlea. (3) See Index.

Chapter 26 (1) A 7; B 14; C 1; D 6; E 2; F 12; G 18; H 3; J 4; K 16; L 10; M 11. (2) (*a*) The terminal bud normally inhibits the development of axillary buds into shoots; (*b*) IAA also inhibits the development of axillary buds; (*c*) the cut surface should have been covered with a similar paste but without the IAA; (*d*) several plants should have been treated with paste only and several with paste plus IAA; and several should have been left untreated—with their terminal buds intact. (3) See Fig. 141. (4) 233. (5) 235 to 236. (6) (*a*) Receptor, nerve impulses, diaphragm, quickly, completely, reflex, oxygen, carbon dioxide; (*b*) see Index.

Chapter 27 (1) See Index. (2) Germination, seedling, mature plant, flowers, pollination, fertilisation, seed formation. (3) Try to base your answer on your records of your own observations (see also p. 252). (4) (*a*) See Fig. 148A; (*b*) X in vagina near cervix; O on ovaries; F in oviduct; I on inner surface of uterus. (5) (*a*) day 14; (*b*) days 11 to 17; (*c*) oestrogen and (*d*) progesterone.

Chapter 28 (1) (*a*) Equally; (*b*) because they have identical genotypes; (*c*) because of environmental influences during their development and growth; (*d*) because they are homozygous and naturally self-pollinating. (2) See Index. (3) (*a* and *b*) This is a monohybrid cross (see Fig. 158); (*c*) by a test cross (see Fig. 158). (4) (*a*) 261; (*b*) meiosis. (5) (*a*) 267; (*b*) as an aid to stock improvement by animal breeding. (6) See incomplete dominance (p. 261) and Fig. 159. (7) (C). (8) (*a*) 46 (see p. 264); (*b*) 264; (*c*) the recessive gene for haemophilia, like the gene for red–green colour blindness (Fig. 163), is sex-linked.

Chapter 29 (1) 254. (2) (D). (3) Similarities in *a*, *b*, *c* and *d* could be due to the evolution of all plants and animals, millions of years ago (see Fig. 1), from organisms which already had these characteristics. (4) See Index. (5) Your answer must be based on your own observations.

Appendix 3

VISUAL AIDS

To order the slide sets and items of equipment listed below, first write to Philip Harris Biological Ltd, Oldmixon, Weston-super-Mare, Avon BS24 9BJ, England, enclosing a stamped addressed envelope and asking for their current Made Simple price list.

Equipment

Hand lens (magnifier) ×10: for examining specimens (Code SS 101)
Hand slide viewer: for examining colour transparencies (Code SS 102)

Colour transparencies

Simpleset 1: Micro-organisms (Code BMS 1)
1 Bacteria: bacilli (p. 51–2)
2 Bacteria: spirilla (p. 51–2)
3 *Euglena* (p. 49)
4 *Amoeba* (p. 49)
5 *Paramecium* (p. 49)
6 *Plasmodium* in red blood corpuscles (p. 107).
7 *Spirogyra* (p. 50)
8 *Mucor* (p. 94)

Simpleset 2: Cells and cell structure (Code BMS 2)
1 Epidermis of leaf with guard cells (p. 201)
2 Root tip (longitudinal section) (p. 146)
3 Plant cell structure and ultrastructure (pp. 141, 142)
4 *Hydra* (longitudinal section) (p. 67)
5 Epithelial cells from the buccal cavity of man (p. 140)
6 Columnar epithelial cells in the gut wall (p. 141)
7 Ultrastructure of animal cell (p. 142)
8 Tooth (tissues in longitudinal section) (p. 152)
9–12 Mitosis in a root tip (pp. 146, 148–9)

Simpleset 3: Tissues and organs (Code BMS 3)
1 Root hair cells of epidermis (p. 198)
2 Root (transverse section) (p. 156)
3 Stem (transverse section) (p. 156)
4 Leaf (transverse section) (p. 172)
5 Skin (vertical section) (p. 162)
6 Hinge joint (longitudinal section) (p. 164)
7 Kidney (section) (p. 205)
8 Renal tubules, and glomerular capillaries (section) (p. 205)
9 Blood (smear) (p. 214)
10 Artery and vein (transverse section) (p. 211)
11 Eye of mammal (horizontal section) (p. 223)
12 Spinal cord (transverse section) (p. 231)

Simpleset 4: Reproduction (Code BMS 4)
1 Yeast (some cells with buds) (p. 93)
2 *Hydra* with bud (p. 241)
3 *Taenia*, scolex producing proglottids (pp. 104–5)
4 *Spirogyra* (conjugation) (p. 242)
5 *Mucor*, stages in sexual reproduction (p. 242)

6 *Hydra* with testes and ovary (p. 243)
7 Flower cut in half (p. 11)
8 Flower bud (longitudinal section) (p. 252)
9–10 Germination of pollen grains on stigma (p. 252)
11 Sperm of man
12 Egg and sperm of rabbit

Appendix 4

FURTHER READING

This reading list is for anyone who has read this book and who wishes to know more about biology. The books listed also provide appropriate background reading or reference works for students who are taking more advanced courses—for example, in the sixth form at school, or at university.

Barrass, R. (1974), *Biology: Food and People—The economic importance of biology*, Hodder & Stoughton, London; St Martin's Press, New York.

Barrass, R. (1981), *Human Biology Made Simple*, Heinemann, London.

Barrass, R. (1978), *Scientists Must Write—A guide to better writing for scientists, engineers and students*, Chapman & Hall, London; Methuen, New York.

Beveridge, W. I. B. (1968), *The Art of Scientific Investigation* (3rd edn), Heinemann, London.

Bold, H. C., and Hundell, C. L. (1977), *The Plant Kingdom* (4th edn), Prentice-Hall, Englewood Cliffs, N.J.

Darwin, C. (1859), *On the Origin of Species by Means of Natural Selection*, John Murray, London.

Delevoryas, T. (1977), *Plant Diversification* (2nd edn), Holt, Rinehart & Winston, New York.

De Witt, W. (1977), *Biology of the Cell: An evolutionary approach*, W. B. Saunders Co., Philadelphia.

Fingerman, M. (1976), *Animal Diversity* (2nd edn), Holt, Rinehart & Winston, New York.

Fuller, W. (Ed.) (1971), *The Social Impact of Modern Biology*, Routledge & Kegan Paul, London.

Handler, P. (Ed.) (1970), *Biology and the Future of Man*, Oxford University Press, New York.

Hanson, E. D. (1972), *Animal Diversity* (3rd edn), Prentice-Hall, Englewood Cliffs, N.J.

Hardy, R. N. (1976), *Homeostasis*, Institute of Biology, Studies in Biology No. 63, Edward Arnold, London.

Hollingsworth, M. J., and K. Bowler (1972), *Principles and Processes of Biology*, Chapman & Hall, London; Halsted Press, New York.

Kormondy, E. J. (1976), *Concepts of Ecology* (2nd edn), Prentice-Hall, Englewood Cliffs, N.J.

Mayer, W. V. (Ed.) (1978), *Biology Teacher's Handbook* (3rd edn), Wiley, New York and London.

Odum, E. P. (1975), *Ecology* (2nd edn), Holt, Rinehart & Winston, New York.

Ray, P. M. (1972), *The Living Plant* (2nd edn), Holt, Rinehart & Winston, New York.

Schmidt-Nielsen, K. (1976), *Animal Physiology: Adaptation and Environment*, Cambridge University Press, London.

Simpson, G. G. (1949), *The Meaning of Evolution*, Yale University Press.

Smith-Keary, P. F. (1974), *Genetic Structure and Function*, Macmillan, London.

Stanier, R. Y., Adelberg, E. A., and Ingraham, J. L. (1977), *General Microbiology* (4th edn), Macmillan, London.

Swanson, C. P., and Webster, P. L. (1977), *The Cell* (4th edn), Prentice-Hall, Englewood Cliffs, N.J.

Wallace, B., and A. M. Srb (1964), *Adaptation* (2nd edn) Prentice-Hall, Englewood Cliffs, N.J.

Appendix 5

GLOSSARY

The terms used in this book are defined when they are first used (or on the page numbers indicated by **bold** print after entries in the Index: e.g. Absorption, 59). Synonyms of some terms are also included in the Index (e.g. Atrium, *see* Auricle). Some other terms, which you may see in other introductions to biology, are defined in this glossary.

Abscission (L. cutting off): the shedding of leaves, flowers or fruits.

Adipose tissue: insulating and storage tissue in dermis (p. 162) which contains many fat-filled cells.

After-birth: embryonic membranes, placenta and umbilical cord expelled from uterus after birth (p. 250).

Air bladder: swim bladder of a fish (p. 165).

Alleles: alternative forms of a gene which may occur as a pair (an allelomorphic pair) in the nucleus of a diploid cell (e.g. SS, Ss, and ss; see p. 259). They occur singly in a gamete (e.g. s or S).

Alternation of generations: diploid plants (sporophyte generation) produce haploid spores which develop into haploid plants (gametophyte generation); these produce eggs and sperms, which fuse in pairs forming diploid cells which develop into diploid plants (e.g. in the life cycle of all bryophytes and tracheophytes).

Anaerobe: organism which can live in the absence of oxygen (see p. 94).

Anaphase: third stage in mitosis (see p. 148).

Androecium: all the stamens of a flower.

Aqueous humor: tissue fluid between cornea and lens of eye (Fig. 137).

Atom: smallest part of an element that can take part in a chemical reaction.

Autecology: the study of one species and its environment.

Birth control: limiting the number of children born, by avoidance of sexual intercourse, contraception or abortion.

Blood stream: blood flowing in a circulatory system (p. 211).

Calorie = kilocalorie = 4.2 MJ = the amount of heat required to raise the temperature of 1000 cm³ water by 1 °C.

Calorific value: energy content of food measured in calories.

Carpals: wrist bones (Fig. 164, p. 270).

Caterpillar: larva of a butterfly or moth.

Cellular respiration: respiration.

Centrum: cylindrical part of vertebra, ventral to spinal cord.

Cerebro-spinal fluid: fills spinal canal (Fig. 141, p. 231) and ventricles of brain; similar to tissue fluid (pp. 215–16).

Chlorenchyma: those parenchyma cells of the stem which contain chloroplasts.

Chrysalis: pupa of butterfly or moth.

Chymase (rennin): enzyme in gastric juice, which clots milk.

Cleavage: production of many cells, by mitosis, from an egg cell (usually after fertilisation).

Clone: organisms with identical genotypes produced from one organism by asexual reproduction (e.g. a colony of bacteria which has developed from one spore).

Codominance: blending or incomplete dominance (pp. 261–2).

Coelenterata: Cnidaria (p. 40) and the comb-jellies (animals which resemble cnidarians but which do not have nematocysts).

Coleoptile: shoot sheath of grass seedling (Fig. 4).

Coleorhiza: root sheath of grass seedling (Fig. 4).

Complete metamorphosis (in insects): metamorphosis in a pupal stage, as in t house-fly (Fig. 12).

Compound: chemical substance with molecules that contain more than one kind atom.

Corm: swollen underground stem base; an organ of perennation.

Distribution (geographical): occurrence of organisms in nature.

Divisions: major groups of plants (see Table 7). See also **Phylla.**

Element: a substance that contains only one kind of atom.

Endolymph: fluid which fills the semicircular canals, sacculus, utriculus (and cavity of cochlea, see Fig. 136). See also **Perilymph.**

Endothelium: a layer of cells, one cell thick, similar to epithelium but lining internal cavity (e.g. lining blood circulatory system, and abdominal, pleur and pericardial cavities).

Epigeal: germination in which seed leaves are pulled above the soil as the sho grows (see also **Hypogeal**).

Etiolation: development of plants in the dark (see Fig. 10B).

External respiration: gaseous exchange.

Fallopian tube: oviduct.

Fauna: all the animals in any area.

Flora: all the plants in any area.

Fructose: a six-carbon sugar.

Gametophyte: see **Alternation of generations.**

Ganglion: a swelling along the length of a nerve, which contains the cell bodies many neurones (e.g. dorsal root ganglion, pp. 230, 231).

Germs: not a scientific term; refers to the bacteria and viruses that cause diseases in germ warfare), or to a gamete (as in germ cell).

Graafian follicle: follicle with developing egg, and with fluid-filled cavity, in ova (see Fig. 149).

Guttation: exudation of drops of water at ends of veins of leaves.

Gynoecium: all the carpels of a flower.

Haemocoel: blood-filled cavity of animal with an open circulatory system (see F 127).

Heterophytic and **heterozoic** nutrition: unnecessary terms (see Heterotrop nutrition, p. 126 and p. 180).

Hilum: scar on seed coat where the seed was attached in the fruit.

Holophytic: mode of nutrition of producers (see p. 126).

Holozoic: mode of nutrition of animals (see p. 84; Herbivores, carnivores a omnivores).

Hydrotropism: positive growth response of roots towards water.

Hymen: thin membrane across opening of vagina in a virgin.

Hypogeal: germination in which seed leaves remain in soil (see also **Epigeal**).

Imago: fully formed insect (after metamorphosis).

Incomplete metamorphosis (in insects): metamorphosis, as in locusts (see Fig. 1 without a pupal stage in the life cycle.

Incubation: period when a disease is developing in the body, before symptoms appe See also Incubation, p. 118.

Incus: bone of middle ear (anvil, Fig. 136).

Innate behaviour: inborn responses of mammals.

Instars: stages in an insect's development.

Internal respiration: respiration.

Invertebrates: all animals without backbones, including some chordates (not a natural grouping).

Kilocalorie (see **Calorie**).

Labyrinth: the inner ear (Fig. 136).

Larynx: voice box; part of trachea next to pharynx (Fig. 103A).

Lenticels: porous areas in bark of twig, through which gaseous exchange takes place.

Leucocyte: white blood corpuscle (see p. 214).

Lymphocyte: kind of white blood corpuscle. Some produce antibodies (p. 214) but they are not phagocytes. Others act against foreign cells (as in a graft).

Malleus: bone of middle ear (hammer, Fig. 136).

Malpighian layer: layer of dividing cells (germinative layer) in epidermis of skin (p. 161 and Fig. 89).

Metacarpals: hand-bones (Fig. 164, p. 270). See also **Carpals** and **Phalanges**.

Metaphase: second stage in mitosis (see p. 148).

Molecule: the smallest part of any substance that can exist alone.

Myriapoda: Chilopoda and Diplopoda (see p. 42).

Nastic movements: responses of leaves or petals of plants caused by changes in turgor (see p. 158).

Navel: place on surface of abdomen to which umbilical cord was connected (see Figs. 150 and 151B).

Nymph: larva of an insect which does not have a pupal stage in its life cycle (e.g. locust, Fig. 15).

Ommatidia: essentially similar units of a compound eye (Fig. 135).

Peptidase: a protease enzyme in the intestine.

Pericarp: ovary wall.

Perilymph: fluid which fills cavities 1 and 3 of cochlea (Fig. 136); see also **Endolymph**.

Phalanges: bones of digits (fingers and toes). See Fig. 164, p. 270.

Phyla (s. phylum): major groups of animals (see Table 7). See also **Divisions**.

Pileus: cap of mushroom (Fig. 20B).

Plumule: young shoot (see Fig. 4, p. 9).

Presbyopia: long-sightedness in elderly (p. 224).

Prophase: first stage in mitosis (see p. 148).

Protandry: development of sperms before eggs (preventing self-fertilisation).

Protogyny: development of eggs before sperm (preventing self-fertilisation).

Protophyta: unicellular protists which resemble plants in their mode of nutrition.

Protoplasm: a term which was used for the cytoplasm and nucleus of a cell when scientists believed that there was one living material, essentially different from non-living matter. With the development of cytology and biochemistry this misleading term is no longer needed.

Protozoa: unicellular protists which resemble animals in their mode of nutrition.

Pteridophyta: clubmosses, horse-tails and ferns; three classes of spore-bearing tracheophytes (p. 39).

Ptyalin: the salivary amylase of mammals (p. 90).

Radicle: young root (see Fig. 4, p. 9).

Renin: hormone secreted by kidneys which is concerned in the regulation of blood pressure.

Rennin (chymase): enzyme in gastric juice which clots milk.

Safe period: misleading name for the days during each 28-day menstrual cycle when sexual intercourse is least likely to be followed by pregnancy (see Rhythm method, p. 249).

Salt: compound formed in a chemical reaction: acid + alkali = salt + water.

Saprophyte: a plant which is a saprobiont.

Saprozoite: an animal which is a saprobiont.

Sclerotic coat: fibrous layer of the eye, continuous with cornea (Fig. 137).

Serum: the fluid which remains after blood in a container has clotted.

Somatic cell: body cell (not a gamete).

Spawn: eggs of fish or frog; or laying of these eggs.

Spermatophyta: cone-bearing plants and flowering plants; two classes of seed-bearing tracheophytes (p. 39).

Sporophyte: see **Alternation of generations.**

Stapes: bone of middle ear (stirrup, Fig. 136).

Stipe: stalk of mushroom (Fig. 20B).

Strobila: tape of tapeworm (Fig. 21A).

Taxes: unlearnt responses of animals, involving movement towards or away from source of stimulation.

Taxonomy: the study of the principles and practice of classification (p. 34).

Telophase: last stage in mitosis (see p. 148).

Terrestrial organism: organism that lives on land.

Tetrapods: four-footed vertebrates (amphibians, reptiles, birds and mammals), see p. 65.

Tissue respiration: respiration.

Translocation: transport of organic molecules from one part of a plant to another

Transmitter substance: a chemical secreted by a nerve cell, which induces either a nerve impulse in another nerve cell or the response of an effector.

Uptake: the movement of materials into a living cell (see intake, p. 185).

Vas deferens: sperm duct (Fig. 148).

Vector: organism that contributes to the spread of disease by carrying parasite (e.g. house-fly, p. 21 and p. 110).

Vitreous humor: transparent jelly between lens and retina of eye (Fig. 137).

Vulva: external parts of reproductive system of a female mammal (see Fig. 148 inner and outer lips).

Worms: flatworms, nematode worms and segmented worms (p. 40 and p. 42).

Index

Index

Numbers in bold print indicate the pages on which terms are defined or illustrated. Note that some terms that are not used in this book, but which you may see in other introductions to biology, are explained in the Glossary (p. 285).